THIRD
PRINT
PRICE GUIDE

▲

EDWIN G. WARMAN

▼

A CHECK-LIST AND PRICE GUIDE
TO
N. CURRIER, CURRIER & IVES, KELLOGG
AND OTHER PRINTMAKERS

—————

Published By
E. G. WARMAN PUBLISHING INC.
8 Frankhoover Street
Uniontown, Penna.

Additional Copies Can Be Obtained
From the Publisher

Published by
E. G. WARMAN PUBLISHING INC.
8 Frankhoover Street
Uniontown, Penna.

PRICE: $4.75 per COPY

REVISED EDITION
FIRST PRINTING NOVEMBER 1969

INTRODUCTION

New Print Price Guide---a book about prints and prices---and the men who made them. The volume is divided into two parts. The first and largest section concerns Nathaniel Currier, Currier & Ives and Charles Currier. The Curriers were the leading printmakers of their day and are believed to have issued more prints on popular subjects than all the other lithographers of their era.

The second section pertains to the leading contemporaries of the Curriers who produced prints of a type similar to theirs. The outstanding competitor was the Kellogg brothers. Other lesser business rivals were Haskell and Allen, Sarony & Major, Prang and Duval.

The prices incorporated within the book are average current retail prices. Values were determined by compiling all available prices and arriving at an average.

Certain groups of prints have made advances in price since the writer issued "Price Guide to 5000 Currier & Ives Prints" over nineteen years ago. Increased values have been especially noted in the following: Horses, The West, Hunting and Fishing, Ships, Hudson Valley Views, Eastern City Views and Flowers and Fruit. Children, Military, Political and Animal groups have shown increases on a smaller scale. As in the past, Religious subjects have not made any appreciable increase. Prints of this group were issued in vast quantities and there is little demand for them among collectors.

Edwin G. Warman

TECHNICAL INFORMATION

N. Currier and Currier & Ives prints were issued in three standard sizes. At various times a few miniatures and a considerable number of store cards were issued. The three standard sizes are:

Small Folio - about 7.8" x 12.8"
Medium Folio - about 13" x 20"
Large Folio - about 18" x 27"

The sizes are of the printed area excluding the margins.

At various times prints were made with a slightly larger or smaller printed area than the standard sizes listed above. With the exception of a few miniatures, sheet music and store cards they fall into the size group nearest their size. For example, a print 12-1/2" x 17-3/4" would be classed as a "Medium Folio."

The values given in this list are for those in fine condition. Prints that have trimmed margins, stains or tears, are less desirable and are worth considerably less--the amount depending upon the degree of damage.

A HISTORY OF CURRIER & IVES

The prints of N. Currier and Currier and Ives present a panorama of life when America was developing. It is to Nathaniel Currier that we owe a debt of gratitude for his ability to record and preserve the activities of the people of this important era.

Nathaniel Currier was born in the year 1813. In 1828, at 15 years of age, he was apprenticed to the firm of William & John Pendleton, in Boston, the first successful lithographers in this country.

Currier finished his apprenticeship five years later and went to Philadelphia to work. One year later he went to New York with the intention of forming a partnership with John Pendleton. Pendleton received another attractive offer and declined to go through with the proposed business project. Currier then went into partnership with Stodart in 1834. The partnership was dissolved in 1835, and Currier moved to #1 Wall Street where he continued his own business.

Two years later, N. Currier moved to factory quarters at #2 Spruce Street, and established a retail and wholesale store at #148 Nassau Street.

The earliest print by N. Currier is not exactly known. Some authorities believe that "Ruins of the Planter's Hotel, New Orleans, May 15, 1835," is the first. Others contend the portrait of William P. Dewees, Professor of Obstetrics at the University of Pennsylvania, with the name "N. Currier" imprinted, and dated 1834, is the earliest. The latter print was probably a commercial job and was not a part of the regular line of N. Currier prints.

N. Currier's brother, Charles, had space in the plant but advertised independently and took commission jobs of his own. There are between 50 and 100 known prints bearing the inscription "C. Currier." Charles invented a superior lithographic crayon which was much in demand at that time.

In 1852, Charles Currier recommended his brother-in-law, James M. Ives, to Nathaniel as a bookkeeper. James was proficient and took an interest in the business to such an extent that Currier turned most of the affairs of business over to him. In 1857, he was admitted as a partner, and since that year the firm was known as "Currier & Ives."

The company did not depend on the retail store for its sole outlet, but appointed distributors in other cities and countries. They also did an extensive mail order business and sent out numerous catalogues. The company maintained a distributor in London and many prints were sold from there to France, Germany, and other European countries.

The smaller uncolored prints sold for six cents each wholesale, and retailed for around 15 cents. The small colored prints retailed at 25 cents to 40 cents; while the medium folios sold for 60 cents and the large folios from $1.50 to $3.00.

The firm employed a dozen or more women who applied the colors to the prints by hand.

No one colorist ever completed a print, but would apply just one color and pass it to the next for the second color, and so on, in an assembly line fashion, until the print was completed.

The large prints were usually sent out, a dozen at a time, to an artist of ability who received the sum of $1.00 for doing a complete job of coloring. Many young artists availed themselves of this opportunity to keep body and soul together while waiting to receive recognition.

The firm employed various artists full time at different periods. For about ten years Louis Maurer was at his best with horse prints and scenes from American Life. Another full time artist was Fanny Palmer. She was very versatile and adept at painting rural scenery, flowers, marine subjects, and railroad and river scenery.

Thomas Worth is best known for his Darktown Comic Series and for his horse prints.

Arthur F. Tate, like Worth, was not an employee of the firm, but was also a frequent contributor. He was an exacting artist and his work was of top quality. His outdoor life subjects are the most sought after prints today and command some of the highest prices.

George B. Durrie was another contributor. No more than a dozen different subjects bearing his name are known to have been lithographed, but his work depicting Farm Life, especially Winter scenes, is as much sought after by collectors as Tate's works.

Charles Parsons contributed Railway scenery and marine subjects to the long list of the firms prints. James E. Butterworth, another artist, contributed marine scenes. At various times other artists of the period contributed work. Many must remain anonymous due to the fact that their names were often omitted.

In 1880, Nathaniel Currier retired from the firm and was succeeded by his son, Edward. In 1888, he died of a heart attack. James Ives remained active with the firm until 1895, a short time before his death. He was succeeded by his son, Chauncey.

In 1902, Edward Currier sold his interest to Chauncey Ives. Ives started liquidating the business and in 1907 sold the firm to Daniel W. Logan. Logan planned to continue this business, but was forced to close due to ill health.

Thus, the firm that had served the people as printmakers for 73 years closed its doors for the last time.

CHRONOLOGY OF THE FIRM

Stodart & Currier: 1834-35, at #137 Broadway.
N. Currier: 1835-36, at #1 Wall Street.
N. Currier: 1836-38, at #148 Nassau Street.
N. Currier: 1838-57, at #152 Nassau Street.
Currier & Ives: 1857-72, at #152 Nassau Street.
Currier & Ives: 1872-74, at #125 Nassau Street.
Currier & Ives: 1875-94, at #123-125 Nassau St.
Currier & Ives: 1894-96, at #108 Fulton Street.
Currier & Ives: 1896-1907, at #33 Spruce Street.
Charles Currier: located at #33 Spruce Street.

CURRIER & IVES PRINTS

— A —

AARON CLARK, Mayor of New York City; N. Currier; 1837.. Small... $70.00
ABBEY OF CLARE-GALWAY .... Small... 20.00
ABBOTSFORD .... Medium. 35.00
ABIGAIL; 1846 .... Small... 20.00
ABRAHAM'S DREAM; 1864 .... Small... 30.00
ACADEMY WALTZ; N. Currier .... Small... 22.50
ACCEPTED, THE .... Small... 18.50
ACCOMMODATION TRAIN, THE; 1875........................ Small... 65.00
ACROSS THE CONTINENT; "Westward the Course of Empire
  Takes Its Way" .... Large . 4250.00
ACTRESS, THE .... Small... 21.50
ADA; N. Currier .... Small... 18.50
ADAM AND EVE DRIVEN OUT OF PARADISE............... Small 30.00
ADAM AND EVE IN THE GARDEN OF EDEN; 1848 .... Small... 30.00
ADAM NAMING THE CREATURES; N. Currier; 1847 .... Small... 35.00
ADELAIDE; N. Currier; 1846 .... Small... 18.50
ADELINE; N. Currier; 1849 .... Small... 18.50
ADIEU AT FONTAINBLEAU .... Large... 48.50
ADMIRAL FARRAGUT'S FLEET ENGAGING THE REBEL
  BATTERIES AT PORT HUDSON, March 14th, 1863. .... Small... 60.00
ADMIRAL PORTER'S FLEET RUNNING THE REBEL
  BLOCKADE OF THE MISSISSIPPI AT VICKSBURG,
  April 16th, 1863 .... Small... 32.50
AESTHETIC CRAZE; 1882 .... Small... 24.50
AFFAIR OF HONOR, AN; "The Critical Moment" .... Small... 24.50
AFFAIR OF HONOR, AN; "Stray Shot" 1884 .... Small... 24.50
AFRICA; 1870 .... Small... 30.00
AFRICAN JUNGLE, THE .... Small... 37.50
AFTER MARRIAGE; "Experience" .... Small... 40.00
AFTER THE BATH .... Small... 20.00
AGE OF BRASS, THE; 1869 .... Small... 65.00
AGE OF IRON, THE; 1869 .... Small... 65.00
AGNES; N. Currier; 1846... Small... 20.00
AGRICULTURAL HALL; 1876.................................... Small... 32.50
AIN'T I SOME; N. Currier .... Small... 25.00
AIN'T THEY CUNNING?.. Small... 25.00
ALABAMA STATE MARCH, THE; N. Currier .... Small... 18.00
ALARM, THE; 1861 .... Small... 48.00
ALICE; N. Currier; 1844 .... Small... 20.00
ALL BROKE UP; 1884 .... Small... 25.00
"ALL HAIL THE POWER OF CHRIST'S NAME".............. Small... 12.50
ALL NICE AND HOT; N. Currier................................. Small... 30.00
ALL PRIMED .... Small... 20.00
ALL RIGHT .... Small... 32.50
ALL SO TIRED .... Small... 18.50
ALL THE WORLD IS SCHEMING................................ Small... 15.00
ALL WRONG; N. Currier .... Small... 32.50
ALMIRA; N. Currier; 1845 .... Small... 20.00
ALNWICK CASTLE, SCOTLAND .... Medium. 40.00
ALONZO AND CORA; N. Currier .... Small ,.. 35.00
AMANDA; N. Currier; 1846 .... Small... 18.50
AMATEUR MUSCLE IN THE SHELL; 1879.................... Medium. 60.00
AMATEUR MUSCLE IN THE SHELL; 1879 .... Small... 48.00
AMBUSCADE; THE .... Medium. 500.00

AMELIA; N. Currier; 1845 .... Small ..... $ 18.50
AMELIA .... Small 18.00
AMERICA; 1870 .... Small 30.00
AMERICA; N. Currier .... Small 30.00
AMERICAN AUTUMN FRUITS .... Small 48.00
AMERICAN BEAUTY, THE .... Small 24.50
AMERICAN BROOK TROUT; 1872 .... Small 55.00
AMERICAN BUFFALOES .... Small 80.00
AMERICAN CHAMPION YACHT "PURITAN," THE; 1885 Small 90.00
AMERICAN CHOICE FRUITS; 1869 .... Large 80.00
AMERICAN CHOICE FRUITS .... Large 75.00
AMERICAN CLIPPER SHIP OFF SANDY HOOK LIGHT
    IN A SNOWSTORM .... Small 240.00
AMERICAN CLIPPER SHIP "WITCH OF THE WAVE" ..... Small 395.00
AMERICAN CLUB HUNT; "Halt On The Scent," 1884 ..... Small 50.00
AMERICAN CLUB HUNT; "Taking A Header," 1884.. .....Small 50.00
AMERICAN COAST SCENE, DESERT ROCK LIGHT
    HOUSE, MAINE ....Medium... 900.00
AMERICAN COTTAGE NO. 1; N. Currier ....Small 45.00
AMERICAN COUNTRY LIFE; "May Morning," 1855 ....Large 275.00
AMERICAN COUNTRY LIFE; "October Afternoon"; 1855.Large 275.00
AMERICAN COUNTRY LIFE; "Pleasures of Winter";
    1855 ....Large 500.00
AMERICAN COUNTRY LIFE "Summer's Evening,"; 1855. Large 325.00
AMERICAN DEAD GAME; 1866 .... Large 45.00
AMERICAN ECLIPSE; 1879 .... Small 80.00
AMERICAN EXPRESS TRAIN; N. Currier; 1853 .... Small 300.00
AMERICAN EXPRESS TRAIN; (Parsons) 1855 .... Large 1800.00
AMERICAN EXPRESS TRAIN; (Palmer) 1864 .... Large 1500.00
AMERICAN FARM LIFE; 1868 .... Medium .. 125.00
AMERICAN FARM SCENE; "In The Olden Time" .... Small 48.00
AMERICAN FARM SCENES, NO. 1; (Spring)................ Large 225.00
AMERICAN FARM SCENES, NO. 2; (Summer) .... Large 215.00
AMERICAN FARM SCENES, NO. 3 (Autumn) .... Large 215.00
AMERICAN FARM SCENES, NO. 4; (Winter) .... Large ... 700.00
AMERICAN FARMYARD – EVENING; 1857 .... Large 160.00
AMERICAN FARMYARD – MORNING; 1857 .... Large 175.00
AMERICAN FEATHERED GAME –MALLARD AND CAN-
    VAS BACK DUCKS; N. Currier; 1854; (Oval) .... Medium... 120.00
AMERICAN FEATHERED GAME – PARTRIDGES; (Oval). Medium... 110.00
AMERICAN FEATHERED GAME – WOODCOCK AND
    GOLDEN EYE; N. Currier ....'Medium... 120.00
AMERICAN FEATHERED GAME – WOODCOCK AND
    SNIPE; N. Currier; 1854; (Oval) .... Medium... 120.00
AMERICAN FEATHERED GAME – WOODCOCK AND
    SNIPE; N. Currier .... Medium... 110.00
AMERICAN FIELD SPORTS; "A Chance for Both Barrels,"
    1857 .... Large 400.00
AMERICAN FIELD SPORTS; "Flush'd"; 1857.............. Large 400.00
AMERICAN FIELD SPORTS; "On A Point"; 1857 .... Large 400.00
AMERICAN FIELD SPORTS; "Retrieving"; 1857.......... Large 395.00
AMERICAN FIREMAN, THE; "Always Ready"; 1858 ..... Medium... 95.00
AMERICAN FIREMAN, THE; "Facing the Enemy; 1858 ... Medium... 95.00
AMERICAN FIREMAN, THE; "Prompt to the Rescue"
    1858 .... Medium ... 95.00
AMERICAN FIREMAN, THE; "Rushing to the Conflict"
    1858 .... Medium ... 90.00
AMERICAN FOREST GAME; 1866 .... Large 110.00

```
AMERICAN FOREST SCENE; Maple Sugaring" 1855 ...... Large..... 975.00
AMERICAN FRONTIER LIFE; "The Hunter's Stratagem"
   1862 .................................................................. Large.....1200.00
AMERICAN FRONTIER LIFE; "On the Warpath" 1863 .. Large.....1500.00
AMERICAN FRUIT PIECE; 1859  .......................... Large..... 90.00
AMERICAN FRUIT PIECE .................................. Small .... 48.50
AMERICAN FRUITS; 1861  ................................ Small .... 40.00
AMERICAN GAME; 1866 ................................... Large..... 45.00
AMERICAN GAME  FISH; 1866 ............................. Large..... 115.00
AMERICAN GIRL; 1871 .................................... Small .... 50.00
"AMERICAN GIRL" AND "LADY THORN" In Their Great
   Match for $2,000; 1869 ................................ Large..... 300.00
AMERICAN HOMESTEAD (AUTUMN); 1869 ............. Small .... 95.00
AMERICAN HOMESTEAD (SPRING); 1869 ............... Small .... 85.00
AMERICAN HOMESTEAD (SUMMER); 1868 .............. Small .... 75.00
AMERICAN HOMESTEAD (WINTER); 1868 ............... Small .... 200.00
AMERICAN HUNTING SCENES; "An Early Start" 1863... Large..... 575.00
AMERICAN HUNTING SCENES; "A Good Chance" 1863 . Large..... 650.00
AMERICAN JOCKEY CLUB RACES, JEROME PARK ..... Large..... 700.00
AMERICAN LANDSCAPE; "Early Morning" ................. Large..... 300.00
AMERICAN LANDSCAPES (Four prints on one page).......Small ...... 60.00
AMERICAN LANDSCAPE; "Sacandaga Creek" (Oval) ..... Small ...... 32.50
AMERICAN MOUNTAIN SCENERY; 1868 .................. Medium.... 95.00
AMERICAN NATIONAL GAME OF BASE BALL, THE;
   "Grand Match For the Championship etc." 1862 ......... Large......3000.00
AMERICAN PRIVATEER "GENERAL ARMSTRONG" ..... Small ...... 200.00
AMERICAN PRIZE FRUIT; 1862  ........................... Large...... 125.00
AMERICAN PRIZE FRUIT  ................................. Small ...... 55.00
AMERICAN RAILROAD SCENE; 1872 ..................... Small ...... 215.00
AMERICAN RAILROAD SCENE; 1874 ..................... Small ...... 215.00
AMERICAN RAILROAD SCENE; 1871; "Snowbound" ...... Small ...... 395.00
AMERICAN RAILWAY SCENE AT HORNELLSVILLE;
   1876 ................................................... Large..... 2150.00
AMERICAN RIVER SCENERY; "View On The Androscoggin,
   Maine" ................................................. Medium... 175.00
AMERICAN SCENERY, PALENVILLE, N.Y. ............... Small ..... 65.00
AMERICAN SHIP RESCUING THE OFFICERS AND CREW
   OF A BRITISH MAN OF WAR; 1863 ...................... Medium... 175.00
AMERICAN SLOOP YACHT MAYFLOWER; 1886 ......... Large..... 125.00
AMERICAN SLOOP YACHT VOLUNTEER; 1888............. Large..... 140.00
AMERICAN SPECKLED BROOK TROUT; 1864 ............ Large..... 120.00
AMERICAN STEAMBOATS ON THE HUDSON; 1874........ Large..... 350.00
AMERICAN SUMMER FRUITS; 1875 ..................... Small ..... 40.00
AMERICAN TAR, THE; "Don't Give Up The Ship", N.
   Currier; 1845 .......................................... Small ..... 60.00
AMERICAN THOROUGHBREDS ............................. Small ..... 125.00
AMERICAN TROTTING STUD, ETHAN ALLEN, POCA-
   HONTAS; 1866 ......................................... Large..... 550.00
AMERICAN TROTTING STUD, MAMBRINO PILOT, FLORA
   TEMPLE; 1866 ......................................... Large..... 525.00
AMERICAN WHALER; N. Currier  ......................... Small ..... 335.00
AMERICAN WHALERS CRUSHED IN THE ICE; "Burning
   the Wrecks to Avoid Danger to other Vessels" ........ Small ..... 325.00
AMERICAN WINTER SCENE; "The Falls" (Oval).......... Small..... 65.00
AMERICAN WINTER SCENES; "Evening" 1854............. Large..... 600.00
AMERICAN WINTER SCENES; "Morning" 1854 ............ Large..... 800.00
AMERICAN WINTER SPORTS; "Deer Shooting on the
   Shattagee; N. Currier; 1855   ........................... Large..... 695.00
```

```
AMERICAN WINTER SPORTS; "Trout Fishing on
    Chateaugay Lake", N. Currier; 1856 ..................... Large .... $650.00
AMONG THE HILLS ............................................. Medium ...   80.00
AMONG THE PINES; "A First Settlement" ................. Small .....   62.50
ANCIENT CROSS OF CLONMACNOISE ........... .......... Small .....   20.00
ANGEL FOOTSTEPS; 1878 ................................. Small .....   18.50
ANGEL GABRIEL, THE ....................................... Small .....   12.00
ANGEL OF PRAYER, THE; (Oval). .......................... Small .....   11.50
ANGEL OF THE BATTLE FIELD; 1865 .................... Small .....   22.50
ANGEL OF THE COVENANT; (Oval) ...................... Sm all ....   12.00
ANGELINE; N. Currier; 1846 ................................ Small .....   20.00
ANIMAL CREATION; 1875 ................................... Small ,....   35.00
ANN; N. Currier; 1848 ......................................... Small .....   20.00
ANN MARIA; N. Currier ...................................... Small .....   20.00
ANNIE ............................................................ Small .....   18.50
ANNUNCIATION, THE; N. Currier; 1844 ................. Small .....   12.00
ANTELOPE SHOOTING; "Fatal Curiosity". .............. Medium ...  200.00
ANXIOUS MOMENT; "A Three Pounder Sure" 1874 ...... Medium ...  175.00
ANXIOUS MOTHER, THE ................................... Small .....   30.00
ANXIOUS NURSE, THE .................................... Small .....   40.00
ANY PORT IN A STORM; 1884 ........................... Small .....   30.00
APOLLO; 1884 ................................................ Small .....   55.00
APPLES; 1868 ................................................ Small .....   27.50
APPLES AND PLUMS; 1870 ................................ Small ....   37.50
APRIL SHOWERS, THE ..................................... Small ....   50.00
AQUARIUM, THE ............................................. Small ....   30.00
ARABIAN; N. Currier; 1846 ................................ Small .....   40.00
ARABS BRIDE, THE; N. Currier ........................... Small .....   30.00
ARABY'S DAUGHTER; N. Currier .......................... Small .....   27.50
ARGUING THE POINT; N. Currier; 1855 ................. Large .....  250.00
ARION; 1892 .................................................. Small .....   60.00
ARISTOCRACY OF COLOR; N. Currier ................... Small .....   35.00
ARISTOTLE; 1893 ........................................... Small .....   55.00
"ARISTOTLE," "MARIE FRANK" AND "RED VIRGIL"
    1893 ........................................................ Small .....   67.50
ARKANSAS TRAVELLER, THE; 1870 .................... Small .....   60.00
ARMOURED STEEL CRUISER "NEW YORK" 1893 ...... Small .....   60.00
ART GALLERY ............................................... Small ....   45.00
ARTHUR CHAMBERS ....................................... Medium ...   95.00
ARTIST IN HAIR; 1872 .................................... Small .....   32.50
ARTISTS' CREEK, NORTH CONWAY ..................... Small .....   70.00
AS KIND AS A KITTEN; 1879 ............................. Small .....   40.00
ASCENSION, THE; N. Currier; 1844 ...................... Small .....   10.00
ASCENSION OF THE VIRGIN; N. Currier; 1848 .......... Small .....   10.00
ASIA ............................................................ Small .....   20.00
ASKING A HAND; 1887 (Comic) ............................ Small .....   22.50
ASLEEP; N. Currier; 1848 .................................. Small .....   15.00
ASSASSINATION OF PRESIDENT LINCOLN, THE; 1865 Small .....   45.00
ASSUMPTION OF THE HOLY VIRGIN ..................... Small .....   10.00
ASTORIA, L.I; "From the New York Side"; 1862 ........ Medium ...  300.00
ASTORIA INSTITUTE; N. Currier ......................... Small .....   48.00
AT THE FAIR GROUNDS; 1890 ........................... Large .....  295.00
AT THE FAIR GROUNDS, 1894 ........................... Large ·····  295.00
AT THE FOOT OF THE CROSS ........................... Small .....   10.00
ATALIBA RECEIVING THE LAST EMBRACES OF HIS
    FAMILY; N. Currier ...................................... Small .....   27.50
ATLANTIC MISSISSIPPI AND OHIO R.R.; 1864 .......... Large .....  875.00
```

ATTACK AND MASSACRE OF CREW OF SHIP "TON-
QUIN" (Miniature) .... Miniature. $ 45.00
ATTACK OF THE GUNBOATS UPON THE CITY AND
CASTLE OF SAN JUAN DE ULLOA; N. Currier;
1847... Small 65.00
ATTACK OF THE LION; N. Currier .... Small 40.00
ATTACK ON THE CASTLE OF CHAPULTEPEC; N.
Currier; 1848 .... Small 42.50
ATTACK ON THE HOME GUARD; 1863................... Large 60.00
ATTACK ON THE WIDOW McCORMACK'S HOUSE; "On
Boulagh Common, Ireland, July 29th", 1848; N.
Currier; 1848 .... Small 42.50
ATTACKING THE BADGER; N. Currier.................... Small 62.50
THE AUBURN HORSE; 1866 .... Large 200.00
AUGUSTA; N. Currier; 1848 .... Small 20.00
AUTUMN; N. Currier; (From an English print) .... Small 30.00
AUTUMN; C. & I; 1871; (Girl's Head) .... Small 21.50
AUTUMN FOLIAGE.. Small 27.50
AUTUMN FRUITS.. Medium.... 75.00
AUTUMN FRUITS .... Small 45.00
AUTUMN FRUITS AND FLOWERS .... Small 27.50
AUTUMN GIFT, THE; 1870 .... Small 25.00
AUTUMN IN NEW ENGLAND; "Cider Making", 1866 .. Large 375.00
AUTUMN IN THE ADIRONDACKS, LAKE HARRISON . Small 85.00
AUTUMN ON LAKE GEORGE .... Small 60.00
AWAKE; N. Currier; 1848 .... Small 12.50
AWFUL CONFLAGRATION OF THE STEAMBOAT
"LEXINGTON"... Small 120.00
AWFUL EXPLOSION OF THE "PEACEMAKER;" N.
Currier; 1844 .... Small 125.00
AWFUL WRECK OF THE MAGNIFICENT STEAMER
"ATLANTIC"; N. Currier; 1846 .... Small 100.00
AXTEL — RECORD 2:12 .... Small 45.00
AZTEC CHILDREN, THE .... Small 50.00

— B —

BABES IN THE WOODS; "Young Partridges"; 1868 ... Small 75.00
BABY'S FIRST VISIT .... Small 20.00
BACKED TO WIN; 1880 .... Small 40.00
BAD BREAK; 1879 .... Small 45.00
BAD CASE OF HEAVES, A; 1875 .... Small 45.00
BAD DREAM, A; N. Currier .... Small 32.50
BAD EGG, A .... Small 30.00
BAD HUSBAND, THE; 1870 .... Small 48.50
BAD MAN AT THE HOUR OF DEATH, THE .... Small 24.50
BAD POINT ON A GOOD POINTER, A; 1879............ Small 57.50
BAD STREAK, A; 1879 .... Small 25.00
BALK ON A SWEEPSTAKE; 1881 .... Small 45.00
BALLS ARE ROLLING — CLEAR THE TRACK .... Small 50.00
BALTIMORE BAKERY .... Medium..... 50.00
BALTIMORE CLIPPER; (Rare) .... Small 500.00
BALTIMORE IN 1880; 1880 .... Small 95.00
BANKS OF DOON, THE .... Medium..... 50.00
BAPTISM OF CHRIST .... Small 10.00
BAPTISM OF JESUS CHRIST; 1893....................... Small 10.00
BAPTISM OF POCAHONTAS, THE .... Small 30.00

```
BAPTISMAL CERTIFICATE ................................. Small..... $ 10.00
BARBER, THE ................................................ Small.....   35.00
BARD, THE; 1887 ........................................... Small.....   48.00
BARE CHANCE A; 1879 .................................... Small.....   40.00
BAREFACED CHEEK; 1881 ................................ Small.....   40.00
BAREFOOT BOY; 1872 ...................................... Small.....   25.00
BAREFOOT GIRL, THE ...................................... Small.....   22.50
BARK THEOXENA, THE (RARE)........................... Large ....  700.00
BARN FLOOR, THE .......................................... Large ....  295.00
BARNUM'S GALLERY OF WONDERS, NO. 5; "Infant
   Hoosier Giant." (Weight, 431 lbs.) ..................... Small.....   45.00
BARNUM'S GALLERY OF WONDERS, NO. 14; "The
   Wonderful Albino Family" .............................. Small.....   45.00
BARNUM'S GALLERY OF WONDERS, NO. 26; "What Is It?"
   or "Man Monkey" ....................................... Small.....   60.00
BARON'S CASTLE, THE ..................................... Small.....   40.00
BASE HIT, A; 1882 .......................................... Small.....   70.00
BASS FISHING AT MACOMB'S DAM, HARLEM RIVER, N.Y.;
   N. Currier; 1852 ......................................... Large ....  500.00
BATTERY, NEW YORK BY MOONLIGHT; N. Currier ..... Small.....  190.00
BATTLE AT BUNKER'S HILL; N. Currier ................. Small.....   48.50
BATTLE AT CEDAR MOUNTAIN, THE...................... Small.....   42.50
BATTLE AT FIVE FORKS, VA., THE....................... Small.....   45.00
BATTLE AT MISSIONARY RIDGE, GA. ..................... Small.....   45.00
BATTLE OF ANTIETAM, MD., THE......................... Small.....   45.00
BATTLE OF BATON ROUGE, LA............................ Small.....   45.00
BATTLE OF BENTONVILLE, NORTH CAROLINA......... Small.....   48.00
BATTLE OF BOONEVILLE — OR THE GREAT MISSOURI
   "LYON" HUNT............................................ Small.....   42.50
BATTLE OF BUENA VISTA; N. Currier ................... Small.....   48.00
BATTLE OF BUNKER'S HILL; N. Currier ................. Small.....   55.00
BATTLE OF BULL RUN, VA. ............................... Small.....   40.00
BATTLE OF CEDAR CREEK, VA. .......................... Small.....   37.50
BATTLE OF CERRO GORDO; N. Currier; 1847 ........... Small.....   45.00
BATTLE OF CHAMPION HILLS, MISS. ..................... Small.....   45.00
BATTLE OF CHANCELLORSVILLE, VA. .................... Small.....   37.50
BATTLE OF CHATTANOOGA, TENN. ....................... Small.....   37.50
BATTLE OF CHICKAMAUGA, GA. .......................... Small.....   39.50
BATTLE OF CHURUBUSCO; N. Currier; 1847 ........... Small.....   42.00
BATTLE OF CLONTARF; N. Currier ....................... Small.....   37.50
BATTLE OF COAL HARBOR, VA. .......................... Small.....   40.00
BATTLE OF CORINTH, MISS. ............................... Small.....   48.00
BATTLE OF FAIR OAKS, VA. 1862 ....................... Large ....   70.00
BATTLE OF FAIR OAKS, VA. 1862 ....................... Small.....   40.00
BATTLE OF FREDERICKSBURG, VA. 1862 ............... Small.....   45.00
BATTLE OF GETTYSBURG, PA., THE; 1863 ............. Large ....  135.00
BATTLE OF GETTYSBURG, PA., THE ..................... Small.....   45.00
BATTLE OF JONESBORO, GA., 1864 ...................... Small.....   42.50
BATTLE OF LEXINGTON, THE.............................. Small.....   40.00
BATTLE OF MALVERN HILL, VA. ......................... Small.....   42.50
BATTLE OF MEXICO, THE; N. Currier; 1848 ........... Small.....   45.00
BATTLE OF MILL SPRING, KY. ............................ Small.....   47.50
BATTLE OF MONTEREY; N. Currier: 1846 .............. Small.....   37.50
BATTLE OF MURFREESBORO, TENN.; 1862 .......... Large ....   87.50
BATTLE OF NEW ORLEANS, THE; N. Currier; 1842 ... Small.....   45.00
BATTLE OF NEWBERN, N.C., THE; 1862 .............. Small.....   42.50
BATTLE OF PEA RIDGE, ARK.; 1862 ..................... Small.....   40.00
BATTLE OF PETERSBURG, VA. ............................ Small.....   40.00
```

```
BATTLE OF PITTSBURGH, TENN., THE; 1862 ......... Small.....  $ 40.00
BATTLE OF RESACA DE LA PALMA; N. Currier; 1846  Small.....    38.50
BATTLE OF SACRAMENTO; N. Currier; 1847 ...........  Small.....    48.50
BATTLE OF SHARPSBURG, MD., THE .................... Small.....    35.00
BATTLE OF SPOTTSLYVANIA, VA. THE ................ Small.....    40.00
BATTLE OF THE BOYNE .................................. Small.....    37.50
BATTLE OF THE GIANTS; "Buffalo Bulls on the
   American Prairies." ................................... Small.....   450.00
BATTLE OF THE KINGS, THE; 1884 ................... Large....   150.00
BATTLE OF THE WILDERNESS, VA., THE ............... Large....   135.00
BATTLE OF THE WILDERNESS, VA., THE .............. Small.....    45.00
BATTLE OF WATERLOO; N. Currier ................... Small.....    35.00
BATTLE OF WILLIAMSBURG, VA. ..................... Small.....    40.00
BAY GELDING "ALLEY," By Volunteer, Record 2:19;
   1879 ................................................... Small.....    60.00
BAY OF ANNAPOLIS, NOVA SCOTIA, THE ............... Small.....    67.50
BE NOT WISE IN THINE OWN EYES; 1872 ............... Small.....    12.50
BEACH SNIPE SHOOTING; 1869 ......................... Medium..   450.00
BEAR HUNTING (A Winter Scene) ..................... Small.....   575.00
BEAR HUNTING; "Close Quarters" ................... Small.....   225.00
BEATRICE CENCI .................................... Small.....    12.50
BEAU AWAKE .......................................... Small.....    14.00
BEAUTIES OF BILLIARDS: "A Carom On the Dark Red"
   1869 ................................................... Large....   120.00
BEAUTIES OF THE BALLET; N. Currier ................ Small.....    20.00
BEAUTIFUL BLONDE ................................... Medium..    20.00
BEAUTIFUL BRUNETTE ................................. Small.....    20.00
BEAUTIFUL DREAMER, THE ........................... Small.....    15.00
BEAUTIFUL EMPRESS, THE; (Eugenie, Empress of
   France) (Oval) ....................................... Small.....    25.00
BEAUTIFUL PAIR; 1872; (Comic)...................... Small.....    30.00
BEAUTIFUL PERSIAN, THE; (Oval)..................... Small.....    18.00
BEAUTIFUL QUADROON, THE........................... Small.....    17.50
BEAUTY ALSEEP ...................................... Small.....    18.00
BEAUTY AWAKE ...................................... Small.....    18.00
BEAUTY OF THE ATLANTIC; (Head)..................... Small.....    20.00
BEAUTY OF THE MISSISSIPPI ......................... Small.....    20.00
BEAUTY OF THE NORTH, THE; (Oval).................. Small.....    20.00
BEAUTY OF THE NORTH WEST ........................ Medium..    20.00
BEAUTY OF THE PACIFIC, THE ....................... Small.....    20.00
BEAUTY OF THE RHINE .............................. Small.....    18.00
BEAUTY OF THE SOUTH (Oval)........................ Small...     20.00
BEAUTY OF THE SOUTH WEST, THE .................. Small.....    20.00
BEAUTY OF VIRGINIA ................................ Small.....    20.00
BED TIME ............................................ Small.....    15.00
BEFORE MARRIAGE; "Anticipation" ................... Small.....    35.00
BEG, SIR; (Child and Dog) ........................... Small.....    25.00
BEGGING A BITE; (Girl and Dog) ..................... Small.....    25.00
BEGGING A CRUST .................................. Medium..    30.00
BELL RINGERS, THE; N. Currier ..................... Small.....    40.00
BELLA; 1876 .......................................... Small.....    50.00
BELLE HAMLIN; 1889.................................. Small.....    55.00
BELLE HAMLIN AND JUSTINA; 1877 .................. Small.....    60.00
BELLE OF CHICAGO .................................. Small .....   18.00
BELLE OF NEW YORK ................................ Small.....    18.50
BELLE OF SARATOGA, THE; N. Currier .............. Medium..    22.50
BELLE OF THE EAST, THE ........................... Medium..    21.50
BELLE OF THE SEA, THE; N. Currier.................. Small.....    20.00
```

```
BELLE OF THE WEST, THE; N. Currier; 1846 .............. Small..... $  22.50
BELLE OF THE WINTER, THE ............................ Medium..    140.00
BELLY-PUNCH, THE; 1876 ................................ Small....    60.00
BELTED WILL'S TOWER, NAWORTH ...................... Small....    35.00
BENDING HER BEAU; 1880................................ Small....    37.50
BENJAMIN FRANKLIN; "The Statesman and Philosopher"
   N. Currier; 1847 ..................................... Small....    80.00
BESSIE; 1872 ........................................... Small....    15.00
BEST HORSE, THE .... .................................. Small....    40.00
BEST IN THE MARKET; 1879 ............................ Small....    24.50
BEST LIKENESS, THE; 1858 ............................. Small....    37.50
BEST SCHOLAR, THE.................................... Small....    30.00
BEST TIME ON RECORD, THREE HEATS; GOLDSMITH
   MAID AND JUDGE FULLERTON........................... Small....    68.50
BETHESDA FOUNTAIN, CENTRAL PARK, N.Y. ........... Small....    50.00
BETROTHED, THE; N. Currier ........................... Small....    25.00
BETWEEN TWO FIRES; 1879.............................. Small....    65.00
BEWILDERED HUNTER, THE; "Puzzle Picture" .........Small....    50.00
BIBLE AND TEMPERANCE, THE; N. Currier ............. Small....    65.00
BIG THING ON ICE, A; 1862 ............................ Small....    90.00
BILLIARDS – A KISS; 1874 ............................. Small....    48.50
BILLIARDS – DOUBLE CAROM; 1874 ..................... Small....    48.50
BILLIARDS – FROZE TOGETHER; 1874 ................... Small....    48.50
BILLIARDS – PLAYED OUT; 1874 ........................ Small....    48.50
BILLY BOYCE – PACER .................................. Small....    55.00
BILLY EDWARDS; "Lightweight Champion Of The World" Medium .   100.00
BIRD TO BET ON, THE; 1872 ........................... Small....    25.00
BIRDIE AND PET....................................... Miniature    20.00
BIRDS EYE VIEW OF THE COLUMBIAN EXPOSITION AT
   CHICAGO; 1892 ...................................... Large....    70.00
BIRDS EYE VIEW OF GREAT SUSPENSION BRIDGE ...... Large....    95.00
BIRDS EYE VIEW OF THE HOME OF WASHINGTON........ Small....    80.00
BIRDS EYE VIEW OF THE PAUPER LUNATIC ASYLUM;
   BLACKWELL'S ISLAND, NEW YORK ..................... Small....    45.00
BIRD'S NEST, THE ..................................... Small....    17.50
BIRTH OF OUR SAVIOR; 1867 .......................... Small....    12.50
BIRTHPLACE OF GENERAL FRANK PIERCE, THE; N.
   Currier; 1852 ....................................... Small....    45.00
BIRTHPLACE OF HENRY CLAY, THE; N. Currier ....... Small....    50.00
BIRTHPLACE OF SHAKESPEARE, THE; N. Currier ..... Medium..    45.00
BIRTHPLACE OF WASHINGTON, THE ..................... Small....    90.00
BITE ALL AROUND; 1879 ............................... Small....    37.50
BITING LIVELY; 1882 .................................. Small....    37.50
BLACK BASS SPEARING; "On the Restigouche, New
   Brunswick"......................................... Medium..   675.00
BLACK BLOND, THE; 1882 .............................. Small.....    18.50
"BLACK CLOUD" Record 2:17¼; 1882.................... Small....    60.00
BLACK DUCK SHOOTING; 1879 ......................... Small....    60.00
BLACK EYED BEAUTY, THE ............................. Small....    20.00
BLACK EYED SUSAN; N. Currier; 1848................... Small....    25.00
BLACK GELDING "FRANK," Record 2:20; 1877.......... Small....    65.00
"BLACK HAWK"; N. Currier; 1850 ..................... Medium..   220.00
"BLACK HAWK" AND "JENNY LIND", 1850; N. Currier Large.....   295.00
BLACK MOUNTAIN...................................... Small.....    35.00
BLACK SQUALL, A; 1879 .............................. Small.....    32.50
BLACKBERRY DELL ..................................... Medium...    50.00
BLACKFISH NIBBLE, A; 1880 ........................... Small.....    45.00
```

BLACKWELL'S ISLAND, EAST RIVER FROM 82nd STREET,
   N.Y.; 1880 .... Medium... $ 200.00
"BLACKWOOD, JR." .... Small 48.50
BLESSED SHEPHERDESS .... Small 10.00
BLESSED VIRGIN MARY .... Small 10.00
BLESSING OF A WIFE .... Small 35.00
BLESSING OF LIBERTY, THE; N. Currier .... Small 32.00
BLOCKADE ON THE "CONNECTICUT PLAN" .... Small 48.00
BLOOD WILL TELL; 1879 .... Small 45.00
BLOOMER COSTUME, THE; N. Currier, 1851 .... S mall 35.00
BLOOMER COSTUME, TURKISH; N. Currier; .... Small 32.50
BLOWER; "The King of the Road"; N. Currier .... Small 37.50
BLUE EYED BEAUTY .... Small..... 20.00
BLUE EYED MARY .... Small..... 20.00
BLUE FISHING .... Small 110.00
BLUE MONDAY .... Small 24.50
BOATSWAIN, THE; N. Currier .... Small 40.00
BODINE; "Trotting Whirlwind of the West"; 1876 .... Small 60.00
BODY OF GEN. ROBERT E. LEE LYING IN STATE, THE
                                                                   Small 25.00
BODY OF HIS HOLINESS POPE PIUS IX LYING IN STATE
                                                                   Small 20.00
BODY OF THE MARTYR PRESIDENT, ABRAHAM LINCOLN;
   1865 .... Small 42.50
BODY OF THE MOST REVEREND ARCHBISHOP HUGHES
   LYING IN STATE .... Small 18.50
BOLTED .... Small 35.00
BOMBARDMENT AND CAPTURE OF FORT FISHER, N.C.
                                                                     Small 55.00
BOMBARDMENT AND CAPTURE OF FORT HENRY, TENN.
                                                                    Small 57.50
BOMBARDMENT AND CAPTURE OF FORT HINDMAN, ARK.
                                                                  Small 48.50
BOMBARDMENT AND CAPTURE OF FREDERICKSBURG
                                                                     Small 40.00
BOMBARDMENT AND CAPTURE OF ISLAND "NUMBER
   TEN" ON THE MISSISSIPPI RIVER; 1862 .... Large 95.00
BOMBARDMENT OF FORT PULASKI, GEORGIA; 1862 . Small 45.00
BOMBARDMENT OF FORT SUMTER .... Small 55.00
BOMBARDMENT OF ISLAND "NUMBER TEN" IN THE
   MISSISSIPPI RIVER; 1862 .... Small 45.00
BOMBARDMENT OF THE FORTS AT HATTERAS INLET,
   N. C. .... Small 50.00
BOMBARDMENT OF TRIPOLI; N. Currier; 1846 .... Small 95.00
BOMBARDMENT OF VERA CRUZ; N. Currier 1847 .... S mall 48.50
BONEFACED CHEEK .... Small 37.50
"BONESETTER"; 1879 .... Small 60.00
BONNIE YOUNG CHIEFTAIN; THE; N. Currier .... Medium... 32.00
BONNINGTON LINN; (Oval) .... Small 48.50
BOOMERANG, A; 1880 .... Small 37.50
BOSS HOSS DRIVEN BY THE KING PIN, THE .... Small .....: 48.00
BOSS OF THE MARKET, THE; 1880 .... Small 35.00
BOSS OF THE RING, THE; 1869 .... Small 32.50
BOSS OF THE ROAD, THE; 1877 .... Small 42.50
BOSS OF THE ROAD, THE; 1884 .... Large..... 70.00
BOSS OF THE TRACK, THE; 1881 .... Small 40.00
BOSS ROOSTER, DE; 1882 .... Small 30.00
BOSS STATE CARRIER, THE 1884 .... Small 37.50
BOSS TEAM, THE; 1882 .... Small 37.50

```
BOTHWELL BRIDGE ON THE CLYDE .......................... Medium ..... $ 50.00
BOTHWELL CASTLE ON THE CLYDE .......................... Medium .....   48.50
BOUND DOWN THE RIVER; 1870 ....... ................... Small.... .....  165.00
BOUND TO HEAR BEECHER; 1881 ............................ Small ........   25.00
BOUND TO SHINE; 1877 ..................................... Small ........   27.50
BOUND TO SMASH; 1877 .................................... Small ........   27.50
BOUQUET, THE; N. Currier; 1846 ......................... Small ........   67.50
BOUQUET OF FRUIT; 1875 .................................. Small ........   67.50
BOUQUET OF ROSES; 1862 .................................. Small ........   67.50
BOUQUET OF THE VASE, THE; 1870 ....................... Small ........   67.50
BOWER OF BEAUTY ........................................ Small ........   20.00
BOWER OF ROSES, THE ................................... Medium .....   67.50
BOY AND DOG ............................................. Small ........   40.00
BOY OF THE PERIOD, THE ................................. Small ........   50.00
BOYNE WATER, THE ...................................... Small ........   30.00
BOZ; (Charles Dickens); N. Currier ...................... Small ........   62.50
BRACE OF MEADOW LARKS; 1879 ......................... Small ........   40.00
BRACK DOG WINS, DE; 1889 .............................. Small ........   25.00
BRANCH AND THE VINE, THE ............................. Small ......   22.50
BRANCH CANNOT BEAR FRUIT, THE; 1872 ............... Small ........   22.50
BRANDING SLAVES; N. Currier; 1845 .................... Small ........  110.00
BRANDY SMASH; 1884 ..................................... Small ........   32.50
BRASS MORTARS TAKEN IN THE COLD SPRING; 1862 .. Medium .....   80.00
BRAVE BOY OF THE WAXHAWS, THE; 1876 .............. Small ........   67.50
BRAVE WIFE, THE ........................................ Small ........   37.50
BREAKING IN; "A Black Imposition" 1881 ............... Small ........   25.00
BREAKING OUT; "A Lively Scrimmage" 1881 ............. Small ........   25.00
BREAKING THAT "BACKBONE" ............................ Small ........   60.00
BRER THULDY'S STATUE; "Liberty Frightenin' De World"
                                                        Small ........   32.50
BRIAN BOROIHME; N. Currier ............................. Small ........   24.00
BRIC-A-BRAC MANIA; 1882 ................................ Small ........   35.00
BRIDAL BOUQUET, THE .................................. Small ........   49.50
"BRIDAL VEIL" FALL, YO-SEMITE VALLEY, CALIF. ... Small. .......   85.00
BRIDAL WREATH, THE .................................... Small ........   28.50
BRIDE, THE; N. Currier; 1847 ............................. Small ........   22.50
BRIDE & BRIDEGROOM, THE ............................. Small ........   22.50
BRIDE OF LAMMERMOOR, THE; N. Currier ............... Small ........   20.00
BRIDE OF THE WHITE HOUSE, THE; (Mrs. Grover Cleveland)
                                                        Small ........   27.50
BRIDESMAID; THE; 1857 .................................. Small ........   28.50
BRIDGE, THE ............................................. Small ........   22.50
BRIDGE AT THE OUTLET, LAKE MEMPHREMAGOG ...... Small ........   45.00
BRIDGET; N. Currier .................................... Small ........   20.00
BRIG; N. Currier ......................................... Small ........   95.00
BRIG. GEN. FRANZ SIGEL; 1861 ......................... Small ........   30.00
BRIG. GEN. IRWIN McDOWELL............................ Small ........   30.00
BRIG. GEN. LOUIS BLENKER ............................. Small ........   30.00
BRIG. GEN. MICHAEL CORCORAN ......................... Small ........   30.00
BRIG. GEN. NATHL. LYON; 1861 ......................... Small ........   3 0.00
BRIG. GEN. ROBERT ANDERSON; "The Hero of Fort Sumter"
                                                        Small ........   30.00
BRIG. GEN. W. S. ROSECRANS, U.S. ARMY .............. Small ........   30.00
BRIG. GEN. W. T. SHERMAN, U. S. A. ................... Small ........   32.00
BRIG. GEN. WM. SPRAGUE, U. S. A. ..................... Medium......   40.00
BRIG "VISION" CAPTAIN DONOVAN, THE ............... Small......   67.50
BRIGAND, THE; N. Currier ............................... Small ........   38.50
BRIGHAM YOUNG ........................................ Medium .....   48.00
```

BRILLIANT CHARGE OF CAPTAIN MAY; N. Currier; 1846
Small........ $35.00
BRILLIANT NAVAL VICTORY; 1862 .... Small........ 67.50
BRING UP YOUR HORSES; 1886 .... Large........ 145.00
BROADWAY BELLE, A .... Small........ 20.00
BROADWAY, NEW YORK, FROM THE WESTERN UNION
  TELEGRAPH BUILDING, LOOKING NORTH; 1875 ... Large........ 1400.00
BROADWAY, NEW YORK, SOUTH FROM THE PARK; N.
  Currier .... Small........ 125.00
BRONZE STATUE OF ANDREW JACKSON .... Small........ 20.00
BROOK, THE .... Small........ 35.00
BROOK, SUMMER, THE .... Small........ 35.00
BROOK TROUT FISHING; "An Anxious Moment"; 1862 .. Large........ 600.00
BROOK TROUT FISHING; 1872 .... Small........ 175.00
BROOK TROUT — JUST CAUGHT; 1858 .... Medium...... 65.00
BROTHER AND SISTER; N. Currier .... Small........ 35.00
BRUSH FOR THE LEAD, A; 1867 .... Large........ 395.00
BRUSH ON THE HOMESTRETCH, THE; 1869.............. Large 175.00
BRUSH ON THE ROAD; "Best Two in Three"; N. Currier;
  1872 .... Small........ 80.00
BRUSH ON THE ROAD, A; MILE HEATS; "Best Two In
  Three"; N. Currier; 1853 .... Medium 125.00
BRUSH ON THE SNOW .... Large........ 200.00
BRUSH WITH WEBSTER CARTS, A; 1884.................... Small........ 175.00
BUCK TAKING THE POT .... Small........ 33.50
BUD OF THE DRIVING PARK; 1876........................... Small........ 50.00
BUDS OF PROMISE; N. Currier .... Small........ 20.00
BUFFALO AND CHICAGO STEAM PACKET "EMPIRE
  STATE"; N. Currier .... Small........ 115.00
BUFFALO BULL, CHASING BACK .... Large 250.00
BUFFALO CHASE, THE .... Large 235.00
BUFFALO DANCE — TO MAKE THE BUFFALOES COME Medium 125.00
BUFFALO HUNT ON SNOW SHOES; "Winter on the
  Northern Prairies"... Medium...... 245.00
BUFFALO HUNT; "Surrounding the Herd" .... Medium...... 225.00
BUFFALO HUNT — THE SURPRISE .... Medium...... 180.00
BUFFALO HUNT UNDER THE WHITE WOLF SKIN ...... Medium...... 225.00
BULL-DOZED; 1875 .... Small........ 27.50
BULLY TEAM, THE; (Scaldine and Early Nose) 1882 ...... Small........ 55.00
BURIAL OF CHRIST, THE; N. Currier .... Small........ 12.50
BURIAL OF DESOTO; 1876 .. .. Small........ 15.00
BURIAL OF THE BIRD, THE .... Small........ 15.00
BURNING GLASS, THE; 1860 .... Medium 60.00
BURNING OF CHICAGO, THE; 1871 .... Small........ 110.00
BURNING OF THE CITY HALL, N. Y.......................... Small........ 150.00
BURNING OF THE CLIPPER SHIP "GOLDEN LIGHT" .. Small 95.00
BURNING OF THE "HENRY CLAY," NEAR YONKERS:
  N. Currier; 1852 .... Small........ 90.00
BURNING OF THE INMAN LINE STEAMSHIP "CITY OF
  MONTREAL"; 1887... Small........ 75.00
BURNING OF THE NEW YORK CRYSTAL PALACE .... Large........ 395.00
BURNING OF THE NEW YORK CRYSTAL PALACE .... Small 95.00
BURNING OF THE "OCEAN MONARCH"; N. Currier;
  1848 .... Small........ 65.00
BURNING OF THE PALACE STEAMER "ROBERT E.
  LEE"; 1882 .... Small........ 65.00
BURNING OF THE SPLENDID STEAMSHIP "ERIE" OFF
  SILVER CREEK, LAKE ERIE; N. Currier .... Small........ 90.00

```
BURNING OF THE STEAMSHIP "AUSTRIA" ................. Small..... $ 50.00
BURNING OF THE STEAMSHIP "GOLDEN GATE" ........ Small..... 75.00
BURNING OF THE STEAMSHIP "NARRAGANSETT" ..... Small..... 65.00
BURNING OF THE THRONE, PARIS; N. Currier ,........... Small..... 25.00
BURNING OF THE U.S. SHIP OF THE LINE "PENNSYL-
    VANIA"; 1861 ................................................... Small..... 100.00
BURNING OF WARWICK CASTLE, Dec. 3, 1871 ...........Small..... 35.00
BUSTIN' A PICNIC ..................................................Small..... 25.00
BUSTIN' THE POOL; 1889 .........................................Small..... 25.00
BUSTIN' THE RECORD...............................................Small..... 55.00
BUTT OF THE JOKERS, THE; 1879 ...........................Small..... 35.00
BUTTERMILK FALLS; (Oval) .....................................Small..... 25.00
BY THE SEASHORE; 1868 .........................................Medium.. 50.00
BYRON AND MARIANNA; N. Currier .........................Small..... 20.00
BYRON IN THE HIGHLANDS ....................................Small..... 20.00
BYRON'S FIRST LOVE; N. Currier .............................Small.... 20.00


                            - C -


CAKE WALK, DE; 1883 .............................................. Small.....$ 22.50
CAIRN'S QUICK STEP; N. Currier ............................ Small..... 20.00
CALIFORNIA BEAUTY, THE    ................................. Small..... 15.00
CALIFORNIA GOLD; N. Currier ................................ Small..... 195.00
CALIFORNIA "OCCIDENT" (Formerly "Wonder"); 1873.. Small..... 60.00
CALIFORNIA SCENERY; "Seal Rocks — Point Lobos" ..Small..... 60.00
CALIFORNIA WONDER HINDA ROSE,, THE; Record 2:19½;
    1883 ................................................................. Small..... 65.00
CALIFORNIA YO-SEMITE FALLS .............................. Small..... 65.00
CALIFORNIAN SEEKING THE ELEPHANT; N. Currier... Small..... 50.00
CAMPING IN THE WOODS; "A Good Time Coming" 1863. Large.... 375.00
CAMPING IN THE WOODS; "Laying Off"; 1863 .......... Large.... 375.00
CAMPING OUT ....................................................... Small..... 60.00
CAMPING OUT; "Life in the Woods"; 1879 ............... Medium.. 129.00
CAMPING OUT; "Some of the Right Sort"; N. Currier;
    1856 ................................................................ Large.... 380.00
CAN YOU KEEP A SECRET? 1872 ........................... Small..... 16.50
CANADIAN VOYAGEURS WALKING A CANOE UP THE
    RAPID   ........................................................... Small..... 65.00
CANADIAN WINTER SCENE ..................................... Medium.. 240.00
CANAL SCENE, MOONLIGHT; (ERIE) ........................ Small..... 72.50
CANARY BIRD, THE    ............................................ Small..... 16.50
CAN'T BE BEAT; 1880 ............................................. Small..... 27.50
CAN'T PLAY; N. Currier ........................................ Small..... 20.00
CAN'T YOU TALK? (Child and Animal) ..................... Small..... 20.00
CANVAS-BACKS ..................................................... Small..... 87.50
CAPABILITY AND AVAILABILITY; N. Currier ............. Small..... 45.00
CAPITAL CIGAR, A ................................................. Miniature 15.00
CAPITAL JOKE, A ................................................... Small..... 21.50
CAPITOL AT WASHINGTON; N. Currier .................... Small..... 57.50
CAPITULATION OF VERA CRUZ; N. Currier; 1847 ........ Small..... 40.00
CAPT. CHARLES WILKES, U.S.N.   ........................... Small..... 35.00
CAPT. JOHN T.CAIRNS    N. Currier ....................... Miniature 15.00
CAPTURE AND FALL OF CHARLESTON, S.C. ........... Small..... 40.00
CAPTURE OF AN UNPROTECTED FEMALE, or CLOSE
    OF THE REBELLION .......................................... Small..... 40.00
CAPTURE OF ANDRE, 1780; N. Currier; 1845 .............. Small..... 50.00
CAPTURE OF ATLANTA, GA. N. Currier ................... Small..... 35.00
```

```
CAPTURE OF GENERAL LA VEGA ........................... Small..... $ 32.50
CAPTURE OF JEFF DAVIS, THE ............................. Small..... 40.00
CAPTURE OF ROANOKE ISLAND .............................. Small..... 50.00
CAPTURING A WILD HORSE ................................. Medium .. 125.00
CAPTURING THE WHALE; N. Currier ....................... Small..... 195.00
CARDINAL IMPOSING THE BERETTA, THE; 1875 ......... Small..... 15.00
CARDINAL JAMES GIBBONS ................................. Small..... 15.00
CARDINAL McCLOSKEY ..................................... Small..... 15.00
CARES OF A FAMILY, THE ................................ Large .... 650.00
CARES OF A FAMILY, THE ................................ Small .... 100.00
CARLO'S ABC's .......................................... Small..... 22.00
CARLO'S FIRST LESSON .................................. Medium .. 27.50
CAROLINE; N. Currier; 1844.............................. Small..... 20.00
CAROLINE; N. Currier; 1846 ............................ Small..... 20.00
CARRIER DOVE, THE ..................................... Small..... 18.50
CARRIER DOVE — THE DEPARTURE; N. Currier........... Small..... 18.50
CARRIER DOVE — THE RETURN; N. Currier .............. Small..... 18.50
CASH ON DELIVERY; 1868 ................................ Small..... 60.00
CASH SYSTEM; 1877 ..................................... Small..... 35.00
CASSIUS M. CLAY OF KENTUCKY; N. Currier; 1846 ....... Small..... 35.00
CASTLE, BLARNEY, IRELAND, THE ........................ Small..... 35.00
CASTLE GARDEN, NEW YORK, FROM THE BATTERY;
    N. Currier; 1848 ................................... Small..... 200.00
CASTLE OF CHILLON, LAKE OF GENEVA ................ Small..... 37,50
CASTLE OF CHILLON, LAKE OF GENEVA ................ Medium .. 50.00
CATASTROPHE; N. Currier ............................... Small..... 24.50
CATCHING A TROUT; "We Hab You Now, Sar"; N. Currier;
    1854 ............................................... Large.... 300.00
CATHERINE; N. Currier; 1845 ........................... Small..... 25.00
CATHERINE HAYES; N. Currier ........................... Small..... 28.50
CATHOLIC MEMORY; N. Currier .... ..................... Small..... 12.50
CAT NAP, A; 1858 ...................................... Medium .. 50.00
CATS-PAW, THE ......................................... Small..... 30.00
CATTERSKILL FALL, THE ................................ Small..... 48.50
CATTSKILL CREEK ....................................... Miniature 32.50
CATTSKILL MOUNTAINS .................................. Large .... 300.00
CAUGHT IN THE ACT .................................... Small..... 30.00
CAUGHT NAPPING; 1879 ................................. Small..... 22.50
CAUGHT ON THE FLY; 1879............................... Small..... 48.00
CAUSE AND EFFECT; "Natural Result" 1887 ............. Small..... 27.50
CAUSE AND EFFECT; "Timely Warning" 1887............. Small..... 27.50
CAVALRY TACTICS BY THE HORSE GUARDS; 1887..... Small ..... 40.00
CAVED IN — THE BUSTED SCULLER; 1876............. Medium .. 45.00
CECELIA; N. Currier ................................... Small ..... 20.00
CEDARS OF LEBANON..................................... Small..... 25.00
CELA WINDER; 1883 .................................... Small..... 27.50
CELEBRATED BOSTON TEAM "MILL BOY" AND
    "BLONDINE"; 1882 .................................. Large.... 160.00
CELEBRATED CLIPPER BARK GRAPESHOT; N. Currier Small..... 150.00
CELEBRATED CLIPPER SHIP "DREADNOUGHT"........ Small..... 75.00
CELEBRATED CLIPPER SHIP "DREADNOUGHT" OFF
    TUSKAR LIGHT....................................... Small..... 75.00
CELEBRATED ETHIOPIAN MELODIES; N. Currier......... Small..... 15.00
CELEBRATED "FOUR-IN.HAND" STALLION TEAM...... Large .... 235.00
CELEBRATED HORSE "DEXTER", The King of the Turf;
    1865 .............................................. Large.... 165.00
CELEBRATED HORSE "DEXTER," The King of the World;
    1867 .............................................. Large .... 165.00
```

CELEBRATED HORSE "GEORGE M. PATCHEN," The
Champion of the Turf" 1860 .... Large ... $150.00
CELEBRATED HORSE "JOHN STEWART" 1869 .... Large ... 140.00
CELEBRATED HORSE "LEXINGTON"; N. Currier, 1855. Large ... 425.00
CELEBRATED KOOK FAMILY .... Large ... 300.00
CELEBRATED MARE "FLORA TEMPLE," The Queen of
the Turf" 1853 ....Large ... 65.00
CELEBRATED PACING MARE "POCAHONTAS"; N.
Currier; 1855 ....Large... 185.00
CELEBRATED PLOUGH HORSE "CAPTAIN LEWIS"......Small. ... 60.00
CELEBRATED STALLION TRIO, A ....Large ... 70.00
CELEBRATED STALLIONS "GEORGE WILKES," AND
"COMMODORE VANDERBILT"; 1866 ....Large ... 150.00
CELEBRATED TERRIER DOG "MAJOR" Performing His
Wonderful Feat of Killing 100 Rats in 8 Minutes, 58 Sec-
onds; N. Currier ....Large ... 95.00
CELEBRATED TROTTER "MOOSE" Record 2:19½; 1881 .Small.... 55.00
CELEBRATED TROTTING HORSE " CAMORS "; 1874 ....Small.... 60.00
CELEBRATED TROTTING HORSE "GLOSTER," 1874 ....Small.... 60.00
CELEBRATED TROTTING HORSE, HENRY; 1872 ....Small.... 60.00
CELEBRATED TROTTING HORSE "HOPEFUL" Record
2:14¾; 1880 ....Large.... 150.00
CELEBRATED TROTTING HORSE "HOPEFUL" Record
2:14¾; 1881 ....Large.... 150.00
CELEBRATED TROTTING HORSE "JUDGE FULLERTON"
1874 ....Large.... 165.00
CELEBRATED TROTTING HORSE "PROSPERO"; 1877.. Small.... 125.00
CELEBRATED TROTTING HORSE "TRUSTEE" 1848.... Large.... 150.00
CELEBRATED TROTTING MARE "DAISYDALE" Record
2:19¾; 1881 ....Small.... 50.00
CELEBRATED TROTTING MARE "FLORA TEMPLE"
1872 ....Small.... 55.00
CELEBRATED TROTTING MARE "HATTIE WOODWARD"
1881 ....Large... 175.00
CELEBRATED TROTTING MARE "HUNTRESS"; 1873 ....Small.... 70.00
CELEBRATED TROTTING MARE "LADY THORN"; 1866 Large.... 165.00
CELEBRATED TROTTING MARE "LUCILLE GOLDDUST"
Record 2:16¼; 1877 .... Small.... 65.00
CELEBRATED TROTTING MARE "LUCY"—Passing the
Judges Stand; 1872 .... Large.... 175.00
CELEBRATED TROTTING MARE "LULA"; 1874.......... Small.... 55.00
CELEBRATED TROTTING MARES "MAUD'S" AND
"ALDINE"; 1883 ....Large.... 175.00
CELEBRATED TROTTING MARE "WIDOW McCHREE";....Large.... 185.00
CELEBRATED TROTTING STALLION "ALEXANDER"
Record 2:19; 1882 ....Large.... 150.00
CELEBRATED TROTTING STALLION "ETHAN ALLEN"Small.... 65.00
CELEBRATED TROTTING STALLIONS "ETHAN ALLEN"
AND "GEORGE M. PATCHEN"; 1858..............Large.... 195.00
CELEBRATED TROTTING STALLION "FRANCIS
ALEXANDER" 1882 .... Large.... 165.00
CELEBRATED TROTTING STALLION "GEORGE
WILKES" (Originally "Robert Fillingham") 1866 .... Large.... 165.00
CELEBRATED TROTTING STALLION "JAY GOULD".... Small.... 55.00
CELEBRATED TROTTING STALLION "WOODFORD
MAMBRINO"; 1878 ....Small.... 60.00
CELEBRATED TROTTING STALLIONS "YOUNG WOFUL"
AND "ABDALLAH CHIEF" ....Large.... 195.00

CELEBRATED TROTTING TEAM "EDWARD" AND
  "SWIVELLER" ....Large.... $200.00
CELEBRATED WINNING HORSES AND JOCKEYS OF THE
  AMERICAN TURF; 1888 ....Large.... 215.00
CELEBRATED WINNING HORSES AND JOCKEYS OF THE
  AMERICAN TURF; 1889 ....Large.... 225.00
CELEBRATED WINNING HORSES AND JOCKEYS OF THE
  AMERICAN TURF; 1891 (Painted by Charles Zellinsky)Large.... 245.00
CELEBRATED YACHT "AMERICA" ....Small.... 95.00
CENTENNIAL EXHIBITION BUILDINGS, PHILA. 1875.....Small.... 50.00
"CENTERVILLE" AND "BLACK DOUGLAS"; 1853 ......Large.... 175.00
CENTRAL PARK IN WINTER ....Small.... 300.00
CENTRAL PARK IN WINTER, SLEIGHING ....Small.... 300.00
CENTRAL PARK — THE BRIDGE ....Small.... 75.00
CENTRAL PARK — THE DRIVE; 1862 ....Medium.. 120.00
CENTRAL PARK — THE LAKE; 1862 ....Medium.. 120.00
CENTRAL PARK, WINTER — THE SKATING CARNIVAL..Small.... 195.00
CENTRAL PARK, WINTER — THE SKATING POND; 1862 Large.... 1275.00
CENTRE HARBOR, LAKE WINNIPISEOGEE, N. H. .... Large.... 210.00
CERITO IN THE SYLPHIDE; N. Currier; 1846 .... Small.... 30.00
CERTIFICATE OF BAPTISM; N. Currier (German) .... Small.... 12.00
CERTIFICATE OF HONOR; 1863............................... Small.... 12.00
CHAMPION IN DANGER, THE; 1882 .... Small.... 60.00
CHAMPION IN LUCK, THE; 1882 .... Small.... 60.00
CHAMPION IRISH SETTER, "ROVER"'' .... Small.... 140.00
CHAMPION PACER JOHNSTON; Record 2:10 .... Large.... 160.00
CHAMPION PACER "MASCOT" Record 2:04; 1892 .... Small.... 55.00
CHAMPION PACER "MASCOT",Record 2:04 .... Large.... 185.00
CHAMPION RACE, A; (Jay Eye See and Maud S.)........... Large.... 150.00
CHAMPION ROWIST — THE PRIDE OF THE CLUB; 1876 Medium.. 40.00
CHAMPION SLUGGER — KNOCKING 'EM OUT; 1883 .... Small.... 32.00
CHAMPION STALLION "DIRECTUM" Record 2:06½ ...... Small.... 57.50
CHAMPION STALLION "GEORGE WILKES"; 1888 .... Large.... 135.00
CHAMPION STALLION "MAXY COBB" Record 2:13¼ ..... Large.... 135.00
CHAMPION STEER OF THE WORLD; 1877 .... Small.... 60.00
CHAMPION TROTTING QUEEN "ALIX"; 1893 ....Small.... 65.00
CHAMPION TROTTING QUEEN "ALIX"; Record 2:03¾;
  ·1894 .... Large.... 150.00
CHAMPION TROTTING STALLION "NELSON" 1891....... Large.... 165.00
CHAMPION TROTTING STALLION "SMUGGLER" 1875... Large.... 175.00
CHAMPIONS AT CLOSE QUARTERS; 1892 ....Small.... 60.00
CHAMPIONS OF BALL RACKET; "At the Close of the
  Season " 1885 ....Small.... 50.00
CHAMPIONS OF BALL RACKET; "On the Diamond Field"
  1886 .... Small.... 50.00
CHAMPIONS OF THE BARN; 1876 .... Small.... 30.00
CHAMPIONS OF THE BARN YARD .... Small.... 27.50
CHAMPIONS OF THE FIELD .... Small.... 175.00
CHAMPIONS OF THE MISSISSIPPI; "A Race for the Buck-
  horns" 1866 ....Small.... 275.00
CHAMPIONS OF THE UNION....................................... Large.... 65.00
CHANCES OF BILLIARDS, THE; "A Scratch All Around"
  1869 .... Large.... 135.00
"CHANG" AND "ENG." (World Renowned Siamese Twins)
  1860 .... Small.... 48.00
CHANGE OF BASE, A; 1883 .... Small.... 30.00
CHANGE OF DRIVERS UNDER THE RULE, A; 1876....... Small.... 50.00
CHANGED MAN; 1879 .... Small.... 35.00

CHAPPAQUA FARM, WESTCHESTER COUNTY, N.Y., 1872..Small...$ 55.00
CHARLES; N. Currier; 1845 .... Small... 22.50
CHARLES F. ADAMS; N. Currier; 1848............................ Small... 32.50
CHARLES O. SCOTT — THE PRIZE BABY BOY IN 1855;
    N. Currier; 1855.. Small... 35.00
CHARLES ROWELL; "The Celebrated Pedestrian"............. Small... 45.00
CHARLES STEWART PARNELL, M.P............................... Small... 25.00
CHARLES STEWART PARNELL, M.P., 1881 .... Small... 25.00
CHARLES SUMNER .... Small... 25.00
CHARLES WESLEY, A. M., N. Currier............................ Small... 22.50
"CHARLEY FORD" 1880 .... Small... 55.00
CHARLEY — THE PRIZE BABY BOY; 1857 .... Small... 27.50
CHARLIE IS MY DARLING; 1872 .... Small... 22.50
CHARLOTTE; N. Currier .... Small... 22.50
CHARTER OAK! CHARTER OAK! ANCIENT AND FAIR...... Small... 25.00
CHASE (THE) — IN THE OLDEN TIME; N. Currier .... Small... 47.50
CHATHAM SQUARE, NEW YORK; N. Currier .... Small... 200.00
CHECK, A; "Keep Your Distance"; N. Currier .... Medium. 560.00
CHERRY TIME; 1866 .... Small... 40.00
"CHESTNUT HILL" 1879 .... Small... 50.00
CHICAGO AS IT WAS .... Small... 100.00
CHICAGO IN FLAMES..Small... 110.00
CHICAGO PLATFORM AND CANDIDATE, THE . ... Small... 35.00
CHICKY'S DINNER .... Small... 25.00
CHIEF COOK AND BOTTLE WASHER; N. Currier .... Small... 25.00
CHILD JESUS, THE.. Small... 12.50
CHILDHOOD'S HAPPY DAYS; 1863 ....Medium. 50.00
CHILDREN AT PLAY.. Small... 35.00
CHILDREN IN THE WOODS, THE .... Small... 35.00
CHILDREN'S PIC-NIC, THE .... Small... 37.50
CHINCHA ISLANDS, THE .... Small... 45.00
CHINESE JUNK KEYING, THE; N. Currier; 1847 .... Small... 60.00
CHIP OFF THE OLD BLOCK, A; N. Currier...................... Medium 57.50
CHOICE APPLES .... Small... 37.50
CHOICE BOUQUET; 1872 .... Small... 55.00
CHOICE SEGARS AND FINE TOBACCO (Adv.) .... Small... 25.00
CHOICE FRUIT; 1865 .... Large .. 75.00
CHRIST AND THE ANGELS...Small... 12.50
CHRIST AND THE WOMAN OF SAMARIA AT JACOB'S WELL;
    N. Currier .... Small... 12.50
CHRIST AT THE WELL; N. Currier; 1846 .... Small... 12.00
CHRIST BEARING HIS CROSS; N. Currier .... Small... 12.00
CHRIST BEFORE PILATE; N. Currier; 1847 .... Small... 12.00
CHRIST BLESSING THE CHILDREN .... Small... 12.00
CHRIST HEALING THE BLIND; N. Currier .... Small... 12.00
CHRIST HEALING THE SICK .... Small... 12.00
CHRIST IN THE GARDEN OF GETHSEMANE .... Small... 12.00
CHRIST IS OUR LIGHT — OUR STAR OF REDEMPTION ..... Small... 12.00
CHRIST RESTORETH THE BLIND; N. Currier; 1846.......... Small... 12.00
CHRIST RESTORETH THE BLIND; N. Currier; 1847.......... Small... 12.00
CHRIST STILLING THE TEMPEST; 1871 .... Small... 12.00
CHRIST THE CONSOLER .... Small... 12.00
CHRIST WALKING ON THE SEA; N. Currier .... Small... 12.00
CHRIST WEEPING OVER JERUSALEM .... Small... 12.00
CHRIST'S ENTRY INTO JERUSALEM .... Small... 12.00
CHRIST'S SERMON ON THE MOUNT; "The Parable of the
    Lily" 1866 .... Small... 12.00
CHRISTIAN'S HOPE; 1874... Small... 12.00

CHRISTIAN'S REFUGE, THE; 1868 .... Small... 12.00
CHRISTMAS SNOW .... Miniature 72.50
CHRISTOPHER COLUMBUS; 1892 .... Small... 45.00
CHRISTUS CONSOLATUS .... Small... 12.00
CIRCULATING MEDIUM, A .... Small... 45.00
CITY HALL AND COUNTY COURT HOUSE, NEWARK, N.J. Small... 195.00
CITY HALL, NEW YORK; N. Currier .... Small... 125.00
CITY HALL AND VICINITY, NEW YORK CITY .... Small... 140.00
CITY HOTEL, BROADWAY, N.Y., N. Currier; (RARE) .... Small... 200.00
CITY OF BOSTON, THE; 1873 .... Large.. 185.00
CITY OF BROOKLYN; 1879 .... Small... 100.00
CITY OF BROOKLYN; Fireman's Certificate) .... Small... 18.50
CITY OF CHICAGO, THE; 1874 .... Large .. 200.00
CITY OF CHICAGO; (Steamship) 1892 .... Large.. 165.00
CITY OF JUNGO; N. Currier; 1840,................................. Small... 35.00
CITY OF MEXICO; "From the Convent of San Cosme" N.
   Currier; 1847 .... Small... 40.00
CITY OF NEW ORLEANS, THE; 1885 .... Large .. 150.00
CITY OF NEW ORLEANS, THE .... Small... 80.00
CITY OF NEW YORK; N. Currier; 1844 .... Small... 160.00
CITY OF NEW YORK; N. Currier; 1855 .... Large.. 450.00
CITY OF NEW YORK AND ENVIRONS; 1875.................... Small... 275.00
CITY OF NEW YORK FROM JERSEY CITY; N. Currier;
   1849 .... Small... 175.00
CITY OF NEW YORK, THE; (Equitable Life Bldg.) 1876 .... Large.. 220.00
"CITY OF PEKING," Pacific Mail Steamship Co. .... Small... 50.00
CITY OF PHILADELPHIA, THE 1875 .... Large.. 195.00
CITY OF ST. LOUIS, THE; 1874................................. Large... 215.00
CITY OF SAN FRANCISCO, THE .... Small... 130.00
CITY OF SAN FRANCISCO, BIRD'S-EYE VIEW FROM THE
   BAY, LOOKING SOUTHWEST; 1878 .... Large.. 225.00
CLAM BOY ON HIS MUSCLE .... Small... 35.00
CLARA; N. Currier; 1849 .... Small... 20.00
CLARISSA; N. Currier .... Small... 20.00
CLEAN SWEEP, A; 1889 .... Small... 30.00
CLEAR GRIT; (Dog and Rat)................................... Small... 35.00
CLEARING, A; "On the American Frontier .... Small... 125.00
CLEVELAND FAMILY, THE; 1893 .... Small... 25.00
CLEVELAND SMILE, THE .... Small... 30.00
CLIFTON HALL, BRISTOL COLLEGE, PA. N. Currier ...... Small... 35.00
CLIPPER SHIP "ADELAIDE; 'Hove to for a Pilot' " .... Large ..2500.00
CLIPPER SHIP "COMET" OF N.Y., N. Currier .... Large..1500.00
CLIPPER SHIP "CONTEST": N. Currier; 1853 .... Large..2450.00
CLIPPER SHIP "DREADNOUGHT"; N. Currier; 1854 .... Large ..1500.00
CLIPPER SHIP "DREADNOUGHT",— OFF TUSKAR LIGHT;
   N. Currier; 1856 .... Large..1200.00
CLIPPER SHIP "FLYING CLOUD"; N. Currier; 1852 .... Large..2400.00
CLIPPER SHIP "GREAT REPUBLIC"; N. Currier; 1853 ... Large..1000.00
CLIPPER SHIP "GREAT REPUBLIC" .... Small... 125.00
CLIPPER SHIP "HURRICANE"; N. Currier; 1852 .... Large..3500.00
CLIPPER SHIP IN A SNOW SQUALL, A .... Small... 200.00
CLIPPER SHIP "LIGHTNING"; N. Currier; 1854 .... Large..2250.00
CLIPPER SHIP "NIGHTINGALE"; N. Currier; 1854 .... Large..3000.00
CLIPPER SHIP "OCEAN EXPRESS"; N. Currier; 1856 ...... Large..1200.00
CLIPPER SHIP "QUEEN OF CLIPPERS"; N. Currier ...... Small... 200.00
CLIPPER SHIP "RACER"; N. Currier; 1854 .... Large..2850.00
CLIPPER SHIP "RED JACKET"................................ Small... 195.00
CLIPPER SHIP "RED JACKET"; N. Currier; 1855 .... Large..1500.00

CLIPPER SHIP "SOVEREIGN OF THE SEAS"; N. Currier
  1852 .... Large. $2400.00
CLIPPER SHIP "SWEEPSTAKES"; N. Currier; 1853 .... Large. $2250.00
CLIPPER SHIP "THREE BROTHERS" .... Small... 200.00
CLIPPER SHIP "THREE BROTHERS"; 1875 .... Large... 750.00
CLIPPER SHIP "YOUNG AMERICA"; N. Currier; 1853 ...... Large...2450.00
CLIPPER SHIPS HOMEWARD BOUND .... Small... 225.00
CLIPPER YACHT "AMERICA", THE; N. Currier .... Medium 350.00
CLIPPER YACHT "AMERICA" OF N. Y., N. Currier .... Small... 200.00
CLOSE CALCULATION, A; "Don't You Wish You May Get
  It?" N. Currier .... Small... 32.50
CLOSE FINISH, A; 1874 .... Small... 65.00
CLOSE HEAT, A; 1873 .... Large .. 215.00
CLOSE LAP ON THE RUN IN A; 1886 .... Large... 180.00
CLOSE QUARTERS; 1866 .... Large... 200.00
COACHING SCENE .... Small... 45.00
COCK-A-DOODLE-DO; (Rooster) .... Small... 40.00
COCK OF THE WALK; 1879 .... Small... 60.00
COD FISHING — OFF NEWFOUNDLAND; 1872 .... Small... 375.00
COL. E. L. SNOW; C. Currier .... Small... 20.00
COL. ELMER E. ELLSWORTH .... Small... 20.00
COL. FRANK P. BLAIR; "First Regiment Missouri Volun-
  teers" 1861 .... Small... 20.00
COL. FREMONT'S LAST GRAND EXPLORING EXPEDITION
  IN 1856; (Political Cartoon) .... Small... 40.00
COL. H. S. RUSSELL'S "SUMGGLER" 1876 .... Small... 55.00
COL. HARNEY AT THE DRAGOON FIGHT AT MADELIN,
  NEAR VERA CRUZ; N. Currier; 1847 .... Small... 35.00
COL. JOHN E. WOOL; N. Currier; 1847 .... Small... 25.00
COL. JOHN O'MAHONEY .... Small... 25.00
COL. MAX WEBER .... Small... 25.00
COL. MICHAEL CORCORAN .... Small... 25.00
COL. MICHAEL CORCORAN AT THE BATTLE OF BULL
  RUN, VA. .... Small... 25.00
COL. RICHARD M. JOHNSON; N. Currier; 1846.......... Small... 22.50
COLORED BEAUTY; 1872 .... Small... 15.00
COLORED BELLE, THE .... Small... 15.00
COLORED INFANTRY .... Large... 75.00
COLORED VOLUNTEER, THE (Oval)........................ Large... 25.00
COLORED VOLUNTEER MARCHING INTO DIXIE, THE .....Small... 18.50
COLORING HIS MEERSCHAUM; 1879 .... Small... 25.00
COLUMBIA; (Girl's Head).................................... Small... 20.00
COM. ANDREW H. FOOTE .... Small... 30.00
COM. FARRAGUT'S FLEET, PASSING THE FORTS ON THE
  MISSISSIPPI; 1862 .... Small... 45.00
COMBAT AT THE MILITARY STATION OF CHATEAU D'EAU;
  N. Currier; 1848 .... Small... 40.00
COME INTO THE GARDEN, MAUD .... Small... 18.00
COME TAKE A DRINK; 1868 .... Small .. 32.50
COMING FROM THE TROT; 1869 .... Large... 250.00
COMING IN "ON HIS EAR"; 1875 .... Small... 40.00
COMING MATCH; 1881 .... Small... 27.50
COMING THE PUTTY; N. Currier; 1853 .... Small... 95.00
COMING UP SMILING; 1884 .... Small... 30.00
COMMANDER IN CHIEF, THE; 1863 .... Small... 40.00
COMMODORE NUTT, THE; (Midget) .... Small... 48.50
COMMON LOT; THE; N. Currier .... Small... 18.00

COMPAGNIE GENERALE TRANS-ATLANTIQUE STEAMER
"LA BOURGOGNE" .... Small ... 48.50
COMPAGNIE GENERALE TRANS-ATLANTIQUE STEAMER
"LA BRETAGNE" .... Small ... 48.50
COMPAGNIE GENERALE TRANS-ATLANTIQUE STEAMER
"LA CHAMPAGNE" .... Small ... 48.50
COMPAGNIE GENERALE TRANS-ATLANTIQUE STEAMER
"LA GASCOGNE" .... Small ... 48.50
CAMPAGNIE GENERALE TRANS-ATLANTIQUE STEAMER
"L'AQUITAINE" .... Small ... 48.50
CAMPAGNIE GANERALE TRANS-ATLANTIQUE STEAMER
"LA LORRAINE" .... Small ... 48.50
COMPAGNIE GENERALE TRANS-ATLANTIQUE STEAMER
"LA TOURAINE" .... Small ... 45.00
CONFEDERACY — THE SECESSION MOVEMENT .... Small ... 40.00
CONGRESSIONAL SCALES — A TRUE BALANCE; N. Currier
1850 .... Small ... 40.00
CONSTITUTION AND GUERRIERE, THE; N. Currier; 1846. Small ... 165.00
CONSTITUTION AND JAVA; N. Currier 1846 .... Small ... 150.00
CONTESTED SEAT, A; (Political Cartoon) .... Small ... 40.00
COOLING STREAM, THE .... Medium. 75.00
COON CLUB HUNT; "Hot On The Scent" 1885 .... Small ... 40.00
COON CLUB HUNT; "Taking a Header" 1885 .... Small ... 40.00
COPPED AT A COCK FIGHT; 1884 .... Small ... 35.00
CORDELIA HOWARD AS "EVA" IN "UNCLE TOM'S
CABIN" C. Currier .... Small ... 32.50
CORINTHIAN RACE, A; "A High-Toned Start" 1883 .... Small ... 35.00
CORINTHIAN RACE, A; "A Low-Toned Finish" 1883 ...... Small ... 35.00
CORNELIA: N. Currier; 1846 .... Small ... 20.00
CORNWALLIS IS TAKEN; 1876 .... Small ... 125.00
"CORONET" AND "DAUNTLESS" 1887 .... Small ... 60.00
CORRECT LIKENESS OF MR. H. ROCKWELL'S HORSE
ALEXANDER; N. Currier .... Small ... 50.00
CORSAIRS ISLE, THE .... Medium. 40.00
COTTAGE BY THE CLIFF, THE .... Small ... 35.00
COTTAGE BY THE WAYSIDE, THE .... Small ... 35.00
COTTAGE DOORYARD — EVENING, THE; N. Currier .... Medium. 48.50
COTTAGE LIFE — SPRING; 1856 .... Medium. 45.00
COTTAGE LIFE — SUMMER; 1856 .... Medium. 45.00
COTTAGES, THE .... Miniature 22.50
COTTER'S SATURDAY NIGHT .... Small ... 37.50
COTTON PLANTATION ON THE MISSISSIPPI, A; 1884 ..... Large... 250.00
COURAGEOUS CONDUCT OF A YOUNG GIRL; N. Currier;
1875 .... Small ... 32.50
COURSE OF TRUE LOVE, THE; 1875 .... Small ... 20.00
COUSINS, THE; N. Currier .... Small ... 16.50
COVE OF CORK, THE .... Small ... 30.00
COZZEN'S DOCK, WEST POINT, HUDSON RIVER .... Medium. 200.00
CRACK SHOT; 1879 .... Small ... 32.50
CRACK SHOTS IN POSITION; 1875 .... Small ... 37.50
CRACK SLOOP IN A RACE TO THE WINDWARD, A; (Yacht
"Gracie") 1882 .... Large .. 200.00
CRACK TEAM AT A SMASHING GAIT, A; 1869 .... Large... 150.00
CRACK TROTTER, A; "Coming Around" 1880 .... Small ... 45.00
CRACK TROTTER, A; "A Little Off" 1880 .... Small ... 45.00
CRACK TROTTER BETWEEN THE HEATS; 1875 .... Medium 55.00
CRACK TROTTER IN THE HARNESS OF THE PERIOD .... Medium 50.00
CRADLE OF LIBERTY, THE; 1876 .... Small ... 37.50

CRAPS — A CLOSE CALL; 1890 ....Small.... $ 27.50
CRAPS — A BUSTED GAME; "Sebben and Iebben — Scoops
de Crowd"; 1890 .... Small.... 27.50
CRAYON STUDIES; N. Currier .... Small..... 37.50
CRAYON STUDIES; N. Currier (Stream, bridge, man, fishing,
cows) ....Small..... 35.00
CREAM OF LOVE; 1879 ....Small..... 30.00
CREATING A SENSATION; "The Bully Boy On a Bicycle"
1881 .... Small..... 32.50
CROMWELL'S BRIDGE, GLENGARIFF, IRELAND ....: Small..... 35.00
CROSS AND ANCHOR OF ROSES .... Small..... 20.00
CROSS AND CROWN; 1871 .... Small..... 15.00
CROSS MATCHED RACE; 1891 ....Medium .. 50.00
CROSS MATCHED TEAM, A; 1878 .... Small..... 35.00
CROSSED BY A MILK TRAIN; 1884 ....Small..... 50.00
CROW QUADRILLES, THE; N. Currier; 1837..................Small..... 16.50
CROWD THAT SCOOPED THE POOLS, THE; 1878 ....Small..... 35.00
CROWING MATCH ....Small..... 25.00
CROWN OF THORNS, THE ....Small..... 12.00
CROW'S NEST, NORTH RIVER; N. Currier ....Small..... 100.00
"CROXIE" Record 2:19¼ ....Small.... 65.00
CRUCIFIXION, THE; N. Currier; 1847 ....Small..... 10.00
CRYSTAL PALACE, THE; N. Currier ....Small..... 65.00
CRYSTAL PALACE, THE MAGNIFICENT BUILDING FOR
THE WORLD'S FAIR OF 1851, HYDE PARK, LONDON Small..... 65.00
CUMBERLAND VALLEY; 1865 .... Large..... 200.00
CUP THAT CHEERS, THE; 1884 .... Small..... 25.00
CUPID'S OWN; 1879 .... Small..... 25.00
CURFEW BELL, THE .... Small..... 25.00
CUSTER'S LAST CHARGE; 1876 .... Small..... 100.00
CUSTOM HOUSE, NEW YORK; N. Currier .... Small..... 275.00
CUTTER "GENESTA," R.Y.S. 1885 .... Small..... 75.00
CUTTER "MADGE" .... Small..... 70.00
CUTTER YACHT "BIANCA"; 1854 , ... Large..... 300.00
CUTTER YACHT "GALATIA" ....: Small..... 75.00
CUTTER YACHT "MARIA"; N. Currier; 1852 .... Medium... 200.00
CUTTER YACHT "SCUD" OF PHILADELPHIA; N. Currier
1855 .... Large..... 265.00
CUTTER YACHT "THISTLE" 1887............................. Small..... 75.00

— D —

DAIRY FARM, THE .... Small..... 35.00
DAISY AND HER PETS; 1876..................................... Small..... 22.50
"DAN RICE" 1868 .... Large..... 165.00
DANCING LESSON, THE .... Small..... 22.50
DANGER SIGNAL, THE; 1884 .... Large 495.00
"DANIEL D. TOMPKINS" AND "BLANK NEGRE"; N.
Currier; 1851 .... Medium... 200.00
DANIEL IN THE LIONS DEN; N. Currier...................... Small..... 20.00
DANIEL O'CONNELL; N. Currier............................... Small..... 20.00
DANIEL WEBSTER; "New England's Choice for Twelfth
. President of the U. S., N. Currier; 1848................... Small..... 57.50
DANIEL WEBSTER; "DEFENDER of the Constitution" N.
Currier; 1851 .... Small..... 55.00
DANIEL WEBSTER; N. Currier; 1852 .... Small..... 60.00
DARGLES GLEN, IRELAND .... Medium... 32.50

DARKTOWN SPORTS — WINNING EASY; 1885................ Small.... 40.00
DARKTOWN TALLY-HO — STRAIGHTENED; 1889 ....Small....$ 40.00
DARKTOWN TALLY-HO — TANGLED UP; 1889................Small.... 40.00
DARKTOWN TOURISTS — COMING BACK ON THEIR DIG..Small.... 40.00
DARKTOWN TOURISTS — GOING BACK ON THEIR
   BLUBBER; 1886 ....Small.... 40.00
DARKTOWN TOURNAMENT — CLOSE QUARTERS; 1890 ...Small.... 40.00
DARKTOWN TOURNAMENT — FIRST TILT; 1890 ....Small.... 40.00
DARKTOWN TRIAL — THE JUDGE'S CHARGE; 1887 ....Small.... 40.00
DARKTOWN TRIAL — THE VERDICT; 1887.....................Small.... 40.00
DARKTOWN TROLLEY — CLAR DE TRACK; 1896 ....Small.... 48.00
DARKTOWN TROLLEY — THROUGH CAR IN DANGER; 1896
                                                                                    Small.... 48.50
DARKTOWN TROTTER READY FOR THE WORD; 1892 .... Small.... 40.00
DARKTOWN WEDDING — THE PARTING SALUTE; 1892 ... Small.... 40.00
DARKTOWN WEDDING — THE SEND OFF; 1892...............Small.... 40.00
DARKTOWN YACHT CLUB, THE; "Hard Up For A Breeze"
   1885 ....Small.... 40.00
DARKTOWN YACHT CLUB; "In Close I Will" 1896 ....Small.... 40.00
DARKTOWN YACHT CLUB; "Ladies' Day" 1896 ....Small.... 40.00
DARKTOWN YACHT CLUB ON THE WINNING TRACK; 1885
                                                                                    Small.... 40.00
DARLING, I AM GROWING OLD ....Small.... 22.50
DARLING ROSIE ....Small.... 22.50
DARTMOUTH COLLEGE; (RARE) ....Small.... 475.00
DASH FOR THE POLE, A ....Small.... 65.00
DAUGHTER OF THE REGIMENT, THE; N. Currier, 1849...Small.... 30.00
DAUGHTER OF THE SOUTH, A .... Small.... 30.00
DAUGHTERS OF TEMPERANCE; N. Currier .... Small.... 27.50
DAVENPORT BROTHERS; 1864 .... Small.... 40.00
DAWN OF LOVE; 1881 .... Small.... 27.50
DAY BEFORE MARRIAGE, THE; N. Currier; 1847........... Small.... 27.50
DAY BEFORE MARRIAGE — THE BRIDE'S JEWELS .... Small.... 35.00
DAY BEFORE THE WEDDING; N. Currier .... Small.... 35.00
DAY OF REST, THE; 1869.. Small.... 32.00
DEACON'S MARE GETTING THE WORD GO, etc. 1879 ..... Small.... 48.00
DEAD BEAT, A .... Small.... 20.00
DEAD BROKE, 1873 .... Small.... 48.50
DEAD GAME — QUAIL; 1872 .... Small.... 30.00
DEAD GAME — WOODCOCK AND PARTRIDGE; 1872 ...... Small.... 30.00
DEAREST SPOT ON EARTH TO ME; 1878 .... Small.... 32.50
DEATH BED OF THE MARTYR PRESIDENT, ABRAHAM
   LINCOLN; 1865 .... Small.... 58.00
DEATH OF ANDREW JOHNSON; 1875 .... Small.... 20.00
DEATH OF CALVIN; N. Currier; 1846 .... Small.... 20.00
DEATH OF CHARLES SUMNER; 1874 .... Small.... 20.00
DEATH OF COL. EDWARD D. BAKER; 1861................... Small.... 20.00
DEATH OF COL. ELLSWORTH; 1861 .... Small.... 20.00
DEATH OF COL. JOHN J. HARDIN; N. Currier; 1847........ Small.... 20.00
DEATH OF COL. PIERCE M. BUTLER AT THE BATTLE
   OF CHURUBUSCO, MEXICO; N. Currier; 1847............ Small.... 20.00
DEATH OF DANIEL O'CONNELL; N. Currier; 1847.......... Small.... 22.50
DEATH OF GENERAL GRANT; 1885 .... Small.... 22.50
DEATH OF GEN. JAMES A. GARFIELD ; 1881................. Small.... 25.00
DEATH OF GENERAL LYON; 1862 .... Small.... 20.00
DEATH OF GEN. ROBERT E. LEE; 1870 .... Small.... 27.50
DEATH OF GEN. ZACHARY TAYLOR; N. Currier; 1850.... Small.... 22.50
DEATH OF HARRISON; N. Currier; 1841 .... Small.... 20.00
DEATH OF HON. HENRY CLAY; N. Currier; 1852 ....Small.... 20.00

DEATH OF JOHN QUINCY ADAMS; N. Currier; 1848 ....Small....$ 20.00
DEATH OF LIEUT. COL. HENRY CLAY, JR. ....Small.... 20.00
DEATH OF MAJOR GEN. JAMES B. M'PHERSON.............Small.... 20.00
DEATH OF MAJOR RINGGOLD; N. Currier; 1846 ....Small.... 20.00
DEATH OF MINNEHAHA, THE; 1867 ....Large.... 45.00
DEATH OF MONTGOMERY; N. Currier ....Small.... 20.00
DEATH OF NAPOLEON; N. Currier ....Small.... 35.00
DEATH OF POPE PIUS IX; 1878 ....Small.... 20.00
DEATH OF PRESIDENT LINCOLN; 1865 ....Small.... 45.00
DEATH OF ST. PATRICK ....Small.... 20.00
DEATH OF "STONEWALL" JACKSON; 1872 .... Small.... 22.50
DEATH OF TECUMSEH; N. Currier; 1841 ....Small.... 42.50
DEATH OF THE BLESSED VIRGIN ....Small.... 12.50
DEATH OF THE JUST, THE ....Small.... 15.00
DEATH OF THE SINNER, THE ....Small.... 15.00
DEATH OF WARREN AT THE BATTLE OF BUNKER HILL;
    N. Currier ....Small.... 27.50
DEATH OF WASHINGTON; N. Currier; 1841 ....Small.... 35.00
DEATH SHOT, THE ....Small.... 47.50
DECLARATION, THE; N. Currier; 1846 ....Small.... 18.00
DECLARATION COMMITTEE, THE; 1876 ....Small.... 50.00
DECLARATION OF INDEPENDENCE, THE; N. Currier .... Small.... 55.00
DECORATION OF THE CASKET OF GEN. LEE .... Small.... 20.00
DEER AND FAWN .... Small.... 80.00
DEER HUNTING BY TORCHLIGHT .... Medium.. 140.00
DEER HUNTING ON THE SUSQUEHANNA .... Medium.. 120.00
DEER IN THE WOODS .... Small.... 60.00
DEER SHOOTING IN THE NORTHERN WOODS .... Small.... 90.00
DEER SHOOTING IN THE NORTH WOODS .... Medium.. 135.00
DEFENSE OF THE FLAG .... Small.... 25.00
DEFIANCE! (Stag and Deer) .... Small.... 40.00
DELIA; N. Currier .... Small.... 20.00
DELICIOUS COFFEE; 1881 .... Small.... 22.50
DEMOCRACY IN SEARCH OF A CANDIDATE; .... Small.... 35.00
DEMOCRATIC PLATFORM, THE .... Small.... 35.00
DEMOCRATIC REFORMERS; 1876 .... Small.... 35.00
DEPARTED WORTH; N. Currier .... Small.... 22.50
DEPTHS OF DESPAIR, THE .... Small.... 32.50
DESCENT FROM THE CROSS; N. Currier; 1847 .... Small.... 12.00
DESCENT FROM THE CROSS; C. & I. .... Small.... 12.00
DESPERATE FINISH; 1885 .... Small.... 35.00
DESPERATE PEACE MAN .... Small.... 28.50
DESSERT OF FRUIT, A; 1869 .... Small.... 48.50
DESTRUCTION OF JERUSALEM BY THE ROMANS;
    N. Currier .... Large.... 55.00
DESTRUCTION OF TEA AT BOSTON HARBOR. 1846   Large.... 350.00
DESTRUCTION OF THE REBEL MONSTER "MERRIMAC" Small.... 70.00
DESTRUCTION OF THE REBEL RAM "ARKANSAS" .... Small.... 65.00
DEVIL'S GLEN. KILLARNEY, THE .... Small.... 25.00
"DEWDROP" 1886 .... Small.... 65.00
"DEXTER" RECORD 2:17¼; 1871 .... Small.... 65.00
"DEXTER" AND "BUTLER"; 1874 .... Small.... 70.00
"DEXTER," "ETHAN ALLEN" AND "MATE"; 1874....... Small.... 65.00
DEXTER'S TURF RECORD; 1867............................... Small.... 65.00
DEXTEROUS WHIP, A; 1876 .... Small.... 32.50
DICK SWIVELLER; 1878 .... Small.... 65.00
DIRECT; 1891 .... Small.... 60.00
DIRECTOR, RECORD 2:17; 1882 .... Miniature 55.00

```
DISCHARGING THE PILOT; N. Currier; 1856 ............ Large .. $   1275.00
DISCOVERY OF THE MISSISSIPPI, THE; 1876 .......... Small...       50.00
DISLOYAL BRITISH·"SUBJECT", A  .................... Small...       35.00
DISPUTED HEAT — CLAIMING A FOUL; 1878............ Large...       225.00
DISPUTED PRIZE, THE; (Sparrows) ...................... Small...    22.50
DISTANCED; 1878 .............................................. Small...    30.00
DISTANT RELATIONS .......................................... Small...    32.00
DISTINGUISHED MILITIA GEN. DURING AN ACTION .. Small...       37.50
DO YOU LOVE BUTTER; 1878 ............................ Small...    24.00
DOCTOR FRANKLIN; N. Currier .......................... Small...    95.00
DODGE THAT WON'T WORK, A; (Political) .............. Small...    40.00
DODGER (THE) — CARTER H. HARRISON AGAINST THE
    BOODLERS; .............................................. Small...    40.00
DOLLY VARDEN; 1872........................................... Small...    20.00
DOMESTIC BLOCKADE, THE  ............................ Large...       60.00
DOMINO; N. Currier  ...................................... Small...    24.50
DON JUAN, PLATE ONE; N. Currier ...................... Small...    30.00
DON JUAN AND HAIDEE, PLATE TWO; N. Currier .... Small...    30.00
DON JUAN AND LAMBRO, PLATE THREE; N. Currier. Small...    30.00
DON JUAN SEPARATED FROM HAIDEE; N. Currier ... Small...    30.00
DONE GONE BUSTED; 1883 ................................ Small...    32.00
DON'T HURT MY BABY; 1872 ............................ Small...    20.00
DON'T SAY NAY; N. Currier; 1846 ....................... Small...    22.50
DON'T YOU WANT ANOTHER BABY?  ................... Small...    22.50
DON'T YOU WISH YOU MAY GET IT? N. Currier........ Small...    22.50
DOTTY DIMPLE ............................................... Small...    22.50
DOUBLE-BARRELED BREECH LOADER; 1880  ....... Small...    38.50
DOUBLE FISHING; N. Currier  ............................ Small...    27.50
DOVE, THE (Girls and Dove)  ............................ Small...    25.00
DOVE'S REFUGE, THE........................................... Small...    25.00
DOWN CHARGE  ............................................... Small...   125.00
DR. WILLIAM VALENTINE .................................. Medium.     65.00
DRAW POKER — GETTING 'EM LIVELY; 1886........... Small...    40.00
DRAW POKER — LAYING FOR 'EM SHARP; 1886 ...... Small...    40.00
DRAWING CARDS FOR BEGINNERS  ..................... Small...    40.00
DREADFUL WRECK OF THE MEXICO ON HEMPSTEAD
    BEACH; .............................................. Small ...   185.00
DREAMS OF YOUTH; 1869  ................................ Small ...    55.00
DREAMS OF YOUTH ............................................ Medium.    100.00
"DREW" AND "ST. JOHN", THE; 1878 .................... Large...      135.00
DRIVE THROUGH THE HIGHLANDS, THE................ Medium..     85.00
DRIVING FINISH, A; 1891 .................................... Small...   140.00
DRUNKARD'S PROGRESS, THE; N. Currier; 1846 ...... Small...    60.00
DRYBURGH ABBEY, SCOTLAND............................ Small...    30.00
DUBLIN BAY, IRELAND  .................................... Small...    30.00
"DUC DE CHATRES"; 1883  ................................ Small...    50.00
DUDE BELLE; 1883  ......................................... Small...    40.00
DUDE SWELL; 1883  ......................................... Small...    40.00
DUKE AND DUCHESS OF EDINBURGH, THE  .......... Small...    30.00
DUSTED AND DISGUSTED; 1878; (Comic)  .............. Small...    36.50
"DUTCHESS" OF ONEIDA  ................................ Small...    55.00
"DUTCHMAN" N. Currier; 1850 ............................ Medium.    250.00
"DUTCHMAN" AND "HIRAM WOODRUFF"; 1871  .... Small ...   225.00
DUTCHMAN — TO SADDLE  ............................ Small...    67.50
DWIGHT L. MOODY  ......................................... Small...    37.50
DYING BUFFALO BULL  ................................ Medium.    215.00
```

```
E PLURIBUS UNUM; 1875 ..................................Medium..... $ 95.00
EAGER FOR THE RACE; 1893 ...........................Small....... 65.00
EARLY AUTUMN IN THE CATSKILLS .................Medium..... 95.00
EARLY AUTUMN, SALMON BROOK, GRANBY, CONN.;
   1869 ............................................................. Small....... 185.00
EARLY PIETY; N. Currier; 1846 ........................... Small ....... 12.00
EARLY SPRING ......................... .................... Medium..... 95.00
EARLY WINTER; 1869.......................................... Medium..... 550.00
EAST RIVER SUSPENSION BRIDGE; 1890 ............... Small....... 95.00
EASTER CROSS, THE; 1869 ................. ............... Small....... 12.50
EASTER FLOWERS; 1869 ................. ............... Small....... 18.00
EASTER MORNING ......................................... Small....... 12.00
EASTER OFFERING; 1871 .................................. Small....... 12.00
EASTER BEAUTY, THE ................................... Small....... 18.00
EATING CROW ON A WAGER – DE FUST BRACE; 1883;
   (Comic) ...................................................... Small....... 35.00
EATING CROW ON A WAGER – DE LAST LAP; 1883;
   (Comic) ...................................................... Small....... 35.00
ECHO LAKE, WHITE MOUNTAINS; (Oval) ............... Medium..... 95.00
ECHO LAKE, WHITE MOUNTAINS ......................... Small....... 65.00
EDITH............................................................... Small....... 18.00
EDWARD; 1879 (Boy) .............................................. Small....... 18.50
EDWARD''''' Record 2:19 ............................... Small....... 68.50
"EDWARD" AND "SWIVELLER"; 1882 ................... Small....... 70.00
EDWIN FORREST; 1860 ................................... Small....... 59.50
EDWIN FORREST .......................................... Medium..... 45.00
EDWIN FORREST AS METAMORA; N. Currier ............ Small....... 40.00
"EDWIN FORREST"Record 2:11¾; 1878 ................... Small....... 65.00
"EDWIN THORNE" Record 2:17½; 1882 ................... Small....... . 65.00
EGYPTIAN BEAUTY, THE ................................. Small....... 18.50
EGYPTIAN BEAUTY, THE ................................. Medium..... 30.00
EL CAPITAN – FROM MARIPOSA TRAIL................. Small....... 70.00
EL DORADO PAIN ABSTRACTOR, THE; N. Currier; 1846;
                                                   Small....... 48.50
EL NINO CANTIVO ......................................... Small....... 14.50
EL SANTO NINO DE ATOCHA ........................... Small....... 14.00
ELECTRIC LIGHT; 1879 ................................... Small....... 32.50
ELEPHANT AND HIS KEEPERS, THE..................... Small....... 45.00
ELIZA; N. Currier .......................................... Small....... 22.50
ELIZA JANE; N. Currier, 1847.............................. Small....... 22.50
ELIZABETH; N. Currier; 1846              ....... Small....... 20.00
ELLA ............................................................. Small....... 20.00
ELLEN; N. Currier .......................................... Small....... 20.00
ELLEN TREE; "Wrecker's Daughter"; N. Currier........ Small....... 32.50
ELLEN TREE AS HERO IN "WOMAN'S WIT"; N. Currier;
   1838 ............................................................. Small....... 35.00
ELLEN TREE AS ION; N. Currier ........................... Small....... 35.00
ELOPEMENT, THE; N. Currier .............................. Small....... 25.00
EMBLEM OF HOPE .......................................... Small....... 12.00
EMBLEM OF SALVATION; 1874.............................. Small....... 12.00
EMELINE; N. Currier; 1848 .............................. Small....... 18.00
EMILY; N. Currier ......................................... Small....... 18.00
EMMA ............................................................. Small....... 18.00
EMMET'S BETROTHED .................................... Small....... 15.00
EMPEROR, THE; N. Currier .............................. Small....... 24.50
EMPEROR OF NORFOLK; 1888 .............................Small........ 65.00
```

```
EMPRESS EUGENIE; N. Currier ................................ Small ... $ 20.00
EMPRESS EUGENIE AND QUEEN VICTORIA ................ Small ...   24.00
EMPRESS JOSEPHINE ..................................... Small ...   20.00
EMPTY CRADLE; N. Currier ............................... Small ...   14.50
ENCHANTED CAVE, THE; 1867 ............................ Medium.   40.00
ENCHANTED ISLES, THE 1869............................. Small ...   27.50
END OF THE LONG BRANCH, THE; (Political Cartoon) .. Small ...   35.00
ENGLISH BEAUTY, THE .................................. Small ...   45.00
ENGLISH SNIPE; N. Currier .............................. Small ...   90.00
ENGLISH SNIPE; 1871; (C. & I.) .......................... Small ...   85.00
ENGLISH WINTER SCENE, AN.............................. Small ...  120.00
ENGLISH YACHT OFF SANDY HOOK, AN ................... Small ...   95.00
ENOCH ARDEN — THE HOUR OF TRIAL; N. Currier........ Small ...   40.00
ENOCH ARDEN — THE LONELY ISLE; 1869 ................ Large...   60.00
ENTRANCE TO THE HIGHLANDS; 1864 .................... Large...  375.00
ENTRANCE TO THE HOLY SEPULCHRE, JERUSALEM;
    N. Currier; 1849 .......................................... Small ...   15.00
ERIN GO BRAGH; (Rifle Match); 1875 .................... Medium.   50.00
ESCAPE OF SERGEANT CHAMPE, THE;  1876 ............ Small ...   60.00
ESTHER; N. Currier   ..................................... Small ...   18.50
"ETHAN ALLEN" AND "MATE" AND "DEXTER"; 1867. Large...  200.00
"ETHAN ALLEN" AND "MATE" AND "LANTERN" AND
    "MATE"; 1859   ........................................ Large...  220.00
ETTA ...................................................... Small ...   22.50
"EUCHERED"; 1884.................................... Small ...   24.50
EUROPA (HEAD) ........................................ Small ...   22.50
EUROPE; 1870  ......................................... Small ...   20.00
EUROPEAN WAR DANCE; 1877........................... Medium.   75.00
EVACUATION OF RICHMOND, VA., THE; 1865.............. Small ...   65.00
EVANGELINE  ........................................... Small ...   24.50
EVANGELINE  ........................................... Large...   75.00
EVENING OF LOVE, THE  ................................ Small ...   16.50
EVENING PRAYER, THE; N. Currier ...................... Small ...   12.00
EVENING PRAYER, THE; 1862............................. Small ...   12.00
EVENING STAR, THE; (Girl) ............................. Small ...   18.50
EVENTIDE — OCTOBER; "The Village Inn"; 1867  ........ Large ...  235.00
EVENTIDE — THE CURFEW  ............................. Small ...   32.50
EVERYBODY'S FRIEND; 1876 ............................. Medium.   40.00
EVERYTHING COMING DOWN  ........................... Small ...   40.00
EVERYTHING LOVELY; 1880  ............................ Small ...   25.00
EXCITING FINISH; 1895,................................. Small ...   60.00
EXCITING FINISH;  ..................................... Large ..  165.00
EXPRESS STEAMSHIP"AUGUSTA"VICTORIA ............... Small ...   55.00
EXPRESS STEAMSHIP "COLUMBIA"......................... Small ...   55.00
EXPRESS STEAMSHIP "FURST BISMARK", THE........... Small ...   55.00
EXPRESS TRAIN, THE; N. Currier ........................ Small ...  265.00
EXPRESS TRAIN, THE; 1870  ............................ Small ...  200.00
EXPRESS TRAIN, THE; 1870  ............................ Large...  1400.00
EXPULSION OF ADAM AND EVE; N. Currier  ............. Small ...   35.00
EXQUISITE, THE — THE "PET OF THE LADIES" (Oval). Small ...   30.00
EXTRAORDINARY EXPRESS ACROSS THE ATLANTIC;
    N. Currier; 1846 ....................................... Small ...  100.00
```

— F —

```
FAIR BEAUTEOUS QUEEN; N. Currier; (Queen Victoria) ...Small ... $ 18.00
FAIR EQUESTRIAN, THE; 1857 .................................... Small ...   48.50
```

```
FAIR FIELD AND NO FAVOR, A ; 1891 .......................Large...$  135.00
FAIR MOON TO THEE I SING; 1879  .......................... Small...   18.00
FAIR PURITAN, THE   .......................................... Small...   18.00
FAIR START, A   .............................................. Small...   30.00
FAIREST OF THE FAIR, THE   ................................ Small...   20.00
FAIRIE'S HOME, THE ........................................ Large...   65.00
FAIRIE'S HOME, THE; 1868 ................................. Medium.   45.00
FAIRMOUNT WATER WORKS.................................... Medium.   90.00
FAIRY GROTTO, THE; 1867  ................................. Large...   60.00
FAIRY GROTTO, THE; 1867................................... Small...   40.00
FAIRY ISLE, THE   .......................................... Small...   20.00
FAIRY TALES  ............................................... Small...   18.00
FAITH, HOPE, AND CHARITY, 1874  .......................... Small...   15.00
FALL FROM GRACE, A; 1883.................................. Small...   22.50
FALL OF RICHMOND, VIRGINIA, THE; 1865 ................. Large...  125.00
FALL OF RICHMOND, VIRGINIA, THE; 1865 ................. Small...   60.00
FALLING SPRINGS, VA. 1868 ............................... Small...   40.00
FALLS "DES CHATS," OTTAWA RIVER, CANADA.......... Small...   60.00
FALLS OF NIAGARA FROM THE CANADA SIDE  ......... Large...  185.00
FALLS OF NIAGARA FROM CLIFTON HOUSE; N. Currier. Small...   60.00
FALLS OF THE OTTAWA RIVER, CANADA .................. Small...   62.50
"FALSETTO"; 1879 ......................................... Small...   60.00
FAMILY DEVOTION; "Reading the Scriptures"; N. Currier. Small...   12.00
FAMILY GARLAND; 1874..................................... Small...   20.00
FAMILY OF LOUIS KOSSUTH; N. Currier; 1851    .......... Small...   20.00
FAMILY PHOTOGRAPH TREE; 1871  .......................... Small...   16.50
FAMILY RECORD; (Oval)   .................................. Small...   12.50
FAMILY REGISTER; N. Currier; 1845  ...................... Small...   12.50
FAMILY REGISTER; N. Currier; (In German)  ............... Small...   12.50
FAMOUS DOUBLE TROTTING TEAM "SIR MOHAWK" AND
    "NELLIE SONTAG"; 1889 ................................ Large..  200.00
FAMOUS TROTTER MAJOLICA, THE; 1884 .................... Large..  150.00
FAMOUS TROTTING GELDING "GUY"; Record 2:12½ 1888
                                                    Small...   67.50
FAMOUS TROTTING MARE "GOLDSMITH MAID," Record 2:14;
    1871 .................................................. Small...   65.00
FANNIE (C. & I.)   ........................................ Small...   20.00
FANNY; N. Currier; 1846 ......... .......................... Small...   20.00
FANNY ELLSLER; "In the Shadow Dance," N. Currier; 1846
                                                    Small...   25.00
FANNY ELLSLER; "In the Favorite Dance La Cachucha";
    N. Currier ............................................ Small...   25.00
FAREWELL, THE; (Oval) .................................... Small...   20.00
FARM AND FIRESIDE; 1878  ................................ Small...   55.00
FARM LIFE IN SUMMER — THE COOLING STREAM; 1867. Small...   60.00
FARM YARD NO. 1, THE; N. Currier .......................... Small...   45.00
FARM YARD NO. 2, THE; N. Currier .......................... Small...   45.00
FARM YARD IN WINTER, THE; 1861  .......................... Large...  500.00
FARM YARD PETS   ......................................... Small...   40.00
FARM YARD — WINTER   ................................... Small...  125.00
FARMER GARFIELD   ........................................ Small...   35.00
FARMERS DAUGHTER, THE..................................... Small...   22.50
FARMER'S FRIENDS, THE .................................... Small...   25.00
FARMER'S HOME — AUTUMN, THE; 1864 .................... Large...  240.00
FARMER'S HOME — HARVEST, THE; 1864 .................... Large...  265.00
FARMER'S HOME — SUMMER, THE; 1864.................... Large...  225.00
FARMER'S HOME — WINTER, THE; 1863 .................... Large...  500.00
FARMER'S PRIDE, THE; N. Currier; 1852 .................... Small...   20.00
```

```
FARMER'S SON, THE ............................................. Small... $ 24.00
FASHIONABLE TURN OUTS IN CENTRAL PARK; 1869.... Large...   800.00
FAST HEAT, A; 1887 ............................................. Large...   145.00
FAST HEAT, A; 1894 ............................................. Small...    67.50
FAST TEAM AT A SMASHING GATE, A ........................ Large...   160.00
FAST TEAM OUT ON THE LOOSE, A ........................ Small...    67.50
FAST TEAM TAKING A SMASH, A ............................ Small...    67.50
FAST TROTTERS ON A FAST TRACK; 1889 ............... Large...   175.00
FAST TROTTERS ON HARLEM LANE, N. Y. 1870 ........ Large...   350.00
FAST TROTTING IN THE WEST; 1871 ...................... Large..   200.00
FAST TROTTING TO FAST WHEELS; 1893 ................... Large...   120.00
FATHER AND CHILD; N. Currier; 1849 .....................Small...    20.00
FATHER, INTO THY HANDS I COMMEND MY SPIRIT;
    N. Currier; 1850 ............................................. Small...    12.50
FATHER MATHEW; N. Currier; 1848 ......................... Small...    15.00
FATHER'S PET; N. Currier; 1851........................Small...    16.50
FATHER'S PRIDE; N. Currier; 1846 ......................... Small...    20.00
FAVORITE CAT, THE; N. Currier ......................... Small...    25.00
FAVORITE HORSE, THE .......................................... Small...    32.50
FAVORITE IN THE POOLS; 1876 .............................. Small...    24.50
FAVORITE JERSEYS ............................................. Small...    27.50
FAVORITE PONY, A; N. Currier .............................. Small...    30.00
FAVORITE SET OF QUADRILLES FOR THE PIANO ...... Small...    15.00
FAWN'S LEAP, CATSKILLS; (Oval).......................... Small...    35.00
FEAST OF FRUITS, A; (Oval) ............................... Small...    45.00
FEAST OF ROSES; 1873 ....................................... Small...    48.50
FEAST OF STRAWBERRIES, A ............................... Small...    30.00
FEATHER WEIGHT MOUNTING A SCALPER, A; 1881 ...... Small...    38.50
FEEDING THE SWANS ........................................... Medium    34.50
FEEDING THE SWANS .......................................... Small...    20.00
FENIAN VOLUNTEER, THE; 1866 ........................... Small...    22.50
FERNS................................................................. Small...    20.00
FERRY BOAT, THE; N. Currier .............................. Medium.   70.00
FIDELE; N. Currier ............................................. Small...    20.00
FIDO'S LESSON .................................................. Small...    22.50
FIEND OF THE ROAD, THE; 1881 ........................... Large...   110.00
FIFTH AVENUE BELLE, A ...................................... Small...    20.00
FINEST IN THE WORLD; 1885.................................. Small...    55.00
FIRE DEPARTMENT CERTIFICATE; 1877 ................... Medium.   20.00
FIRE DEPARTMENT CERTIFICATE; 1877 ................... Small...    15.00
FIRE ENGINE CO. "PACIFIC" BROOKLYN ................. Small...    40.00
FIREMEN'S CERTIFICATE; 1889             Small ...    20.00
FIRST APPEARANCE OF JENNY LIND IN AMERICA;
    N. Currier; 1850                    ................ Medium.   325.00
FIRST AT THE RENDEZVOUS; N. Currier ................. Small...    22.50
FIRST BIRD OF THE SEASON; 1879 .............. Small...    45.00
FIRST CARE, THE; "The Young Mother"; (Oval) .......... Small...    20.00
FIRST CHRISTMAS MORN, THE .............................. Small...    18.00
FIRST COLORED SENATOR AND REPRESENTATIVES IN
    THE 41st, 42nd CONGRESS; 1872 ......................... Medium.   35.00
FIRST EASTER DAWN, THE .................................Small...    12.50
FIRST FIGHT BETWEEN IRON CLAD SHIPS OF WAR, THE;
    1862 ............................................................. Small...    95.00
FIRST FLIRTATION, THE ...................................... Small...    18.00
FIRST GAME; N. Currier ,.................................... Small...    30.00
FIRST LANDING OF COLUMBUS, THE; 1892 .............. Large...    75.00
FIRST LESSON, THE; N. Currier ........................... Medium.   60.00
FIRST LOVE; N. Currier....................................... Small...    22.50
```

```
FIRST MEETING OF WASHINGTON AND LAFAYETTE;
   1876 ............................................................... Small ...$ 87.50
FIRST PARTING, THE ........................................ Small ...   18.00
FIRST PARTY, THE .......................................... Small ...   18.00
FIRST PLAYMATE, THE ...................................... Small ...   15.00
FIRST PRAYER, 1870 ......................................... Small ...   15.00
FIRST PREMIUM GRAPES ...................................... Medium.   60.00
FIRST PREMIUM POULTRY .................................. Small ...   40.00
FIRST PRESIDENT OF THE MORMONS; 1879 ................ Small ...   50.00
FIRST PRESIDENTS OF THE CHURCH OF JESUS CHRIST
   OF THE LATTER DAY SAINTS ............................ Medium.   75.00
FIRST RIDE, THE; N. Currier; 1849 ........................... Small ...   20.00
FIRST SCHOLAR, THE ......................................... Small ...   18.00
FIRST SMOKE — ALL RIGHT; 1870 ........................... Small ...   45.00
FIRST SNOW, THE ............................................. Medium. 200.00
FIRST STEP, THE "Come to Mama"; 1859 .................. Small ...   18.50
FIRST TOILET; 1873 .......................................... Small ...   18.50
FIRST TROT OF THE SEASON; 1870 ........................... Large...  345.00
FIRST VIOLET, THE .......................................... Small ...   18.50
FIRST UNDER THE WIRE; 1878 ............................... Small ...   48.00
FISH ` OUT OF WATER; N. Currier ........................... Small ...   35.00
FISHERMAN'S COT, THE ...................................... Small ...   25.00
FISHERMAN'S DOG, THE ..................................... Medium.   32.50
FLAG OF THE UNION, THE ................................... Small ...   24.50
"FLEETY GOLDDUST"; 1874 .................................. Small ...   60.00
FLIGHT INTO EGYPT; N. Currier .............................. Small ...   20.00
FLIGHT OF THE MEXICAN ARMY AT THE BATTLE OF
   BUENA VISTA; N. Currier; 1847 ............................. Small ...   45.00
FLIGHT OF THE STAKEHOLDER ............................. Small ...   25.00
FLOATING DOWN TO MARKET; 1870 ........................ Small ...   90.00
FLORA; N. Currier; 1846 ..................................... Small ...   20.00
"FLORA TEMPLE"; N. Currier; 1853 ......................... Large...  225.00
"FLORA TEMPLE" AND "HIGHLAND MAID"; 1853 ....... Large...  200.00
"FLORA TEMPLE" AND "LANCET"; N. Currier .......... Large...  200.00
"FLORA TEMPLE" AND "PRINCESS"; 1859 ............... Large...  210.00
FLORAL BEAUTIES ........................................... Small ...   58.50
FLORAL BOUQUET ........................................... Small ...   60.00
FLORAL CROSS — AUTUMN FLOWERS .................... Small ...   50.00
FLORAL GEMS ................................................. Small ...   50.00
FLORAL GIFT ................................................. Small...   45.00
FLORAL GROUP ............................................... Small ...   45.00
FLORAL OFFERING ........................................... Small ...   45.00
FLORAL TREASURE .......................................... Small ...   35.00
FLORAL TRIBUTE ............................................ Small ...   40.00
FLORAL WREATH ............................................ Small ...   35.00
FLORA'S TREASURE .......................................... Small ...   37.50
"FLORIDA" .................................................... Large...  175.00
FLORIDA COAST .............................................. Small ...   85.00
FLOWER BASKET; 1872 ...................................... Small ...   50.00
FLOWER DANCE, THE; N. Currier 1846 ..................... Small ...   40.00
FLOWER GIRL, THE; N. Currier; 1845 ....................... Small ...   22.50
FLOWER OF THE HAREM, THE; N. Currier ................ Small ...   22.50
FLOWER STAND, THE .................. .................... Small ...   40.00
FLOWER STREWN GRAVE; 1874 ............................. Small ...   15.00
FLOWER VASE, THE; N. Currier; 1848 ..................... Small ...   60.00
FLOWER VASE, THE .......................................... Medium.   80.00
FLOWERS; N. Currier ....................................... Small ...   55.00
FLUSHING A WOODCOCK.................................... Small ...   70.00
```

FLY FISHING; 1879 .... Small .... $ 70.00
"FLYING DUTCHMAN" AND "VOLTIGEUR"; N. Currier. Medium .. 265.00
FOLIAGE; (Four views on same sheet) .... Small 35.00
FOLLY OF SECESSION; 1861 .... Small 37.50
FONT AT EASTER, THE; 1869 .... Small 32.50
FORDING THE RIVER; N. Currier .... Medium .. 85.00
FORDS OF THE JORDAN .... Small 18.00
FOREST SCENE ON THE LEHIGH .... Medium .. 95.00
FOREST SCENE, SUMMER .... Small 60.00
FORK OVER WHAT YOU OWE; 1868 .... Small 37.50
FORT PICKENS, PENSACOLA, FLORIDA .... Small 50.00
FORT SUMTER — CHARLESTON HARBOR, S.C. .... Small 50.00
FOUL TIP, A; 1882 .... Small 35.00
"FOUR-IN-HAND"; 1861 .... Large 145.00
"FOUR-IN-HAND"; 1887 .... Small 70.00
FOUR MASTED STEAMSHIP "EGYPT" OF THE NATIONAL
   LINE; N. Currier .... Small 55.00
FOUR OARED SHELL RACE, A; 1884 .... Large 295.00
FOUR SEASONS OF LIFE, THE — CHILDHOOD; 1868 ..... Large 150.00
FOUR SEASONS OF LIFE, THE — MIDDLE AGE; 1868 ... Large 150.00
FOUR SEASONS OF LIFE, THE — OLD AGE; 1868 .... Large 150.00
FOUR SEASONS OF LIFE, THE — YOUTH; 1868 .... Large 150.00
FOURTH OF JULY — YOUNG AMERICA CELEBRATING .. Large 87.50
FOX CHASE — GONE AWAY; N. Currier .... Small 185.00
FOX CHASE — IN FULL CRY; N. Currier; 1846 .... Small 185.00
FOX CHASE — THE DEATH; N. Currier; 1846 .... Small 185.00
FOX CHASE — THROWING OFF; N. Currier; 1845 .... Small 185.00
FOX HOUNDS; N. Currier .... Small 185.00
FOX-HUNTER, THE; N. Currier .... Small 185.00
FOX-HUNTING — THE DEATH .... Medium .. 325.00
FOX-HUNTING — THE FIND .... Medium .. 325.00
FOX-HUNTING — FULL CRY .... Medium ... 325.00
FOX-HUNTING — THE MEET .... Medium .. 325.00
"FOXHALL"; 1881 .... Small 55.00
"FOXHALL"; 1882 .... Miniature 25.00
FOX'S OLD BOWERY THEATRE, THE LAST SCENE IN
   G. L. FOX'S PANTOMIME, "THE HOUSE THAT JACK
   BUILT." .... Small 150.00
FRAGRANT AND FAIR .... Small 60.00
FRAGRANT CUP; 1884 .... Small 40.00
FRANCIS R. SHUNK — Gov. of Penna., N. Currier .... Small 27.50
FRANKIE AND TIP .... Small 22.00
FRANKLIN PIERCE, "Democratic Candidate for 14th
   President of the U.S., N. Currier; 1852 .... Small 40.00
FRANKLIN PIERCE, "Fourteenth President of the U.S.,
   N. Currier; 1852 .... Small 40.00
FRANKLIN'S EXPERIMENT, 1876 .... Small 125.00
FRAUD AGAINST TRUTH; 1872 .... Small 27.50
FREDERIKSTED; "Island of St. Croix, W. I. .... Medium .. 80.00
FREE FOR ALL; 1875 .... Small 25.00
FREE LUNCH; 1872 .... Small 25.00
FREE TRADE AND PROTECTION; 1888 .... Small 32.50
FREEDMAN'S BUREAU, THE; 1868 .... Small 40.00
FREEDOM TO IRELAND; 1866 .... Small 22.50
FREEDOM TO THE SLAVES .... Small 80.00
"FREELAND"; 1885 .... Small 60.00
FRENCH REVOLUTION, THE; N. Currier; 1848 .... Small 32.50
FRESH BOUQUET, A .... Small 67.50

— 41 —

```
FRIEND CLEVELAND; 1888............................................ Small .... $ 35.00
FRIEND IN NEED, A ............................................... Small ....   16.50
FRIENDSHIP, LOVE, AND TRUTH; 1874 ................... Small ....   18.00
FRIGHTENED BROOD, THE ..................................... Small ....   25.00
FROLICSOME KITS; N. Currier .................................. Small ....   25.00
FROLICSOME PETS ................................................... Small ....   25.00
FROM SHORE TO SHORE .......................................... Small ....   18.00
FRONTIER LAKE, THE ............................................ Small ....   60.00
FRONTIER SETTLEMENT, A .................................... Medium..  125.00
FROZEN UP; 1872 ..................................................... Small ....  275.00
FRUIT; 1861............................................................... Medium..   60.00
FRUIT, NO. 1, THE; N. Currier; 1848............................ Small ....   50.00
FRUIT AND FLOWER PIECE; 1863 ........................... Medium..   98.50
FRUIT AND FLOWERS, NO. 1., N. Currier; 1848 .......... Small ....   48.50
FRUIT AND FLOWERS, CHERRIES, STRAWBERRIES, etc.
                                                                       Small ....   70.00
FRUIT GIRL, THE...................................................... Small ....   18.00
FRUIT VASE; N. Currier; 1847 ................................... Small ....   49.50
FRUITS, AUTUMN VARIETIES; 1871............................ Small ....   35.00
FRUITS AND FLOWERS ............................................. Small ....   48.50
FRUITS AND FLOWERS IN SUMMER .......................... Small ....   48.50
FRUITS AND FLOWERS OF AUTUMN ......................... Medium..   70.00
FRUITS AND FLOWERS OF SUMMER ........................ Medium..   70.00
FRUITS OF INTEMPERANCE, THE; N. Currier .......... Small ....   80.00
FRUITS OF TEMPERANCE, THE; N. Currier; 1848 ....... Small ....   80.00
FRUITS OF THE GARDEN ......................................... Small ....   40.00
FRUITS OF THE GOLDEN LAND; 1871 ....................... Small ....   42.50
FRUITS OF THE SEASON; 1870 ................................. Small ....   40.00
FRUITS OF THE SEASON ......................................... Small ....   40.00
FRUITS OF THE SEASON — AUTUMN ........................ Small ....   40.00
FRUITS OF THE TROPICS; 1871 ............................... 'Small ... .   40.00
FULL HAND, A; 1884 ............................................... Small ....   25.00
FUNERAL OF DANIEL O'CONNELL, THE; N. Currier ..... Small ....   20.00
FUNERAL OF PRESIDENT LINCOLN; 1865 ................. Small ....   95.00
FUST BLOOD, DE; 1882 ............................................ Small ....   40.00
FUST KNOCK-DOWN, DE; 1882 .................................. Small ....   40.00
FUTURITY RACE AT SHEEPSHEAD BAY; 1889 ............ Large....  240.00
```

— G —

```
GALLANT CHARGE OF THE 54th. MASSACHUSETTS REGIMENT;
   N. Currier; 1865 ................................................. Small .... $ 50.00
GALLANT CHARGE OF THE KENTUCKY CAVALRY UNDER
   COL. MARSHALL; N. Currier; 1865 ....................... Small ....   50.00
GALLANT CHARGE OF THE "69th." ON THE REBEL
   BATTERIES ...................................................... Small ....   50.00
GALLANT CHARGE OF THE "69th." ........................... Small ....   50.00
GAME COCK, THE; N. Currier .................................. Small ....   92.50
GAME DOG, A; 1879................................................. Small ....   48.00
GAME OF THE ARROW ............................................ Medium..   80.00
GAP OF DUNLOE, THE ............................................ Small ....   25.00
GARDEN OF GETHSEMANE, THE; N. Currier; 1846 ...... Small ....   15.00
GARDEN, ORCHARD AND VINE; 1867 ....................... Medium..   85.00
GARFIELD FAMILY, THE ......................................... Small ....   32.50
GARNET POOL, THE.................................................. Medium..  135.00
"GARRETT DAVIS"; N. Currier; 1854 ........................ Large....  495.00
GATE OF BELEN, MEXICO; N. Currier; 1848 .............. Small ....   42.50
```

```
GAY DECEIVER, THE; 1871 ............................... Medium ....$ 40.00
GEM OF THE ATLANTIC, THE; N. Currier; 1849 ......... Small ....... 200.00
GEM OF THE PACIFIC, THE; N. Currier; 1849 ............. Small ....... 190.00
GEMS OF AMERICAN SCENERY ........................... Small ....... 95.00
GENERAL AMPUDIA TREATING FOR THE CAPITULATION
    OF MONTEREY, WITH GENL. TAYLOR; N. Currier...Small ....... 42.50
GENERAL AND MRS. WASHINGTON; 1876 ............... Small ....... 45.00
GENERAL ANDREW JACKSON; "The Hero" .............. Small ....... 45.00
GENERAL ANDREW JACKSON; "The Hero of New Orleans"
                                                     Small ....... 48.00
GENERAL ANDREW JACKSON AT NEW ORLEANS ..... Small ....... 45.00
GENERAL ANDREW JACKSON; "The Union Must And
    Shall Be Preserved." ...................................Small ....... 45.00
GENERAL BEM; "The Hungarian Hero", N. Currier .......Small ....... 25.00
GENERAL BENJAMIN F. BUTLER ...................... Small ....... 25.00
"GENL. BUTLER" AND "DEXTER";; 1866 ................. Large ....... 225.00
"GENL. BUTLER" AND "DEXTER" ........................ Small ....... 70.00
GENERAL CHESTER A. ARTHUR; 1880 ................... Medium ..... 45.00
GENERAL D. E. TWIGGS AT THE STORMING OF THE
    FORTRESS OF CHAPULTEPEC; N. Currier ............ Small ....... 50.00
GENERAL DEMBINSKI; N. Currier; 1849.................... Small ....... 35.00
GENERAL E. CAVAIGNAC ................................... Small ....... 35.00
GENL. FRANCIS MARION; 1876 ............................ Small ....... 100.00
GENL. FRANKLIN PIERCE; N. Currier; 1852 ............ Small ....... 45.00
GENL. FRANZ SIGEL; 1862 ................................. Small ....... 30.00
GENL. FRANZ SIGEL AT THE BATTLE OF PEA RIDGE,
    ARK......................................................... Small ....... 50.00
GENL. G. T. BEAUREGARD ............................. Small ....... 40.00
GENL. GARIBALDI; "The Hero of Italy" .................. Small ....... 35.00
GENL. GEO. B. McCLELLAN AND STAFF; 1862; (At
    Williamsburg) ........................................... Small ....... 45.00
GENL. GEO. B. McCLELLAN AND STAFF BEFORE
    YORKTOWN, VA............................................ Small ....... 45.00
GENL. GEORGE WASHINGTON; (Equestrian); N. Currier Small ....... 75.00
GENL. GEORGE WASHINGTON; (Equestrian) ............. Medium ..... 60.00
GENERAL GORGEY; "The Hungarian Patriot ............. Small ....... 35.00
GENERAL GRANT; 1884 .................................... Small ....... 40.00
GENERAL GRANT; (Seated at Desk) ..................... Medium ..... 45.00
GENERAL GRANT AND FAMILY; 1867..................... Small ....... 42.50
GENERAL GRANT AT THE TOMB OF A. LINCOLN:
    1868 ...................................................... Small ....... 40.00
GENERAL HELMUTH VON MOLTKE VON PREUSSEN. Small ....... 18.00
GENERAL ISRAEL PUTNAM; C. Currier ................. Small ....... 67.50
GENERAL JAMES A. GARFIELD; 1880 .................. Small ....... 32.50
GENERAL JAMES IRVIN; N. Currier; 1847 .............. Small ....... 25.00
GENERAL JOHN C. BRECKINRIDGE ...................... Small ....... 25.00
GENERAL JOSEPH E. JOHNSTON; 1861 ................ Small ....... 25.00
GENERAL LAFAYETTE; N. Currier ...................... Small ....... 35.00
GENERAL LEWIS CASS; N. Currier; 1846 .............. Small ....... 22.50
GENERAL MEAGHER AT THE BATTLE OF FAIR OAKS,
    VA. 1862; ................................................ Small ....... 29.50
GENERAL ROBERT E. LEE ............................... Small ....... 48.50
GENERAL ROBERT E. LEE AT THE GRAVE OF
    "STONEWALL" JACKSON .............................. Small ....... 35.00
GENERAL SCOTT'S VICTORIOUS ENTRY INTO THE CITY
    OF MEXICO; N. Currier; 1847 .......................... Small ....... 45.00
GENERAL SHIELDS AT THE BATTLE OF WINCHESTER,
    VA., 1862 ................................................ Small ....... 40.00
```

GENERAL STONEMAN'S GREAT CAVALRY RAID....... Small ....$ 40.00
GENERAL TAYLOR AND STAFF; N. Currier; 1847 ...... Small 45.00
GENL. TAYLOR AT THE BATTLE OF PALO ALTO; N.
  Currier; 1846 ,... Small 45.00
GENERAL TAYLOR AT THE BATTLE OF RESACA DE LA
  PALMA; N. Currier; 1846 .... Small 45.00
GENERAL TOM THUMB; N. Currier   .... Small 42.50
GENERAL TOM THUMB — Barnum's Gallery of Wonders,
  No. 1., N. Currier; 1849 .... Small 45.00
GENERAL TOM THUMB — Barnum's Gallery of Wonders,
  No. 1., "Born in 1832, is 28 in. high, etc." .... Small 35.00
GENERAL TOM THUMB & WIFE, COM. NUTT & MINNIE
  WARREN — "The Greatest Wonders in the World"
  1863 .... Small 50.00
GENERAL TOM THUMB AS HOP O' MY THUMB......... Small 35.00
GENERAL TOM THUMB'S MARRIAGE; 1863 .... Small 50.00
GENERAL TRANSATLANTIC COMPANY'S STEAMER
  "NORMANDIE" .... Small 60.00
GENERAL U. S. GRANT; 1884 .... Small 28.50
GEN. U. S. GRANT; "The Nation's Choice for President
  of the U. S." .... Small 30.00
GEN. U. S. GRANT; "President of the U.S.".............. Small 35.00
GENERAL VIEW OF THE CITY OF TORONTO, N.C. .. Medium...... 80.00
GENERAL VON STEINMETZ VON PREUSSEN............. Small 21.50
GENERAL WILLIAM F. PACKER; "Gov. of Penna.".....Small 16.50
GENERAL WILLIAM H. HARRISON; N. Currier .... Small 35.00
GENERAL WILLIAM J. WORTH; N. Currier; 1847; .... Small 22.50
GENERAL WILLIAM T. SHERMAN............................. Small 27.50
GENERAL WINFIELD S. HANCOCK......................... Small 27.50
GENERAL Z. TAYLOR; "The Hero of the Rio Grande,"
  N. Currier; 1846   .... Small 30.00
GENERAL Z. TAYLOR; "Rough and Ready."; 1846 .....Small 32.00
GENUINE HAVANA, A   .... Small 17.50
GEORGE .... Small 16.50
GEORGE AND LUCY .... Small 18.50
GEORGE AND MARTHA WASHINGTON; (Pair) .... Small 40.00
GEORGE M. DALLAS; N. Currier; 1846 .... Small 22.50
"GEORGE M. PATCHEN," "BROWN DICK" AND "MILLER'S
  DAMSEL" 1859 ....Large...... 225.00
GEORGE W. WILLIAMS ....Small 18.50
GEORGE WASHINGTON (Bust to left); N. Currier .... Medium 48.50
GEORGE WASHINGTON; (Bust to right)................. Medium 55.00
GEORGE WASHINGTON; (in uniform); N. Currier.......... Small 50.00
GEORGE WASHINGTON — First President; N. Currier .. Small 55.00
GEORGE WASHINGTON AND HIS FAMILY .... Large 135.00
GEORGIANA; N. Currier; 1846................................ Small 20.00
GEORGIE; "Quite Tired" .... Small 20.00
GERMAN BEAUTY, THE... Small 20.00
GERTRUDE; N. Currier 1846   .... Small 20.00
GETTING A BOOST; 1882 .... Small 30.00
GETTING A FOOT; 1887 .... Small 27.50
GETTING A HOIST; 1875 .... Small 30.00
GETTING DOWN; N. Currier; (Comic) .... Small 24.00
GETTING IN; N. Currier .... Small 27.50
GETTING OUT; N. Currier .... Small 27.50
GETTING UP; N. Currier; (Comic) .... Small 27.50
GIANT'S CAUSEWAY, THE, Ireland .... Small 32.00
GIFT OF AUTUMN, A; 1875................................... Small 48.00

```
GIRARD AVENUE BRIDGE, FAIRMOUNT PARK, PHILA. ...Small ..$ 45.00
GIRL I LOVE, THE; 1870 ..............................................Small ...  20.00
GIRL OF MY HEART ...........................................Small ...  20.00
GIRL OF THE PERIOD, THE ....................................Small ...  20.00
"GIVE ME LIBERTY, OR GIVE ME DEATH!"..................Small ...  85.00
GIVE US THIS DAY OUR DAILY BREAD; 1872 ..............Small ...  12.50
GIVING HIM TAFFY; 1881..........................................Small ...  18.00
GLEN AT NEWPORT, THE..........................................Small ...  70.00
GLENGARIFF INN, IRELAND......................................Small ...  40.00
GLIMPSE OF THE HOMESTEAD, A; 1863........................Medium. 120.00
GLIMPSE OF THE HOMESTEAD, A; 1865........................Small ...  50.00
GLORIOUS CHARGE OF HANCOCK'S DIVISION ..............Small ...  48.00
GOD BLESS FATHER AND MOTHER; 1876 ...................Small ...  25.00
GOD BLESS OUR HOME ...........................................Small ...  25.00
GOD BLESS OUR SCHOOL; 1874 .............................Small ...  15.00
GOD BLESS THEE AND KEEP THEE............................Small ...  12.00
"GOD IS LOVE"........................................................Small ...  12.00
GOD SAVE MY FATHER'S LIFE; N. Currier ..................Small ...  12.00
GOD SPAKE ALL THESE WORDS; 1876..........................Small ...  11.50
GO IN AND WIN; 1880 ...........................................Small ...  25.00
GOING AGAINST THE STREAM; N. Currier ..................Small ...  42.00
GOING FOR A SHINE; 1888.......................................Small ...  24.50
GOING FOR HIM; 1868 ..............................................Small ...  32.50
GOING FOR THE MONEY; 1891......................................Small ...  50.00
GOING IT BLIND; N. Currier .....................................Small ...  60.00
GOING TO PASTURE — EARLY MORNING.......................Small ...  40.00
GOING TO THE FRONT; 1880 ....................................Small ...  45.00
GOING TO THE MILL; N. Currier ...............................Small ...  40.00
GOING TO THE MILL; 1859 .......................................Medium.  60.00
GOING TO THE TROT — A GOOD DAY AND GOOD TRACK. Large ...  200.00
GOING WITH THE STREAM; N. Currier ...........................Small ...  47.50
GOLD DUST; 1875 ..................................................Small ...  45.00
GOLD MINING IN CALIFORNIA; 1871 ...........................Small ...  240.00
GOLD SEEKERS, THE; N. Currier; 1851 .......................Small ...  235.00
GOLDEN FRUITS OF CALIFORNIA; 1869 .......................Large ...  100.00
GOLDEN MORNING, A; N. Currier ................................Medium.  55.00
GOLDEN MORNING, THE..............................................Small ...  40.00
GOLDSMITH MAID, Record 2:14; 1881 ............................Small ...  55.00
"GOLDSMITH MAID" AND "AMERICAN GIRL"; 1868........Large ..  175.00
"GOLDSMITH MAID" AND "JUDGE FULLERTON"; 1874 . Small ...  80.00
"GOLDSMITH MAID" AND "LUCY"; 1874.......................Small ...  75.00
GOOD CHANCE, A; 1863 ...........................................Large ...  400.00
GOOD DAY'S SPORT, A — HOMEWARD BOUND; 1869 .......Large ...  390.00
GOOD ENOUGH ......................................................Small ...  15.00
GOOD EVENING; (Dog and child) ..............................Small ...  28.00
GOOD FIDO AND NAUGHTY KITTY...............................Small ...  24.50'
GOOD FOR A COLD....................................................Small ...  18.50
GOOD FOR NOTHING ..............................................Medium.  37.50
GOOD FRIENDS, THE ..............................................Small ...  17.50
GOOD HUSBAND, THE; 1870.......................................Small ...  70.00
GOOD LITTLE BROTHER; 1872 ................................Small ...  20.00
GOOD LITTLE GIRL; 1871 ........................................Small ...  20.00
GOOD LITTLE SISTERS, THE ...................................Small ...  20.00
GOOD MAN AT THE HOUR OF DEATH, THE; N. Currier ....Small ...  30.00
GOOD MORNING; (Dog and child) ..............................Small ...  20.00
GOOD MORNING, LITTLE FAVORITE ..........................Small ...  20.00
GOOD NATURED MAN, THE; N. Currier ......................Small ...  21.50
GOOD NIGHT, LITTLE PLAYFELLOW ........................Small ...  20.00
```

```
GOOD OLD DOGGIE ...................................................... Small ... $ 24.50
GOOD OLD ROVER AND KITTIE .................................. Small ...   20.00
GOOD RACE, WELL WON, A; 1887 .............................. Large ...  175.00
GOOD SAMARITAN, THE; N. Currier; 1849 ................... Small ...   14.50
GOOD SEND OFF — GO! A; 1872 ................................. Large ...  165.00
GOOD SHEPHERD, THE ............................................ Small ...   12.50
GOOD SHEPHERDESS; N. Currier; 1846 ....................... Small ...   12.50
GOOD TIMES ON THE OLD PLANTATION ................... Small ...   95.00
GOSPEL ORDINANCE, THE; N. Currier; 1848 ............... Small ...   16.50
GOT 'EM BOTH; 1882 ............................................... Small ...   55.00
GOT THE DROP ON HIM; 1881 ................................... Small ...   33.50
GOVERNING POWER, THE .......................................... Small ...   27.50
GOVERNMENT GUARDS — CONNECTICUT 1st COMPANY.. Small ...   55.00
GOVERNOR RUTHERFORD B. HAYES ......................... Small ...   45.00
GOV. SAMUEL J. TILDEN ......................................... Small ...   32.50
GOVERNOR SPRAGUE — BLACK TROTTING STALLION ... Small ...   65.00
GOVERNOR THOMAS A. HENDRICKS .......................... Small ...   30.00
GOVERNOR WADE HAMPTON ...................................... Small ...   30.00
GRACE DARLING; (Shipwreck); N. Currier ................... Small ...   40.00
GRACE, MERCY AND PEACE ..................................... Small ...   12.50
GRACES OF THE BICYCLE, THE; 1880 ..................... Miniature  16.50
GRACIE ................................................................... Small ...   16.00
GRAF VON BISMARK .............................................. Small ...   20.00
GRAND BANNER OF THE RADICAL DEMOCRACY — FOR
   1864 ............................................................... Small ...   35.00
GRAND CALIFORNIA FILLY "SUNOL" — Record 2:10½.... Small ...   65.00
GRAND CALIFORNIA FILLY "WILDFLOWER"; 1883 .......Small ...   68.50
GRAND CALIFORNIA TROTTING MARE "SUNOL"; 1890 .. Large ...  185.00
GRAND CENTRAL SMOKE; 1876 ................................. Small ...   45.00
GRAND CENTRAL WEDDING; 1876 ............................. Small ...   45.00
GRAND DEMOCRATIC FREE SOIL BANNER; 1848 ......... Small ...   55.00
GRAND DISPLAY OF FIREWORKS; 1883 ....................... Small ...   60.00
GRAND DISPLAY OF FIREWORKS AND ILLUMINATIONS .. Medium.   90.00
GRAND DRIVE, CENTRAL PARK, N. Y., THE, 1869 ....... Large ...  550.00
GRAND FOOTBALL MATCH; Darktown against Blackville;
   "A Kick Off"; 1888 .......................................... Small ...   45.00
GRAND FOOTBALL MATCH; Darktown against Blackville;
   "A Scrimmage"; 1888 ....................................... Small ...   40.00
GRAND FUNERAL PROCESSION IN MEMORY OF GENERAL
   JACKSON; N. Currier ........................................ Small ...  135.00
GRAND FUNERAL PROCESSION OF THE VICTIMS OF THE
   REVOLUTION; N. Currier; 1848 ............................Small ...   40.00
GRAND HORSE "ST. JULIEN, " THE "KING OF TROTTERS"
   1880 ............................................................... Small ...   65.00
GRAND NATIONAL AMERICAN BANNER; N. Currier; 1856. Small ...   40.00
GRAND NATIONAL DEMOCRATIC BANNER, POLK AND
   DALLAS; N. Currier; 1844 ................................. Small ...   42.50
GRAND NATIONAL DEMOCRATIC BANNER, CASS AND
   BUTLER; N. Currier; 1848 ................................. Small ...   40.00
GRAND NATIONAL DEMOCRATIC BANNER; PIERCE AND
   KING; N. Currier; 1852 .................................... Small ...   40.00
GRAND NATIONAL DEMOCRATIC BANNER, BUCHANAN
   AND BRECKENRIDGE; N. Currier; 1856 ................. Small ...   40.00
GRAND NATIONAL DEMOCRATIC BANNER FOR 1860;
   BRECKENRIDGE AND LANE; 1860 ......................... Small ...   40.00
GRAND NATIONAL DEMOCRATIC BANNER, TILDEN; 1876 Small ...   40.00
GRAND NATIONAL REPUBLICAN BANNER, FREMONT AND
   DAYTON: N. Currier; 1846 ................................. Small ...   40.00
```

GRAND NATIONAL REPUBLICAN BANNER FOR 1872.
GRANT AND GREELEY; 1872 ....Small ...$ 40.00
GRAND NATIONAL TEMPERANCE BANNER; N. Currier ...Small ... 35.00
GRAND NATIONAL UNION BANNER FOR 1860 ....Small ... 36.50
GRAND NATIONAL UNION BANNER FOR 1864 ....Small ... 48.50
GRAND NATIONAL WHIG BANNER; "Justice to Harry of
  The West"; N. Currier; 1844 .... Small ... 40.00
GRAND NATIONAL WHIG BANNER; "Onward"; N. Currier. Small ... 40.00
GRAND NATIONAL WHIG BANNER; N. Currier; 1848 .... Small ... 40.00
GRAND NEW STEAMBOAT "PILGRIM," THE LARGEST IN
  THE WORLD; 1883 .... Large ... 195.00
GRAND PACER "FLYING JIB,"; Record 2:05¾ ....Small ... 60.00
GRAND PACER "RICHBALL,"; Record 2:12½ .... Small ... 60.00
GRAND RACER "KINGSTON,"; 1891 .... Large ... 200.00
GRAND RECEPTION OF KOSSUTH; N. Currier; 1851 .... Small ... 85.00
GRAND SALOON OF THE PALACE STEAMER "DREW";
  1878 .... Small ... 95.00
GRAND STALLION; "MAXY COBB,"; Record 2:13¼ .... Small ... 65.00
GRAND THROUGH ROUTE BETWEEN NORTH AND SOUTH;
  1878 ....Large ... 250.00
GRAND TROTTER "CLINGSTONE," Record 2:14; 1883 ...Large ... 265.00
GRAND TROTTER "CLINGSTONE," Record 2:14; 1882 ... Small ... 65.00
GRAND UNITED ORDER OF ODD FELLOWS CHART; 1881 Small ... 18.50
GRAND YOUNG TROTTER, "JAY EYE SEE" Record: 2:10 Small ... 60.00
GRAND YOUNG TROTTING MARE "NANCY HANKS,"; 1890
                                                                  Small ... 65.00
GRAND YOUNG TROTTING STALLION "AXTELL,"; 1899 Small ... 60.00
GRAND YOUNG TROTTING STALLION "AXTELL,"; 1899 Large ... 135.00
GRANDEST PALACE DRAWING ROOM STEAMERS IN THE
  WORLD, "DREW" and "ST. JOHN"; 1878 .... Large ... 200.00
GRANDFATHER'S ADVICE ....Small ... 15.00
GRANDMA'S "SPECS" ....Small ... 15.00
GRANDMOTHER'S PRESENT, THE; N. Currier ....Small ... 15.00
"GRANDPA'S SPECS" .... Small ... 15.00
GRANDPAPA'S CANE..Small ... 15.00
GRANDPAPA'S CANE..Medium. 25.00
GRANDPAPA'S RIDE ....Small ... 27.50
GRANT AND HIS GENERALS; 1865 .... Medium. 75.00
GRANT AND LEE MEETING NEAR APPOMATTOX COURTHOUSE, VA.,
  1868 .... Small ... 48.50
GRANT AT HOME; 1869 ....Small ... 40.00
GRANT IN PEACE ....Small ... 35.00
GRAVE OF STONEWALL JACKSON, LEXINGTON, VA.; 1870
                                                                  Small ... 32.50
GRAY GELDING "JACK" BY PILOT MEDIUM, Record 2:15;
  1888 .... Small ... 60.00
GRAY'S ELEGY — IN A COUNTRY CHURCHYARD; 1864 .. Large ... 95.00
GRAZING FARM, THE; 1867 .... Large ... 195.00
GREAT BARTHOLDI STATUE; (Statue of Liberty) ....Small ... 45.00
GREAT BARTHOLDI STATUE; (Statue of Liberty) .... Large ... 115.00
GREAT BATTLE OF MURFREESBORO, TENN., 1863 ......Small ... 48.50
GREAT BLACK SEA LION. THE MONARCH OF THE ARCTIC
  SEAS; .... Small ... 100.00
GREAT COMMAND, THE; 1866 ....Small ... 20.00
GREAT CONFLAGRATION AT PITTSBURGH, PENNA.,
  N. Currier; .... Small ... 165.00
GREAT DOUBLE TEAM TROT; 1891............................. Small ... 70.00
GREAT DOUBLE TEAM TROT; 1870 .... Large ... 225.00

```
GREAT EAST RIVER BRIDGE; 1872 .......................... Small ... $ 80.00
GREAT EAST RIVER SUSPENSION BRIDGE .............•..Large ... 495.00
GREAT EAST RIVER SUSPENSION BRIDGE; (Between New
    York and Brooklyn) 1881 ......................................Small ...   90.00
GREAT EASTERN; Record 2:19; 1877 ........................... Small ...   65.00
"GREAT EASTERN", THE; (Ship) ...............................Small ...   85.00
GREAT EXHIBITION OF 1851; N. Currier...................... Medium.  130.00
GREAT EXHIBITION OF 1860 .......................................Small ...   48.00
GREAT FAIR ON A GRAND SCALE, A; 1894 .................. Small ...   95.00
GREAT FIELD IN A GRAND RUSH, A; 1888 ................... Large ...  175.00
GREAT FIGHT AT CHARLESTON, S.C., 1863 ........ ........ Small ...   70.00
GREAT FIGHT BETWEEN THE "MERRIMAC" AND
    "MONITOR," 1862 ................................................Small ...  100.00
GREAT FIGHT FOR THE CHAMPIONSHIP BETWEEN JOHN
    C. HEENAN "THE BENICIA BOY," AND TOM SAYERS
    "CHAMPION OF ENGLAND." 1860 ...................... Small ...  165.00
GREAT FIRE AT BOSTON; 1872 ................................. Small ...   72.50
GREAT FIRE AT CHICAGO; 1871............................... Large ...  800.00
GREAT FIRE AT ST. JOHN, N. B., 1877 ....................... Small ...   65.00
GREAT FIRE AT ST. LOUIS, MO. , N. Currier; 1849 .........Small ...  125.00
GREAT FIRE OF 1835 ............................................... Large ...  200.00
GREAT FIRE OF 1835; "The Ruins" ............................. Large ...  200.00
GREAT FIVE MILE ROWING MATCH FOR $4,000; 1867 .... Large ...  600.00
GREAT HORSES IN A GREAT RACE "SALVATOR" AND
    "TENNY"; 1891 ................................................. Large ...  200.00
GREAT INTERNATIONAL BOAT RACE ...................... Small ...  425.00
GREAT INTERNATIONAL YACHT RACE, AUGUST 8,1870 Large ...  850.00
GREAT INTERNATIONAL YACHT RACE OF 1870 ........... Small ...  140.00
GREAT MATCH RACE; "A Dead Heat; 1873 ...................Small ...   85.00
GREAT MISSISSIPPI STEAMBOAT RACE; 1870 ...............Small ...  100.00
GREAT NAVAL VICTORY IN MOBILE BAY ...................Small ...   48.50
GREAT OCEAN YACHT RACE; 1867 ............................Small ...  190.00
GREAT OYSTER EATING MATCH; "The Start"; 1886 ......Small ...   35.00
GREAT OYSTER EATING MATCH; "The Finish"; 1886 ...Small ...   35.00
GREAT PACER JOHNSTON, Record 2:10; 1883................Small ...   65.00
GREAT PACER "SORREL DAN," Record 2:14; 1880:........Small ...   60.00
GREAT POLE MARES, "BELLE HAMLIN" AND "JUSTINA"
                                                        Small ...   70.00
GREAT PRESIDENTIAL SWEEPSTAKES OF 1856............ Medium.   60.00
GREAT RACE AT BALTIMORE; 1877.............................Small ...  190.00
GREAT RACE FOR THE WESTERN STAKES; 1870 .......... Small ...  115.00
GREAT RACE FOR THE MISSISSIPPI; "Between the 'New
    Orleans' and the 'St. Louis;' " 1870 ....................... Large ...  300.00
GREAT RACE ON THE MISSISSIPPI; "Robert E. Lee" de-
    feating the "Natchez"; 1870 ............................... Large ...  300.00
GREAT RACING CRACK HINDOO; 1881 ...................... Small ...   67.50
GREAT REPUBLICAN REFORM PARTY........................ Small ...   50.00
GREAT RIOT AT THE ASTOR PLACE OPERA HOUSE,
    N.Y. ................................................................Small ...  145.00
GREAT ST. LOUIS BRIDGE ACROSS THE MISSISSIPPI......Small ...   77.50
GREAT SALT LAKE, UTAH ......................................Small ...   55.00
GREAT SIRE OF TROTTERS "ELECTIONEER"; 1891,.....Small ...   70.00
GREAT VICTORY IN THE SHENANDOAH VALLEY, VA....Small ...   45.00
GREAT WALK — "Come In As You Can"; 1879 .................Small ...   37.50
GREAT WALK — "Go As You Please"; 1879 ................... Small ...   37.50
GREAT WEST, THE; 1870 .......................................Small ...  135.00
GRECIAN BAND, THE; "Fifth Avenue Style"; 1868.........Small ...   40.00
GREY EAGLE; N. Currier; 1850 ...............................Medium.  165.00
```

```
GREY EDDY; N. Currier; 1855 ........................................ Large ...$200.00
GREY MARE "EMMA B"; Record 2:22½ ..................... Small ...  65.00
GREY MARE "LUCY" – THE PACING QUEEN; 1879 ....... Small ...  60.00
GREY MARE "POLICE GAZETTE," 1879..................... Small ...  60.00
GREY TROTTING WONDER "HOPEFUL"; Record 2:14¾.. Small ...  70.00
GROTTOES OF THE SEA ......................................... Small ...  22.50
GROUP OF FRUIT; 1875 ....................................... Small ...  25.00
GROUP OF LILIES ............................................... Small ...  55.00
GROVER CLEVELAND – PRESIDENT OF THE U.S. ....... Small ...  30.00
GUARDIAN ANGEL, THE ......................................Small ...  12.50
GUION LINE STEAMSHIP "ARIZONA".................... Small ...  50.00
GULICK GUARD, THE; N. Currier; 1838 .................. Small ...  65.00
GUNBOAT CANDIDATE, THE ................................ Small ...  37.50
GUSTAV STRUVE; N. Currier; 1848 ....................... Small ...  20.00
GUY: By Kentucky Prince ..................................... Small ...  48.50
GYPSIES CAMP, THE ........................................... Medium.  35.00
```

– H –

```
H. R. H. PRINCESS LOUISE .................................. Small ...$ 20.00
H. W. BEECHER ................................................. Small ...  25.00
HAIDEE; N. Currier ............................................ Small ...  20.00
HAIL MARY, MOTHER OF GOD................................ Small ...  12.50
HAIR TONIC EXPLOSION; 1884 .............................. Small ...  27.50
HALT BY THE WAYSIDE, A ................................... Small ...  60.00
HAMBLETONIAN; 1871......................................... Small ...  60.00
HAMBURGH- AMERICAN MAIL STEAMER FRISIA .......... Small ...  48.50
HAND-WRITING ON THE WALL, THE ...................... Small ...  21.50
HANNAH; N. Currier; 1846 .................................. Small ...  22.50
HANNIS; 1881 .................................................. Small ...  65.00
HANOVER; 1887................................................ Small ...  60.00
HAPPY FAMILY; (Home Scene); N. Currier.................. Small ...  30.00
HAPPY FAMILY; (Farmyard Scene) ......................... Small ...  35.00
HAPPY FAMILY – RUFFED GROUSE AND YOUNG; 1866. Large ...2500.00
HAPPY HOME, THE; N. Currier................................ Small ...  25.00
HAPPY HOUR, THE; N. Currier .............................. Small ...  25.00
HAPPY LAND, THE; (Oval) ................................... Small ...  16.50
HAPPY LITTLE CHICKS; 1866 ............................... Small ...  25.00
HAPPY LITTLE PUPS ........................................... Small ...  25.00
HAPPY MOTHER, THE; (Deer) ............................... Small ...  120.00
HAPPY NEW YEAR; N. Currier .............................. Small ...  65.00
HARBOR FOR THE NIGHT, A ................................ Small ...  45.00
HARBOR OF NEW YORK, THE ............................... Small ...  195.00
HARD ROAD TO TRAVEL, A; 1862 .......................... Small ...  35.00
HARRIET; N. Currier; 1845 .................................. Small ...  20.00
HARRISBURG AND THE SUSQUEHANNA; 1865 .............. Large ...  265.00
HARRY BASSETT; 1871........................................ Small ...  70.00
HARRY BASSETT AND LONGFELLOW; 1874 ................ Small ...  65.00
HARRY WILKES; 1885 ........................................ Large ...  225.00
HARRY WILKES; Record 2:13¼; 1886 ...................... Small ...  70.00
HARVARD COLLEGE, CAMBRIDGE, MASS; N. Currier .. Small ...  385.00
HARVEST; N. Currier; 1849 ................................. Small ...  37.50
HARVEST DANCE, THE; N. Currier; 1846 .................. Small ...  30.00
HARVEST FIELD, THE; N. Currier; (Oval).................. Medium.  80.00
HARVEST MOON, THE ......................................... Medium.  80.00
HARVEST QUEEN, THE ....................................... Small ...  20.00
HARVESTER, THE ............................................... Medium.  24.50
```

```
HARVESTING .............................................................. Small ...$  65.00
HARVESTING — THE LAST LOAD .............................. Small ...   65.00
HAT THAT MAKES THE MAN; 1879 ............................. Small ...   22.50
HATTIE ...................................................................... Small ...   20.00
HAUNTED CASTLE, THE ........................................... Small ...   27.50
HAUNTS OF THE WILD SWAN, THE; 1872 .................... Small ...   75.00
HAVANA ..................................................................... Small ...   48.50
HAYING - TIME; "The First Load"; 1868 ..................... Large ...  225.00
HAYING - TIME; "The Last Load"; 1868 ...................... Large ...  225.00
HE IS SAVED .............................................................Small ...   14.50
HE LOVES ME ............................................................Small ...   15.00
HEAD AND HEAD FINISH, A; (Poster) ........................ Large ...   67.50
HEADS OF THE DEMOCRACY .................................Small ...   50.00
HEALTH TO THE KING AND BISMARCK; 1870 ................Small ...   20.00
HEART OF DIVINE LOVE .......................................Small ...   12.50
HEART OF JESUS; 1876 ............................................. Small ...   12.00
HEART OF THE WILDERNESS, THE ........................... Medium.   95.00
HEATHEN CHINEE; 1871.............................................Small ...   65.00
HEBE ......................................................................Small ...   20.00
HEIR TO THE THRONE; 1860 .....................................Small ...   45.00
HELEN; N. Currier; 1855 ............................................ Small ...   20.00
HENRIETTA; N. Currier .............................................Small ...   20.00
HENRY; N. Currier; 1845 ............................................Small ...   25.00
HENRY; RECORD 2:20½ ............................................Small ...   60.00
HENRY CLAY; "The Farmer of Ashland"; N. Currier ......Small ...   35.00
HENRY CLAY OF KENTUCKY: N. Currier; 1842 .......... Small ...   35.00
HENRY CLAY — NOMINATED FOR 11TH PRES., N. Currier Small .
HERO AND FLORA TEMPLE; N. Currier; 1856 .............. Large ...  235.00
HEROINE OF MONMOUTH; 1876 (Mollie Pitcher) ............ Small ...   75.00
HEROINE OF THE LIGHTHOUSE, THE ........................Small ...   37.50
HIAWATHA'S DEPARTURE; 1868 ................................Medium.   40.00
HIAWATHA'S WEDDING ...... ................................... Small ...   40.00
HIAWATHA'S WEDDING; 1858 ...................................Large ...   40.00
HIAWATHA'S WOOING; N. Currier ............................. Small ...   37.50
HIAWATHA'S WOOING; 1860 ...................................... Medium.   45.00
HIGH BRIDGE AT HARLEM, N. Y., N. Currier ............. Small ...  120.00
HIGH OLD SMOKE — GO IN FELLERS; 1881 ................ Small ...   27.50
HIGH PRESSURE STEAMBOAT "MAYFLOWER", N. Currier;
   1855 .................................................................Large ...  275.00
HIGH-SPEED STEAM YACHT "STILETTO" ...................Small ...  115.00
HIGH TONED; 1879 ....................................................Small ...   15.00
HIGH WATER IN THE MISSISSIPPI; 1868 ......................Large ...  220.00
HIGHLAND BEAUTY, THE ........................................ Small ...   20.00
HIGHLAND BOY, THE; N. Currier ............................. Small ...   20.00
HIGHLAND GIRL, THE; N. Currier ............................. Small ...   20.00
HIGHLAND FLING; N. Currier; 1846; (Oval) .............. Small ...   27.50
HIGHLAND FLING; 1876 ............................................ Medium.   42.50
HIGHLAND LOVERS THE; N. Currier; 1846 .............. Small ...   22.50
HIGHLAND MARY; 1876 ............................................Small ...   22.50
HIGHLAND WATERFALL; (Oval).................................Small ...   18.00
HIGHLANDER N. Currier; 1854 ...............................Large ...  385.00
HIGHLANDER'S RETURN, THE ..................................Medium.   40.00
HILLSIDE PASTURE — SHEEP ...................................Medium.   45.00
HILLSIDE PASTURES — CATTLE .............................. Small ...   45.00
HIS MOTHER-IN-LAW; 1877 ...................................... Small ...   32.50
HOLD THE FORT ; 1875 ............................................ Small ...   24.50
HOLD YOUR HORSE, BOSSY; 1877.............................. Small ...   30.00
HOLIDAYS IN THE COUNTRY — THE OLD BARN FLOOR . Large ...  350.00
```

```
HOLIDAYS IN THE COUNTRY — TROUBLESOME FLIES;
  1868 ................................................................ Large ....$275.00
HOLY BIBLE, THE .............................................. Small ....   12.00
HOLY CATHOLIC FAITH, THE ........................... Small ....   12.00
HOLY COMMUNION; 1873 ...................................Small ....   12.00
HOLY CROSS, THE ................................................ Small ....   12.00
HOLY CROSS ABBEY ON THE SUIR .................... Small ....   15.00
HOLY EUCHARIST, THE; N. Currier; 1848 ............... Small ....   12.00
HOLY FACE, THE ..................................................... Small ....   12.00
HOLY FAMILY ........................................................... Small ....   12.00
HOLY SACRAMENT OF THE ALTAR ......................Small ....   12.00
HOLY SEPULCHRE, THE ...........................................Small ....   12.00
HOLY VIRGIN PRAY FOR US; 1876 ........................... Small ....   12.00
HOLY WELL, THE; (Ireland) ...................................Small ....   14.50
HOME AND FRIENDS ............................................. Small ....   25.00
HOME FROM THE BROOK — THE LUCKY FISHERMEN;
  1867 .............................................................. Large ....   245.00
HOME FROM THE WAR; 1862 ...................................... Small ....   27.50
HOME FROM THE WOODS — THE SUCCESSFUL SPORTSMEN;
  1867 .............................................................. Large ....   250.00
HOME IN THE COUNTRY, A ....................................... Medium...   100.00
HOME IN THE WILDERNESS, A; 1870 ....................... Small ....   75.00
HOME IN THE WILDERNESS, THE; 1875 .................... Small ....   70.00
HOME IN THE WOODS, A .......................................... Small ....   50.00
HOME OF EVANGELINE, THE; 1864 ........................... Large ....   75.00
HOME OF FLORENCE NIGHTINGALE, THE .............. Medium...   60.00
HOME OF SCOTT, THE; ABBOTSFORD .................... Small ....   30.00
HOME OF THE DEER — MORNING IN THE ADIRONDACKS
                                                          Large ....   750.00
HOME OF THE DEER; 1870 ...................................... Small ....   60.00
HOME OF THE DEER ...............................................Medium...   75.00
HOME OF THE SEAL, THE ...................................... Small ....   50.00
HOME OF THE SOUL, THE; 1876...............................Small ....   15.00
HOME OF WASHINGTON, MT. VERNON; C. Currier; 1852..Medium...   60.00
HOME OF WASHINGTON, MT. VERNON .....................Small ....   45.00
HOME OF WASHINGTON, MT. VERNON .....................Large ....   150.00
HOME "ON SICK LEAVE" ........................................ Small ....   25.00
HOME ON THE MISSISSIPPI, A; 1871 ........................... Small ....   85.00
HOME, SWEET HOME; 1869 ....................................Large ....   125.00
HOME SWEET HOME ............................................. Medium...   50.00
HOME SWEET HOME .............................................. Small ....   35.00
HOME TO THANKSGIVING; 1867 ............................. Large ....4000.00
HOME TREASURES ...............................................Small ....   12.50
HOMEWARD BOUND; N. Currier ............................. Small ....   80.00
HONOR THE LORD; 1872 .......................................Small ....   10.00
HONOR THE LORD WITH THY SUBSTANCE ,.................Small ....   10.00
HON. ABRAHAM LINCOLN; (Facsimile signature); Portrait
  without beard ....................................... Medium...   120.00
HON. ABRAHAM LINCOLN; (Republican Candidate); 1860
  (Oval) ................................................... Small  ... 100.00
HON. ABRAHAM LINCOLN — 16TH PRESIDENT; 1860 ...Medium... 165.00
HON. ABRAHAM LINCOLN; (Republican Candidate); 1860. Large .... 450.00
HON. ABRAHAM LINCOLN — OUR NEXT PRES., 1860 .... Small ....   80.00
HON. CHARLES GAVAN DUFFY; N. Currier; 1849 ........Small ....   25.00
HON. EDWARD EVERETT ....................................Medium...   40.00
HON. HANNIBAL HAMLIN; (Republican Candidate) .........Small ....   30.00
HON. HERSCHEL V. JOHNSON; 1860 .............................Small ....   27.50
HON. HORACE GREELEY; 1872 .................................Small ....   30.00
```

```
HON. HORATIO SEYMOUR.............................................Small ...$ 30.00
HON. JAMES G. BLAINE.............................................Small ....  35.00
HON. JAMES G. BLAINE .............................................Large ....  70.00
HON. JEFFERSON DAVIS .............................................Small ....  50.00
HON. JOHN A. LOGAN  .............................................Small ....  25.00
HON. JOHN BELL, OF TENNESSEE; 1860.....................Small ....  30.00
HON. JOHN C. BRECKINRIDGE; 1860..........................Small ....  30.00
HON. JOSEPH LANE; 1860  .............................................Small ....  27.50
HON. STEPHEN A. DOUGLAS .............................................Small ....  37.50
HON. STEPHEN A. DOUGLAS .............................................Large ....  75.00
HONOUR! N. Currier  .............................................Small ....  37.00
HOOKED! 1874 .............................................Small ....  87.50
HOPEFUL; (Grey Horse)  .............................................Small ....  60.00
HOPEFUL; 1876  .............................................Large ....  150.00
HOPEFUL — Record 2:14¾ .............................................Small ....  65.00
HOPEFUL DRIVER, A .............................................Small ....  40.00
HORACE GREELEY.............................................Medium...  48.50
HORSE CAR SPORTS — GOING TO A CHICKEN SHOW; 1886
                                                          Small ....  27.50
HORSE CAR SPORTS — ON THE BACK TRACK; 1886..... Small ....  27.50
HORSE FAIR, THE .............................................Small ....  45.00
HORSE FOR THE MONEY, THE................................. Small ....  65.00
HORSE, KENNEL AND FIELD; 1893  .........................  Small ....  55.00
HORSE SHED STAKES; 1877 .............................................Small ....  40.00
HORSE THAT DIED ON THE MAN'S HANDS, THE; 1878.. Small ....  30.00
HORSE THAT TOOK THE POLE, THE; 1875 ................ Small ....  40.00
HORSEMAN OF THE PERIOD; 1876  .........................  Small ....  50.00
HORSES AT THE FORD; 1867.............................................Small ....  60.00
HORSES IN A THUNDERSTORM .............................................Small ....  60.00
HORTICULTURAL HALL.............................................Small ....  37.50
HOT RACE FROM THE START, A; 1893 ......................Small ....  60.00
HOT RACE TO THE WIRE; A; 1876 ...........................Small ....  60.00
HOUR OF VICTORY, THE; 1861  .............................Medium...  38.00
HOUSE IN ROXBURY, MASS., THE; N. Currier  .......... Small ....  70.00
HOUSEHOLD PETS; N. Currier; 1845  .........................  Small ....  25.00
HOUSEHOLD TREASURES .............................................Small ....  25.00
"HOVE TO FOR A PILOT"; N. Currier; 1856................. Large ...2950.00
HOW PRETTY!  .............................................Small ....  20.00
HOW SWEET! .............................................Small ....  20.00
HOWLING SWELL — ON THE WAR PATH; 1890..............Small ....  32.50
HOWLING SWELL — WITH HIS SCALP IN DANGER; 1890 .Small ....  32.50
HOWTH CASTLE .............................................Small ....  20.00
HUDSON AT PEEKSKIL, THE  .............................Small ....  89.50
HUDSON, FROM WEST POINT, THE; 1862 .....................Medium...  220.00
HUDSON HIGHLANDS, THE; 1867.............................. Medium...  275.00
HUDSON HIGHLANDS, THE; 1871 .............................Small ....  95.00
HUDSON HIGHLANDS NEAR NEWBURG, N. Y. .............. Small ....  95.00
HUDSON NEAR COLDSPRING, THE .........................Small ....  85.00
HUDSON RIVER — CROW'S NEST .............................Small ....  87.50
HUDSON RIVER STEAMBOAT "BRISTOL".................... Small ....  100.00
HUDSON RIVER STEAMBOAT "ST. JOHN"; 1864 ........Large ....  275.00
HUES OF AUTUMN, THE; "On Racquette River" ............Small ....  90.00
HUG ME CLOSER, GEORGE; (Bear); 1886 ....................Small ....  35.00
HUMMING TROT, A; 1893 .............................................Small ....  65.00
HUNDRED LEAF ROSE; N. Currier  .............................Small ....  48.50
HUNG UP — WITH THE STARCH OUT; 1878  ................Small ....  40.00
HUNGARIAN'S FAREWELL, THE; N. Currier.................Small ....  25.00
HUNGRY LITTLE KITTIES  .............................................Small ....  24.50
```

HUNTER'S DOG, THE; N. Currier ....Small .... $ 95.00
HUNTER'S SHANTY, THE — IN THE ADIRONDACKS; 1861
                                         Large 375.00
HUNTER'S SHANTY, THE .... Small 90.00
HUNTING CASUALTIES, NO. 575 — A TURN OF SPEED
    OVER THE FLATS; N. Currier ....Small 150.00
HUNTING CASUALTIES, NO. 576 — A STRANGE COUNTRY;
    N. Currier ....Small 150.00
HUNTING CASUALTIES, NO. 577 — DISPATCHED TO HEADQUARTERS
    N. Currier ....Small 150.00
HUNTING CASUALTIES, NO. 578 — UP TO SIXTEEN STONE;
    N. Currier .... Small 150.00
HUNTING CASUALTIES, NO. 579 — A RARE SORT FOR THE
    DOWNS; N. Currier .... Small 150.00
HUNTING CASUALTIES, NO. 580 — A MUTUAL DETERMINATION;
    N. Currier ....Small 150.00
HUNTING, FISHING AND FOREST SCENES; 1867 — GOOD
    LUCK ALL AROUND ....Large 395.00
HUNTING, FISHING, AND FOREST SCENES — SHANTYING
    ON THE LAKE SHORE; 1867...............................Large 385.00
HUNTING IN THE NORTHERN WOODS ....Small 150.00
HUNTING ON THE PLAINS; 1871 ....Small 160.00
HUNTING ON THE SUSQUEHANNA ....Medium .. 145.00
HURRY UP THE CAKES; N. Currier .... Small 22.50
HUSH! I FEEL HIM; 1880 ....Small 90.00
HUSH! I'VE A NIBBLE ....Small 85.00
HUSKING; 1861 ....Large 575.00
HYDE PARK — ON THE HUDSON ....Small 65.00

                                        — I —

I AM AS DRY AS A FISH ....Small .... $ 48.50
I SEE YOU; N. Currier ....Small 20.00
"I TOLD YOU SO"; 1860 ....Small 60.00
I WILL NOT ASK TO PRESS THAT CHEEK; 1875 ....Small 20.00
ICE-BOAT RACE ON THE HUDSON ....Small 400.00
ICE COLD SODA WATER; 1879 ....Small 27.50
ICE CREAM BUCKET — FREEZIN' IN; 1889 ....Small 27.50
ICE CREAM BUCKET — THAWING OUT; 1889 ....Small 27.50
ICED LEMONADE; 1879 ....Small 27.50
IDLEWILD — ON THE HUDSON; "The Glen"..................Small 75.00
IMMACULATE CONCEPTION ....Small 12.50
IMPEACHMENT OF DAME BUTLER, FESSENDEN, BUTLER,
    BEN WADE .... Small 37.50
IMPENDING CATASTROPHE, AN .... Small 40.00
IMPENDING CRISIS, THE .... Small 40.00
IMPERIAL BEAUTY, THE .... Small 21.50
IMPERIAL GERMAN MAIL STEAMER "ELBE," OF THE
    NORTH GERMAN LLOYD LINE .... Small 65.00
IMPERIAL GERMAN MAIL STEAMER "FULDA," OF THE
    NORTH GERMAN LLOYD LINE .... Small 60.00
IMPERIAL GERMAN MAIL STEAMER "HAVEL" .... Small 60.00
IMPERIAL GERMAN MAIL STEAMER "WERRA" .... Small 60.00
IMPORTED MESSENGER; 1879 .... Small 65.00
IMPORTED MESSENGER; 1880 .... Small 65.00
IN A TIGHT PLACE — GETTING SQUEEZED; 1860........ Medium .. 75.00
IN AND OUT OF CONDITION; 1877 .... Small 33.50

```
IN FULL BLOOM; 1870 ............................................... Small ....$  20.00
IN FULL DRESS  .................................................... Small ....   20.00
IN GOD IS OUR TRUST; 1874 ..................................... Small ....   10.00
IN MEMORIAM; N. Currier   ..................................... Small ....    8.00
IN MEMORY OF 'St. Paul's churchyard); N. Currier; 1845.. Small ....    7.50
IN THE HARBOR ..................................................... Small .... 125.00
IN THE MOUNTAINS  ............................................... Small ....   90.00
IN THE MOUNTAINS; (Deer)  ..................................... Medium..  120.00
IN THE NORTHERN WILDS — TRAPPING BEAVER  ...... Small ....  140.00
IN THE SPRINGTIME   .............................................. Small ....   40.00
IN THE WOODS ...................................................... Small....   40.00
INAUGURATION OF WASHINGTON; 1876  .................... Small ....   75.00
INCREASE OF FAMILY, AN; 1863 ............................. Medium..   42.50
INDEPENDENT GOLD HUNTER ON WAY TO CALIFORNIA;
    N. Currier  ......................................................Small ....   85.00
INDIAN BALL PLAYERS ..........................................Medium..   90.00
INDIAN BEAR DANCE, THE  .....................................Medium..   87.50
INDIAN BUFFALO HUNT ...........................................Medium..  200.00
INDIAN BEAUTY, THE ..............................................Small ....   30.00
INDIAN BUFFALO HUNT — ON THE PRAIRIE BLUFFS ..Medium..  200.00
INDIAN FALLS.........................................................Small ....   45.00
INDIAN FAMILY; N. Currier .....................................Small ....   40.00
INDIAN LAKE — SUNSET; 1860   .............................Large....  135.00
INDIAN PASS, THE — ROCKY MOUNTAINS ...................Medium..  225.00
INDIAN SUMMER, SQUAM LAKE, N. H., 1868  .... ......... Medium ..  225.00
INDIAN TOWN ....................................................... Small ....   80.00
INDIAN WARRIOR, THE; N. Currier; 1845 ...................... Small ....   60.00
INDIANS ATTACKING THE GRIZZLY BEAR  .............. Medium..  240.00
INFANCY OF JESUS; N. Currier; 1849 ......................... Small ....    8.50
INFANCY OF THE VIRGIN; N. Currier 1849.................. Small ....    8.50
INFANT BROOD, THE ............................................... Small  ....   79.50
INFANT JESUS PREACHING IN THE TEMPLE ............. Small  ....    8.50
INFANT ST. JOHN, THE; N. Currier; 1845   ................ Small ....    8.50
INFANT SAVIOR  ..................................................... Small ....    8.50
INFANT SAVIOUR & ST. JOHN.................................. Small ....    8.50
INFANT SAVIOUR WITH MARY AND JOSEPH................ Small ....    8.50
INFANTRY MANEUVERS — BY THE DARKTOWN VOLUNTEERS;
    1887  ................................................................. Small ....   40.00
INGLESIDE WINTER, THE........................................... Small ....   27.50
INITIATION CEREMONIES OF THE DARKTOWN LODGE . Small ....   28.50
INITIATION CEREMONIES OF THE DARKTOWN LODGE;
    "Grand Boss Charging the Candidate"; 1887 .............. Small ....   28.50
INNOCENCE; N. Currier; 1848 ................................... Small ....   18.50
INQUIS, 1881  ......................................................... Small ....   50.00
INQUIS AND ARCHER; 1881 ...................................... Small ....   55.00
INTERIOR OF FORT SUMTER DURING THE BOMBARDMENT;
                                                                              Small ....   45.00
INTO MISCHIEF; 1857   ............................................ Small ....   35.00
INUNDATION, THE; N. Currier ................................... Small ....   22.50
INVITING GIFT, AN; 1870  ........................................ Small ....   32.50
IRA D. SANKEY — THE EVANGELIST OF SONG ............ Small ....   20.00
IRISH BEAUTY, THE.................................................. Small ....   20.00
IRON R. M. STEAMSHIP "PERSIA" CUNRAD LINE;
    N. Currier:........................................................... Small ....   75.00
IRON STEAMSHIP "GREAT BRITAIN"; N. Currier      Small ....   75.00
IRON STEAMSHIP "GREAT EASTERN"; 1858      ......... Large....  325.00
IROQUOIS; 1882  ..................................................... Large ....  250.00
ISABELLA; C. Currier; 1844   ................................... Small ....   20.00
```

ITALIAN LANDSCAPE ....Small ... $ 27.50
IVY BRIDGE, THE ....Small ...   29.50
IVY CLAD RUINS, THE..Medium.   48.00

— J —

JAMES; N. Currier; 1845 ....Small ...$ 37.50
JAMES BUCHANAN; (Democratic Candidate); N. Currier; ...Small ...   40.00
JAMES BUCHANAN — 15TH PRESIDENT; N. Currier ....Small ...   42.50
JAMES G. BIRNEY; N. Currier; 1844 .... Small ...   24.50
JAMES J. CORBETT .... Medium. 175.00
JAMES K. POLK — 11TH PRESIDENT; C. Currier .... Small ...   30.00
JAMES K. POLK — PEOPLE'S CANDIDATE; N. Currier; 1844
                                                                      Small ...   35.00
JAMES K. POLK; (Race Horse); N. Currier; 1850 ....Medium. 165.00
JAMES MADISON — 4TH PRESIDENT; N. Currier ....Small ...   49.50
JAMES MONROE — 5TH PRESIDENT; N. Currier ....Small ...   49.50
JAMES STEPHENS ....Small ...   27.50
JANE; N. Currier; 1845...Small ...   21.00
JAY EYE SEE — Record 2:14; 1883 ....Small ...   60.00
JAY EYE SEE; 1883 ....Large... 175.00
JAY EYE SEE — THE PHENOMENAL TROTTING GELDING;
     1884 ....Large ... 175.00
JAY EYE SORE — THE GREAT WORLD BEATER; 1885....Small ...   28.50
JEANETTE; N. Currier; 1846 ....Small ...   20.00
JEANIE; N. Currier; 1850 ....Small ...   20.00
JEFF DAVIS ON HIS OWN PLATFORM...........................Small ...   40.00
JEFF'S LAST SHIFT ....Small ...   37.50
JEM MACE; 1870...Medium. 125.00
JENNIE ....Small ...   20.00
JENNIE CRAMER ....Small ...   32.50
JENNY LIND; N. Currier .... Small ...   55.00
JENNY LIND — THE SWEDISH NIGHTINGALE'S GREETING
     TO AMERICA; N. Currier..Medium.   65.00
JEROME EDDY; 1882 ....Small ...   40.00
JERSEY CITY, HOBOKEN AND BROOKLYN; 1858 ....Small ... 100.00
JERUSALEM; N. Currier; 1846 ....Small ...   25.00
JERUSALEM FROM THE MOUNT OF OLIVES; N. Currier .. Small ...   25.00
JESUS AND THE CYRENIAN; N. Currier; 1848 ....Small ...   10.00
JESUS AND THE TWELVE APOSTLES; N. Currier; 1848   . Small ...   10.00
JESUS ASCENDETH INTO HEAVEN..............................Small ...   10.00
JESUS BEARING HIS CROSS; N. Currier; 1848 .... Small ...   10.00
JESUS BLESSING LITTLE CHILDREN; 1866 .... Small ...   10.00
JESUS CONDEMNED TO DEATH; N. Currier; 1848 ....Small ...   10.00
JESUS CONSOLES THE WOMEN OF JERUSALEM; N. Currier;
                                                                      Small ...   10.00
JESUS CRUCIFIED; N. Currier; 1847 ....Small ...   10.00
JESUS DESPOILED OF HIS GARMENTS; N. Currier ....Small ...   10.00
JESUS' FALL FOR THE FIRST TIME; N. Currier .... Small ...   10.00
JESUS' FALL FOR THE SECOND TIME; N. Currier ....Small ...   10.00
JESUS' FALL FOR THE THIRD TIME; N. Currier ....Small ...   10.00
JESUS IMPRINTS HIS FACE ON A CLOTH; N. Currier ......Small ...   10.00
JESUS IN THE TEMPLE ....Small ...   10.50
JESUS IS PLACED IN THE SEPULCHRE; N. Currier .... Small ...   10.00
JESUS LAID IN THE SEPULCHRE .... Small ...   10.00
JESUS MEETING HIS MOTHER; N. Currier .... Small ...   10.00
JESUS MEETS ST. VERONICA; N. Currier .... Small ...   10.00

```
JESUS NAILED TO THE CROSS; 1848 ............................Small ... $  10.00
JESUS OF NAZARETH PASSES BY .............................Small ...    10.00
JESUS ON THE CROSS .................................... ...........Small ...    10.00
JESUS PUT INTO THE SEPULCHRE; N. Currier  ...........Small ...    10.00
JESUS TAKEN FROM THE CROSS.............................. Small ...    10.00
JIB AND MAINSAIL RACE, A; 1882 .............................. Large ...  135.00
JOCKEY'S DREAM, THE; 1880 ...................................Small ...    40.00
JOHN; N. Currier; 1845 .............................................Small ...    42.50
JOHN ADAMS — 2ND PRESIDENT; N. Currier ..................Small ...    48.50
JOHN BROWN; 1863 .................................................Small ...    50.00
JOHN BROWN — THE MARTYR; 1870 ...........................Small ...    35.00
JOHN BROWN — LEADER OF THE HARPER'S FERRY
    INSURRECTION;  ..................................................Small ...    37.50
JOHN BULL MAKES A DISCOVERY ..............................Small ...    30.00
JOHN C. BREKENRIDGE; "Vice-Pres. of the U. S."........Small ...    30.00
JOHN C. CALHOUN; N. Currier; 1853 ...........................Small ...    28.50
JOHN C. FREMONT; N. Currier ...................................Small ...    30.00
JOHN C. HEENAN — THE CHAMPION OF AMERICA; 1860 .Small ...  175.00
JOHN C. HEENAN — CHAMPION OF THE WORLD; 1860  ..Small ...  175.00
JOHN ENNIS; 1879 .................................................. Small ...    60.00
JOHN HANCOCK'S DEFIANCE; 1876 ............................ Small ...    55.00
JOHN J. DWYER — CHAMPION OF AMERICA ................. Medium.    75.00
JOHN J. SULLIVAN; 1883 .........................................Medium .  175.00
JOHN MITCHEL; N. Currier; 1848 ............................... Small...    22.50
JOHN MORRISSEY; 1860 ...........................................Small ...    75.00
JOHN QUINCY ADAMS — 6TH PRESIDENT; N. Currier ......Small ...    37.50
JOHN R. GENTRY — Record 2:00½ ............................. Small ...    55.00
JOHN TYLER — 10TH PRESIDENT; N. Currier  ............. Small ...    40.00
JOHN WESLEY, A .M., N. Currier................................. Small ...    20.00
JOHN WESLEY PREACHING ON HIS FATHER'S GRAVE .. Small ...    20.00
JOHNNY AND LILY.................................................Small ...    20.00
JOLLY DOG, A; 1878  .............................................Small ...    20.00
JOLLY HUNTERS, THE  ..........................................Small ...    27.50
JOLLY JUMPER; 1888 ............................................. Small ...    20.00
JOLLY SMOKER, THE; 1880 ....................................... Small ...    20.00
JOLLY SMOKER, THE; 1880  .................................... Large ...    48.50
JOLLY YOUNG DUCKS; 1866 ..................................... Small ...    35.00
JOSEPHINE; N. Currier; 1848...................................... Small ...    20.00
JOSIE  .................................................................. Small ...    20.00
JUDGE FULLERTON; 1873.......................................... Small ...    75.00
JULIA; N. Currier; 1845 ............................................ Small ...    20.00
JULIA; N. Currier; 1846 ............................................ Small ...    20.00
JULIET  ................................................................Small ...    20.00
JULIETTE  .............................................................Small ...    20.00
JUNE ....................................................................Small ...    20.00
JUNO; (Girl's head)................................................Small ...    20.00
JUNO — A CELEBRATED SETTER; N. Currier.................Small ...    95.00
JUNO; (Pointer); N. Currier ......................................Small ...    95.00
JUST CAUGHT — TROUT AND PICKEREL; 1872 ............Small ...    50.00
JUST MARRIED .....................................................Small ...    21.50
JUST MY STYLE; 1871...............................................Small ...    20.00


                                    — K —

KAISER WILHELM DER GROSSE OF THE NORTH GERMAN
    LLOYD LINE  .................................................. Small ...$  35.00
KATE; N. Currier; 1846 ............................................ Small ...    20.00
```

```
KATE  .............................................................Medium ..$   22.50
KATE .............................................................Small.........   20.00
KATZ-KILLS, IN WINTER, THE  ...........................Small......   60.00
KILKENNY CASTLE, IRELAND  ...........................Small......   27.50
KILLERIES, THE — CONNEMARA ..........................Small......   40.00
KILLINEY HILL, DUBLIN......................................Small......   28.50
KING OF THE FOREST, THE — STAG  ................. Small......   40.00
KING OF THE HOUSE  .......................................Small......   25.00
KING OF THE ROAD, THE; 1866  ...........................Large......  225.00
KING WILLIAM III, CROSSING THE BOYNE; 1846..........Small......   20.00
KINGSTON; 1891  .............................................. Small......   60.00
KISS IN THE DARK, A; 1881......................................Small......   60.00
KISS ME QUICK; N. Currier ..................................Small......   60.00
KITCH-EE-I--AA-BA — OR THE BIG DUCK INDIAN CHIEF
                                                           Small......   35.00
KITTIE IN CLOVER; 1872  ...................................Small......   25.00
KITTIES AMONG THE CLOVER; 1873 .........................Small......   25.00
KITTIES AMONG THE ROSES ...................................Small......   25.00
KITTIES LESSON; 1877 .........................................Small......   25.00
KITTIES ON A FROLIC; 1877  .................................Small......   25.00
KITTY; (Gray kitten); N. Currier............................Small......   25.00
KITTY; (Girl) ..................................................Small......   20.00
KITTY AND ROVER  ......................................... Small......   24.50
KITTY'S BREAKFAST  .................................... Large......   24.00
KITTY'S DINNER  ........................................... Small......   24.00
KNITTING LESSON, THE .......................................Small......   32.50
KONIG WILHELM VON PREUSSEN IN DER SCHLACT VON
     SEDAN IN FRANKREICH .....................................Small......   20.00
KOSSUTH; N. Currier ............................................Small......   24.00
KREMLIN — Record 2:07¾; 1893  .............................. Small......   45.00


                             — L —

LA CRACOVIENNE, AS DANCED BY FANNY ELLSLER. Small......$   24.50
LADDER OF FORTUNE; 1875 ..........................Small......   35.00
LADIES' BOUQUET; 1870 .......................................Small......   40.00
LADIES LOYAL UNION LEAGUE, THE; 1863 ..............Small......   30.00
LADY & MOOR; N. Currier .......................................Small......   21.50
LADY EMMA, GEORGE WILKES AND GENERAL BUTLER;
     1865 ....................................................Large......  200.00
LADY FULTON; 1857  ..........................................Small......   60.00
LADY MAUD; 1876  ...........................................Small......   45.00
LADY MOSCOW; N. Currier; 1850 .............................Large......  175.00
LADY MOSCOW, ROCKET AND BROWN DICK; N. Currier. Large......  200.00
LADY OF THE LAKE; 1870  ................................. Small......   20.00
LADY SUFFOLK; N. Currier; 1850 ........................Medium......  150.00
LADY SUFFOLK; N. Currier; 1852 .............................Large .....  195.00
LADY SUFFOLK — Record 2:26  ..............................Large .....  195.00
LADY SUFFOLK AND LADY MOSCOW; N. Currier; 1850..Large .....  195.00
LADY SUTTON; N. Currier; 1849 ...............................Medium....  125.00
LADY THORN; 1871 ...........................................Small......   60.00
LADY THORN AND MOUNTAIN BOY; 1867.................. Large......  200.00
LADY WASHINGTON; N. Currier  .............................Small......   50.00
LADY WASHINGTON  ........................................Medium....   60.00
LADY WOODRUFF, MILLER'S DAMSEL, GENERAL DARCY
     AND STELLA; 1857 ...........................................Large .....  125.00
LADY'S BOUQUET, THE  ................................... Small......   48.00
```

LAFAYETTE .... Medium.. $ 67.50
LAFAYETTE AT THE TOMB OF WASHINGTON; N. Currier
                                                       Small...... 48.00
LAFAYETTE LAKE, NEAR TALLAHASSEE, FLORIDA ...Small...... 45.00
LAKE AND FOREST SCENERY .... Medium.... 70.00
LAKE GEORGE, N. Y. ....Small...... 40.00
LAKE GEORGE, BLACK MOUNTAIN ....Small...... 35.00
LAKE IN THE WOODS, THE .... Small...... 48.50
LAKE LUGANO, ITALY .... Small...... 25.00
LAKE MEMPHREMAGOG, CANADA .... Small...... 48.00
LAKE MOHONK ....Small...... 70.00
LAKE OF THE DISMAL SWAMP, THE ....Small 35.00
LAKE THUN − NEAR THE ALPS .... Small...... 30.00
LAKE WINNEPOSOGIS, CANADA .... Medium.... 140.00
LAKE WINNIPISEOGEE, NEW HAMPSHIRE .... Large...... 175.00
LAKES OF KILLARNEY, THE; 1868 .... Small...... 25.00
LAKESIDE HOME; 1869 ....Medium.... 70.00
LAMB AND THE LINNET, THE ....Small...... 35.00
LANDING A TROUT; 1879 ....Small...... 45.00
LANDING IN THE WOODS, A ....Small 40.00
LANDING OF COLUMBUS AT SAN SALVADOR; 1876...... Small 35.00
LANDING OF COLUMBUS, OCTOBER 11, 1492; N. Currier
                                                       Small 35.00
LANDING OF THE AMERICAN FORCES UNDER GENERAL
  SCOTT AT VERA CRUZ; N. Currier; 1847 ....Small 65.00
LANDING OF THE PILGRIMS AT PLYMOUTH; N. Currier Small 75.00
LANDSCAPE AND RUINS ....Medium.... 40.00
LANDSCAPE, FRUIT AND FLOWERS; 1862 ....Large 375.00
LANDSCAPE WITH CATTLE ....Medium.... 40.00
LANERCOST PRIORY, ENGLAND ....Medium.... 37.50
LAPPED IN THE LAST QUARTER; 1880 ....Small 32.00
LAST DITCH OF THE CHIVALRY, THE ....Medium.... 35.00
LAST DITCH OF THE DEMOCRATIC PARTY, THE........Small 33.50
LAST GUN OF THE "ARTIC"; N. Currier; 1855 ....Medium.... 95.00
LAST HIT OF THE GAME; 1886 ....Small 39.50
LAST LEADERS OF HUNGARY; N. Currier ....Small 24.00
LAST SHAKE, THE; 1885 ....Small...... 25.00
LAST SHOT, THE; 1858 .... Large......4000.00
LAST SUPPER, THE; N. Currier .... Small 25.00
LAST WAR-WHOOP, THE; N. Currier; 1856 .... Large 2000.00
LAUGH NO. 1, 1879 .... Small 27.50
LAUGH NO. 2; 1879 .... Small 27.50
LAURA; N. Currier; 1846 .... Small 20.00
LAWN TENNIS AT DARKTOWN − A SCIENTIFIC PLAYER
                                                       Small 35.00
LAWN TENNIS AT DARKTOWN − A SCIENTIFIC STROKE
                                                       Small 35.00
LAYING BACK − STIFF FOR A BRUSH; 1878 .... Small 55.00
LE MARECHAL MACMAHON .... Small 20.00
LE PETIT ST. JEAN; N. Currier .... Small 10.00
LE SAUVEUR DU MONDE; N. Currier .... Small 10.00
LEADERS, THE; JAY EYE SEE, 2:10; MAUD S., 2:08¾;
  ST. JULIEN, 2:11¼; 1888 .... Large...... 225.00
LEARN SOMETHING; (Motto) .... Small 18.00
LEARNING TO RIDE .... Small 20.00
LEONORA .... Medium.... 20.00
LES MEMBRES DE GOVERNMENT PROVISOIRE; N. Currier;
  1848 ....Small...... 22.50

− 58 −

```
LETTING THE CAT OUT OF THE BAG ..................... Small... $  30.00
LEVEE NEW ORLEANS, THE; 1884 ......................... Large ..   320.00
LEXINGTON; (Horse) ......................................... Small...    95.00
LEXINGTON OF 1861, THE ............................... Small...    60.00
LIBERTY, 1876 ................................................ Small...    30.00
LIEUT. GEN. N. B. FORREST ........................... Small...    28.50
LIEUT. GENL. ULYSSES S. GRANT AT THE SIEGE OF
  VICKSBURG; 1863 ........................................ Small...    35.00
LIEUT. GENL. ULYSSES S. GRANT — GENL. IN CHIEF..... Small...    35.00
LIEUT.-GENL. WILLIAM T. SHERMAN ................... Small...    35.00
LIEUT.-GENL. WINFIELD SCOTT ...................... - ......... Small...    35.00
LIFE AND AGE OF MAN, THE; N. Currier .............. Small...    40.00
LIFE AND AGE OF WOMAN, THE; N. Currier; 1850 ........ Small...    40.00
LIFE AND DEATH ........................................... Small...    35.00
LIFE IN NEW YORK — CUFFY DANCING FOR EELS CATHERINE
  MARKET .................................................... Small...    85.00
LIFE IN THE CAMP — PREPARING FOR SUPPER; 1863... Large ..   200.00
LIFE IN THE COUNTRY — EVENING ................... Medium.    85.00
LIFE IN THE COUNTRY — MORNING; 1862 .............. Medium    90.00
LIFE IN THE COUNTRY — MORNING ..................... Small...    48.00
LIFE IN THE COUNTRY — THE MORNING RIDE; 1859 .... Large ..   350.00
LIFE IN THE WOODS — RETURNING TO CAMP; 1860 ... Large ..   350.00
LIFE IN THE WOODS — STARTING OUT; 1860 ........... Large ..   350.00
LIFE OF A FIREMAN — THE FIRE; N. Currier; 1854 ........ Large ..   350.00
LIFE OF A FIREMAN — THE METROPOLITAN SYSTEM; 1866
                                                        Large ..   400.00
LIFE OF A FIREMAN — THE NEW ERA ..................... Large ..   400.00
LIFE OF A FIREMAN — THE NIGHT ALARM; N. Currier; 1854
                                                        Large ..   400.00
LIFE OF A FIREMAN — THE RACE; N. Currier; 1854........ Large ..   375.00
LIFE OF A FIREMAN — THE RUINS; N. Currier; 1854 ...... Large ..   300.00
LIFE OF A HUNTER, THE — CATCHING A TARTAR; 1861. Large ..   650.00
LIFE OF A HUNTER, THE — A TIGHT FIX; 1861 ......... Large ..  7500.00
LIFE OF A SPORTSMAN, THE; "Camping in the Woods"..... Small...    85.00
LIFE OF A SPORTSMAN, THE; "Coming Into Camp"........ Small...    85.00
LIFE OF A SPORTSMAN, THE; "Going Out"; 1872 ........ Small...    85.00
LIFE OF A TRAPPER; "A Sudden Halt"; 1866 ............... Large ..  3000.00
LIFE ON THE PRAIRIE; "The Buffalo Hunt"; 1862 ......... Large ..  2750.00
LIFE ON THE PRAIRIE; "The Trapper's Defence"; 1862... Large ..  2750.00
LIGHTNING EXPRESS, THE ............................... Small...   375.00
"LIGHTNING EXPRESS" TRAIN LEAVING THE JUNCTION;
  1863 ....................................................... Large ..  2500.00
"LIGHTNING EXPRESS" TRAIN LEAVING THE JUNCTION
                                                        Small...   500.00
LILLY ....................................................... Small...    20.00
LILLY AND HER KITTY ................................... Small...    25.00
LILY LAKE, NEAR ST. JOHN, N.B. ...................... Small...    50.00
LIME KILN CLUB, DE; "A Temperance Racket"; 1883 ......Small...    27.50
"LIMITED EXPRESS", A; 1884 ........................... Small...    67.50
LINCOLN, ABRAHAM; 16TH PRESIDENT; (Half Length); 1860
                                                        Small...    60.00
LINCOLN, ABRAHAM; 16TH PRESIDENT; (Portrait).......... Small...    60.00
LINCOLN, ABRAHAM; 16TH PRESIDENT; 1861 .............. Small...    60.00
LINCOLN, ABRAHAM ....................................... Medium    65.00
LINCOLN, ABRAHAM — THE NATION'S MARTYR ......... Small...    45.00
LINCOLN, ABRAHAM — THE NATION'S MARTYR ......... Large ..   125.00
LINCOLN ................................................... Medium    80.00
LINCOLN AT HOME; 1867.................................. Small...    60.00
```

```
LINCOLN AT HOME ..........................................................Large ..$ 175.00
LINCOLN FAMILY, THE; 1867 ...............................Small...   60.00
LINCOLN STATUE, THE  ...................................Small...   40.00
LINE SHOT — THE AIM; 1881  ............................Small...   35.00
LINE SHOT — THE RECOIL; 1881............................Small...   35.00
LION AND THE LAMB; N. Currier .........................Small...   18.50
LION HUNTER, THE; N. Currier  ...........................Small...   38.50
LIONS OF THE DERBY, THE; (Comic)........................ Small...   40.00
LISMORE CASTLE, COUNTY WATERFORD ...................Small...   24.50
LITERARY DEBATE IN THE DARKTOWN CLUB — QUESTION
    SETTLED .................................................................Small...   27.50
LITERARY DEBATE IN THE DARKTOWN CLUB — SETTLING
    THE QUESTION ......................................................Small...   27.50
LITTLE ALMS GIVER, THE ...........................................Small...   20.00
LITTLE ANNA  ....................................................... Small...   20.00
LITTLE ANNIE  ....................................................... Small...   20.00
LITTLE ANNIE AND HER KITTIE............................... Small...   20.00
LITTLE ANNIE AND HER KITTIES  ......................... Small...   20.00
LITTLE ASTRONOMER, THE ..................................... Small...   20.00
LITTLE BAREFOOT; 1872  ..................................... Small...   20.00
LITTLE BASHFUL.......................................................Small...   20.00
LITTLE BEAR, THE  ...............................................Small...   20.00
LITTLE BEAU, THE  ...............................................Small...   20.00
LITTLE BEAUTY, THE  ..........................................Small...   20.00
LITTLE BEGGAR  ......................................................Small...   19.50
LITTLE BELLE, THE  ............................................ Small..   19.50
LITTLE BLOSSOM  ................................................ Small...   19.50
LITTLE BLUEBELL  .............................................. Small...   19.50
LITTLE BO-PEEP  ................................................ Small...   19.50
LITTLE BOUNTIFUL................................................. Small ...   19.50
LITTLE BOUQUET; 1872 .........................  ................... Small...   20.00
LITTLE BROTHER; 1865  ..................................... Small...   19.50
LITTLE BROTHER AND I  ...................................... Small...   19.50
LITTLE BROTHER AND SISTER  ............................ Small...   19.50
LITTLE BROTHERS; 1875...........................................Small...   19.50
LITTLE BRUNETTE....................................................... Medium   25.00
LITTLE BUSY BEE; 1872  ..................................... Small...   18.50
LITTLE BUTTERFLY ............................................... Small...   18.50
LITTLE CAROLINE; N. Currier ................................ Small...   18.50
LITTLE CARRIE  .................................................... Small...   18.50
LITTLE CAVALIER, THE  ....................................... Small...   18.50
LITTLE CHARLIE — THE PRIZE BOY; 1859  ............. Small...   19.50
LITTLE CHARLIE AND HIS HORSE; 1874...................... Small...   22.50
LITTLE CHERUBS, THE  ....................................... Small...   18.50
LITTLE CHIEFTAIN.THE  ....................................... Small...   19.50
LITTLE CHILDREN — LOVE ONE ANOTHER  .............. Small...   20.00
LITTLE COLORED PET; 1881..................................... Small...   19.50
LITTLE DAISY .......................................................... Small...   19.50
LITTLE DOLLIE; 1872  ........................................... Small...   19.50
LITTLE DOT; 1872  ................................................ Small...   19.50
LITTLE DRESSMAKER, THE ..................................... Small ..   18.50
LITTLE DRUMMER BOY  ........................................ Small...   20.00
LITTLE EMMA GOING TO SCHOOL ........................... Small...   18.50
LITTLE EMMIE; 1872 ............................................... Small...   19.50
LITTLE EMPEROR, THE  ....................................... Small...   18.50
LITTLE ELLA  ........................................................ Small...   19.50
LITTLE ELLEN  ...................................................... Small...   18.50
LITTLE EVA ........................................................... Small...   18.50
```

```
LITTLE FAIRY .................................................Small...$ 19.50
LITTLE FANNIE ................................................Small...  18.50
LITTLE FAVORITE, THE; N. Currier; (Oval) ....................Small...  20.00
LITTLE FIREMAN, THE; 1857 ...................................Large..  50.00
LITTLE FLORA; 1874 ..........................................Small...  18.50
LITTLE FLOWER GATHERER.......................................Small...  18.50
LITTLE FLOWER GIRL, THE; 1852 ..............................Small...  20.00
LITTLE FOLKS IN THE COUNTRY ................................Small...  18.50
LITTLE FREDDIE .............................................Small...  18.50
LITTLE FRUIT BEARER; 1873 ..................................Small...  18.50
LITTLE FRUIT GIRL, THE; 1863 ...............................Small...  20.00
LITTLE GAME OF BAGATELLE BETWEEN OLD ABE, THE
   RAIL SPLITTER, AND LITTLE MAC, THE GUNBOAT
   GENERAL..................................................Small...  60.00
LITTLE GEORGIE .............................................Small...  18.50
LITTLE GROGGY, A; 1884 .....................................Small...  18.50
LITTLE HARRY ...............................................Small...  18.50
LITTLE HERO ................................................Small...  18.50
LITTLE HIGH STRUNG; 1879; (Comic)...........................Small...  25.00
LITTLE HIGHLANDER, THE .....................................Small...  18.50
LITTLE JAMIE ...............................................Small...  18.50
LITTLE JANE ................................................Small...  18.50
LITTLE JANICE ..............................................Small...  18.50
LITTLE JENNIE ..............................................Small...  18.50
LITTLE JOHNNIE AND BESSIE...................................Small...  22.50
LITTLE JOHNNY ..............................................Small...  20.00
LITTLE JULIA ...............................................Small...  18.50
LITTLE KATE; N. Currier; 1851 ..............................Small...  20.00
LITTLE KITTIE AND HER KITS .................................Small...  25.00
LITTLE KITTIES AMONG THE ROSES .............................Small...  25.00
LITTLE LILY ................................................Small...  18.50
LITTLE LIZZIE ..............................................Small...  18.50
LITTLE LULU ................................................Small...  18.50
LITTLE MAGGIE ..............................................Small...  18.50
LITTLE MAMIE ...............................................Small...  18.50
LITTLE MAMA, THE; N. Currier ...............................Small...  18.50
LITTLE MANLY; 1874 .........................................Small...  20.00
LITTLE MARTHA ..............................................Small...  18.50
LITTLE MARY ................................................Small...  18.50
LITTLE MARY AND HER LAMB ...................................Small...  22.50
LITTLE MAY BLOSSOM; 1874 ...................................Small...  20.00
LITTLE MAY QUEEN ...........................................Small...  20.00
LITTLE MECHANIC, THE .......................................Small...  24.50
LITTLE MERRY BOY ...........................................Small...  18.50
LITTLE MINNIE; 1862 ........................................Small...  18.50
LITTLE MORE GRAPE CAPT; BRAGG, A; N. Currier ...............Small...  35.00
LITTLE MOTHER, THE .........................................Small...  18.50
LITTLE MOURNER; 1872 .......................................Small...  12.50
LITTLE NELLY...............................................Small...  18.50
LITTLE PETS, THE ...........................................Small...  18.50
LITTLE PILGRIMS; 1873 ......................................Small...  20.00
LITTLE PLAYFELLOW, THE; N. Currier .........................Small...  18.50
LITTLE PLAYMATES, THE; N. Currier ..........................Small...  22.50
LITTLE POTATOE BUGS; N. Currier ............................Small...  18.50
LITTLE PROTECTOR, THE; N. Currier ..........................Small...  18.50
LITTLE PRUDY ...............................................Small...  18.50
LITTLE RECRUIT, THE; 1863 ..................................Small...  25.00
LITTLE RED RIDING HOOD .....................................Large..  65.00
```

```
LITTLE RED RIDING HOOD ...................................... Small...    37.50
LITTLE ROSEBUD; 1870 ........................................ Small...    18.50
LITTLE ST. JOHN, THE BAPTIST ............................... Small...    18.50
LITTLE SARAH; N. Currier ................................... Small...    18.50
LITTLE SARAH; 1874 ......................................... Small...    18.50
LITTLE '76 ................................................. Small...    35.00
LITTLE SISTER; 1865........................................ Small...    18.50
LITTLE SISTERS, THE........................................ Medium   32.50
LITTLE SISTER'S FIRST STEP ................................. Small...    18.50
LITTLE SISTER'S RIDE ....................................... Small...    18.50
LITTLE SLEEPY ............................................... Small...    18.50
LITTLE SNOWBIRD ............................................ Small...    20.00
LITTLE STUDENTS, THE; (Oval) ............................... Small...    21.50
LITTLE SUNBEAM ............................................. Small...    18.50
LITTLE SUNSHINE; 1868....................................... Small...    18.50
LITTLE SWEETHEART; 1875..................................... Small...    18.50
LITTLE TEA PARTY, THE....................................... Small...    20.00
LITTLE TEACHER, THE ........................................ Small...    18.50
LITTLE THOUGHTFUL .......................................... Small...    18.50
LITTLE VIOLET; 1874 ........................................ Small...    18.50
LITTLE VOLUNTEER, THE; 1861 ................................ Small...    22.50
LITTLE WANDERER ............................................ Small...    42.50
LITTLE WHITE DOGGIES; 1877 ................................. Small...    25.00
LITTLE WHITE KITTIES EATING CAKE .......................... Small...    25.00
LITTLE WHITE KITTIES — FISHING; 1871 .................. Small...    24.50
LITTLE WHITE KITTIES PLAYING BALL ................. Small...    24.50
LITTLE WILD FLOWER ......................................... Small...    25.00
LITTLE WILLIAM AND MARY .................................... Small...    21.50
LITTLE WILLIE .............................................. Small...    20.00
LITTLE YACHTSMAN; 1875 ..................................... Small...    37.50
LITTLE ZOUAVE, THE; 1861.................................... Small...    22.50
LIVING CHINESE FAMILY, THE; N. Currier .................. Small...    40.00
LIZZIE ..................................................... Medium   20.00
LLEWELLYN — THE GREAT; N. Currier .......................... Small...    27.50
LOADING COTTON; 1870 ....................................... Small...   100.00
LOBSTER SAUCE; N. Currier .................................. Small...    28.00
LOLA MONTEZ AS MARIQUITA; N. Currier ..................... Small...    35.00
LOLA MONTEZ, BELLE OF THE WEST; N. Currier ........... Small...    35.00
LONDON FROM KEW GARDENS .................................... Small...    32.50
LONDONDERRY, IRELAND ....................................... Small...    25.00
LONDONDERRY, ON THE RIVER FOYLE, IRELAND ........ Small...    24.50
LONG ISLAND SOUND; 1869 .................................... Medium  200.00
LONG LIVE THE REPUBLIC; N. Currier ......................... Medium   48.50
LONGFELLOW; (Horse) ........................................ Small...    65.00
LOOK AT MAMA; N. Currier ................................... Small...    18.50
LOOK AT PAPA; N. Currier ................................... Small...    18.50
LOOKING DOWN THE YO-SEMITE ................................. Small...    47.50
LOOKING IN; N. Currier ..................................... Small...    24.00
LOOKING OUT; N. Currier .................................... Small...    24.00
LOOKING UNTO JESUS; 1870.................................... Small...    10.00
LOOKOUT MOUNTAIN, TENNESSEE AND THE CHATTANOOGA
     RAILROAD; 1866 ....................................... Large..  1000.00
LORD BE WITH YOU, THE; 1872 ............................... Small...    10.00
LORD'S PRAYER, THE; N. Currier ............................ Small...    10.00
LORD'S PRAYER AND THE ANGELICAL SALUTATION .... Small...    10.00
LOSS OF THE STEAMBOAT "SWALLOW"; N. Currier ........ Small...    65.00
LOSS OF THE STEAMERBOAT "CAMBRIA"; 1883 ............ Small...    65.00
LOSS OF THE U. S. M. STEAMSHIP "ARTIC"; 1854 ....... Small...    65.00
```

```
LOST; N. Currier ..................................................Small... $  20.00
LOST CAUSE; 1872 ................................................Small...    20.00
LOST IN THE SNOW — DOGS OF ST. BERNARD..............Small...    75.00
LOTTIE ..............................................................Small...    20.00
LOUIS KOSSUTH; N. Currier; 1849 ..........................Small...    25.00
LOUIS KOSSUTH AND HIS STAFF; N. Currier ...........Small...    30.00
LOUIS NAPOLEON BONAPARTE; N. Currier; 1849...........Small...    35.00
LOUISA; N. Currier; 1850 ....................................Small...    20.00
LOUISA V. PARKER AS EVA IN "UNCLE TOM'S CABIN"
    C. Currier ......................................................Small...    32.50
LOVE IS THE LIGHTEST; N. Currier; 1847 .....................Small...    21.50
LOVE IS THE LIGHTEST ............................................Small...    21.50
LOVE LETTER; N. Currier .......................................Small...    22.50
LOVE LIFE AT WINDSOR CASTLE ...........................Small...    27.50
LOVE LIGHT MAKES HOME BRIGHT ............................Small...    22.50
LOVE THE OLD DOG, TOO ......................................Small...    30.00
LOVELY CALM, A; 1878 .........................................Small...    25.00
LOVERS, THE; N. Currier; 1846.................................Small...    20.00
LOVER'S ADIEU, THE; N. Currier; 1852.......................Small...    22.50
LOVER'S LEAP; 1886 ...........................................Small ..    35.00
LOVER'S QUARREL; N. Currier; 1846 ...........................Small...    25.00
LOVER'S RECONCILIATION; N. Currier; 1846 .............. Small...    25.00
LOVER'S RETURN, THE; N. Currier; 1852 ,....................Small...    25.00
LOVER'S WALK, THE; N. Currier; 1849 ........................Small...    25.00
LOVER'S WALK, THE ............................................ Small...    20.00
LOVE'S LIGHT; 1874 ...........................................Small...    20.00
LOVE'S MESSENGER; N. Currier...................................Small...    20.00
LOW PRESSURE STEAMBOAT "ISAAC NEWTON"; N. Currier;
    1855; .........................................................Large .   425.00
LOW WATER IN THE MISSISSIPPI; 1868 ........................Large ..   225.00
LOWER LAKE OF KILLARNEY ...................................Small...    35.00
LOYAL UNION LEAGUE CERTIFICATE; 1863 .................Small...    15.00
LUCILLE — RECORD 2:21; 1878 ...............................Small...    65.00
LUCKY ESCAPE, THE; N. Currier ...........................Medium     75.00
LUCRETIA; N. Currier .........................................Small...    20.00
LUCY; N. Currier ............................................. Small...    20.00
LUDWIG KOSSUTH, THE HUNGARIAN LEADER; N. Currier;
    1849 ..........................................................Small...    25.00
LUGGELAW, COUNTY WICKLOW ..............................Small...    22.50
LUKE BLACKBURN; (Horse); 1880..............................Small...    65.00
LULA; BAY MARE; 1876 ........................................Large ..   200.00
LUSCIOUS PEACHES ............................................Small...    37.50
LUXURY OF TOBACCO, THE ...................................Small...    40.00
LYDIA; N. Currier .............................................Small...    20.00


                              — M —


MAC-CUT-MISH-E-CA-CU-CAC; (Indian Chief) ...............Small... $  48.50
MACHINERY HALL ..............................................Small...    30.00
MADAME CELESTE AS "MIMI"; N. Currier; 1848 ...........Small...    32.50
MADISON, CAPITOL OF WISCONSIN; C. Currier ...........Small...    95.00
MADLLE. AUGUSTA IN LA BAYADERE; N. Currier ........Small...    25.00
MADLLE. CELESTE AS THE WILD  ARAB BOY; N. Currier
                                                               Small...    25.00
MADDLE. FANNY ELLSLER IN LA TARENTULE ...........Small...    25.00
MADONNA DI SAN SISTO ........................................Small...    15.00
MADONNA OF THE SHAWL.......................................Small...    15.00
```

```
MAGGIE ...................................................................Small...$   20.00
MAGIC CURE; 1890 ................................................. Small...   25.00
MAGIC GROTTOES; 1871 ...........................................Small...   27.50
MAGIC LAKE .................................................... Medium.   40.00
MAGIC LAKE .................................................... Small...   21.50
MAGNIFICENT BUILDING FOR THE WORLD'S FAIR OF
   1861 ..................................................... Small...   48.50
MAGNIFICENT O'CONNELL FUNERAL CAR; N. Currier;
   1847 ....................................................... Small ...   60.00
MAGNIFICENT STEAMSHIP "BRITANIC" OF THE WHITE
   STAR LINE; ............................................... Small...   65.00
MAGNIFICENT STEAMSHIP "CITY OF NEW YORK" OF THE
   INMAN LINE ............................................... Small...   65.00
MAGNIFICENT STEAMSHIP "CITY OF PARIS" OF THE
   INMAN LINE ...............................................Small...   65.00
MAGNIFICENT STEAMSHIP "CITY OF ROME".................Small...   65.00
MAGNIFICENT STEAMSHIP "GERMANIC"......................Small...   65.00
MAGNIFICENT STEAMSHIP "NEW YORK" OF THE AMERICAN
   LINE ...................................................... Small...   65.00
MAGNIFICENT STEAMSHIP "PARIS" OF THE AMERICAN
   LINE ...................................................... Small...   65.00
MAGNIFICENT STEAMSHIP "ST. LOUIS" OF THE AMERICAN
   LINE ......................................................Small...   65.00
MAIDEN ROCK, MISSISSIPPI RIVER............................Small...   60.00
MAIDEN'S PRAYER .............................................. Small...   20.00
MAIN BUILDING; 1876 ........................................Small ...   30.00
MAIN OF COCKS, A; "The First Battle" ...................... Medium.   88.00
MAJOLICA; 1885; Record 2:15 ...............................Large ...  175.00
MAJ. GENL. AMBROSE E. BURNSIDE, COMMANDER-IN-
   CHIEF OF THE ARMY OF THE POTOMAC; 1862......... Small...   30.00
MAJ. GENL. AMBROSE E. BURNSIDE AT THE BATTLE OF
   FREDERICKSBURG, VA. .....................................Small...   32.50
MAJ. GENL. FRANZ SIGEL — HERO OF THE WEST.........Small...   30.00
MAJ. GENL. GEORGE B. McCLELLAN ..........................Small...   30.00
MAJ. GENL. GEORGE G. McCLELLAN AT THE BATTLE OF
   ANTIETAM, MD.1862 ...................................... Small...   30.00
MAJ. GENL. GEORGE G. MEADE AT THE BATTLE OF
   GETTYSBURG; 1863 .......................................Small...   37.50
MAJ. GENL. GEORGE G. MEADE, COMMANDER-IN-CHIEF
   ETC. ......................................................Small ...   30.00
MAJ. GENL. HENRY W. HALLECK..............................Medium.   30.00
MAJ. GENL. HENRY W. HALLECK .............................Small...   30.00
MAJ. GENL. JOHN C. FREMONT................................Small...   30.00
MAJ. GENL. JOHN E. WOOL ..................................... Medium.   35.00
MAJ. GENL. JOHN E. WOOL ..................................... Small...   35.00
MAJ. GENL. JOSEPH HOOKER; (On Horseback) ............ Small...   30.00
MAJ. GENL. JOSEPH HOOKER COMMANDER-IN-CHIEF OF
   THE "ARMY OF THE POTOMAC"; 1862 ................Small...   30.00
MAJ. GENL. JOSEPH HOOKER — AT THE BATTLE OF
   ANTIETAM ................................................ Small...   30.00
MAJ. GENL. NATHANIEL P. BANKS............................ Small...   30.00
MAJ. GENL. PHILIP SHERIDAN, U. S. ARMY ................ Small...   30.00
MAJ. GENL. PHILIP SHERIDAN RALLYING HIS TROOPS AT
   THE BATTLE OF CEDAR CREEK, VA. ................... Small...   30.00
MAJ. GENL. Q. A. GILLMORE, U. S. ARMY ................... Small...   30.00
MAJ. GENL. U. S. GRANT AT THE SIEGE OF VICKSBURG;
                                                   Small...   30.00
MAJ. GENL. WILLIAM S. ROSECRANS, U. S. ARMY.......... Small...   30.00
```

```
MAJ. GENL. WILLIAM ROSECRANS AT THE BATTLE OF
  MURFREESBORO ................................................... Small...$  32.50
MAJ. GENL. WILLIAM T. SHERMAN, U. S. ARMY  ........ Small...   30.00
MAJ. GENL. WINFIELD SCOTT; GENERAL-IN-CHIEF OF
  U.S. ARMY; N. Currier; 1846  ................................... Small..   35.00
MAJ. GENL. WINFIELD SCOTT AT VERA CRUZ; 1864  .. Small..   40.00
MAJ. GENL. WINFIELD SCOTT HANCOCK AT THE BATTLE
  OF SPOTTSYLVANIA COURT HOUSE, VA.  ............... Small..   40.00
MAJ. GENL. ZACHARY TAYLOR BEFORE MONTEREY; 1848;
  N. Currier ....................:.................................:....... Small..   30.00
MAJOR ROBERT ANDERSON ..................................... Small..   30.00
MAJOR SAMUEL RINGGOLD; N. Currier; 1846 .................. Small..   30.00
MA-KO-ME-TA; (BEAR'S OIL) Indian Chief; C. Currier ...... Small..   42.50
MAMA'S DARLING  ............................................... Large..   50.00
MAMA'S DARLINGS; 1877 .............................................. Small..   22.50
MAMA'S JEWEL  ........................................................ Small..   20.00
MAMA'S PET; N. Currier; 1847............................................ Small..   20.00
MAMA'S ROSEBUD; 1858  ....:.......................................Medium   22.50
MAMBRINO  .....................................................Small..   90.00
MAMBRINO PILOT, DAISY BURNS AND ROSAMOND ..........Large..  225.00
MAMMA'S TREASURE ...............................  ..................Medium   30.00
MAMMOTH IRON STEAMSHIP "GREAT EASTERN"  .......... Small..   60.00
MAN OF WORDS – MAN OF DEEDS. WHICH DO YOU THINK
  THE COUNTRY NEEDS? 1868  ................................. Small..   40.00
MAN THAT GAVE BARNUM HIS TURN, THE  ............... Small..   65.00
MAN THAT KEPT THE BRIDGE, THE; 1881 ................... Small..   30.00
MAN THAT KEPT THE GATE, THE ...............................Small...   30.00
MAN THAT KNOWS A HORSE, THE (Comic) 1877 ..............Small..   37.50
MAN WHO DRIVES TO WIN, THE; 1876  .........................Small..   30.00
MANAGING A CANDIDATE  .......................................Small..   40.00
MANIFESTATION OF THE SACRED HEART  .............  ....Small..   10.00
MANSION OF THE OLDEN TIME, A ...............................Small..   55.00
MAP OF CENTREVILLE, MICHIGAN; N. Currier ..............Large..   65.00
MAP OF MT. VERNON; C. Currier  ...............................Small..   75.00
MAPLE SUGARING, EARLY SPRING IN THE NORTHERN
  WOODS; 1872  .................................................. Small..  225.00
MARCUS MORTON – GOV. OF MASS.; N. Currier  ....:......Small...   30.00
MARGARET; N. Currier; 1846  ...:................................Small...   20.00
MARGUERITE; N. Currier  ........................................Small...   20.00
MARIA; N. Currier; 1845  ........................................Small...   20.00
MARINE BARK "CATALPA"; N. Currier .........................Small...  195.00
MARINE BARK "THE AMAZON"; N. Currier ..................Small...  195.00
MARION'S BRIGADE CROSSING THE PEDEE RIVER, S.C. ..Small...   65.00
MARRIAGE, THE; 1847 ..............................................Small...   20.00
MARRIAGE CERTIFICATE; N. Currier; 1848  ...............Small...   18.50
MARRIAGE CERTIFICATE FOR COLORED PEOPLE.........Small...   15.00
MARRIAGE EVENING, THE; N. Currier  ......................Small...   20.00
MARRIAGE MORNING, THE; N. Currier  ....................Small...   20.00
MARRIAGE OF THE FREE SOIL AND LIBERTY PARTIES;
  (Political Cartoon)  ............................................ Small...   45.00
MARRIAGE VOW, THE; N. Currier .................................. Small...   20.00
MARRIED; N. Currier; 1845  ....................................... Small...   20.00
MARTHA; N. Currier  ................................................ Small...   20.00
MARTHA WASHINGTON  ............................................. Medium   50.00
MARTHA WASHINGTON  ............................................. Small..   42.50
MARTIN VAN BUREN, CHAMPION OF DEMOCRACY ........ Small...   36.50
MARTIN VAN BUREN – 8TH PRESIDENT; N. Currier ....... Small...   48.50
MARTIN VAN BUREN – 8TH PRESIDENT; N. Currier ....... Medium   50.00
```

```
MARTIN VAN BUREN — FREE SOIL CANDIDATE............Small...$  27.50
MARY; N. Currier; 1845     ...........................................Small...   27.50
MARY AND HER LITTLE LAMB...................................Medium     30.00
MARY ANN; N. Currier   ...........................................Small...   20.00
MARY ELIZABETH; N. Currier; 1846 .............................Small...   20.00
MARY JANE; N. Currier; 1846 ....................................Small...   20.00
MARY, QUEEN OF SCOTS, LEAVING FRANCE; 1870........Small...   24.50
MARY'S LITTLE LAMB.................................................Small...   30.00
MASHERS, THE; 1884    ...............................................Small...   35.00
MASONIC CHART; 1876 ..............................................Small...   18.50
MASTER R. W. OSBORN; (Midget) N. Currier....................Small...   40.00
MATCH AGAINST TIME, A; 1878 ...............................Small...   48.50
MATER DOLOROSA; N. Currier ..................................Small...   20.00
MATERNAL AFFECTION; N. Currier; 1845.....................Small...   20.00
MATERNAL HAPPINESS; N. Currier; 1849 ....................Small...   20.00
MATERNAL PIETY; N. Currier ....................................Small...   18.00
MATILDA; N. Currier  ..............................................Small...   20.00
MATING — IN THE WOODS, "RUFFED GROUSE"; 1871 .....Small...   150.00
MATTIE............................................................Small...   20.00
MATTIE HUNTER; 1881 ...............................................Small..   65.00
MATTIE HUNTER — RECORD 2:15; 1879    .....................Small...   65.00
MAUD S. — RECORD 2:08¾; 1881 ...................................Small...   65.00
MAUD S. AND ALDINE ...............................................Small...   65.00
MAUD S. AND ST. JULIEN; 1884 ...................................Small...   65.00
MAY QUEEN; 1876   .........  ...........................................Small...   22.50
MAY QUEEN; (Horse); 1876 ........................................Small...   65.00
"MAYFLOWER"SALUTED BY THE FLEET; 1886 ............Large..   160.00
MAZEPPA, PLATE 1; N. Currier; 1846 ...........................Small...   18.00
MAZEPPA, PLATE 2; N. Currier; 1846 ........................... Small...   18.00
MAZEPPA, PLATE 3; N. Currier; 1846  ..........................Small...   18.00
MAZEPPA, PLATE 4; N. Currier; 1846 ...........................Small...   18.00
McDONOUGH'S VICTORY ON LAKE CHAMPLAIN; 1846 ....Small...   115.00
MEADOW IN SPRINGTIME, THE TWIN LAMBS; 1867 .........Large..   95.00
MEADOWSIDE COTTAGE ...........................................Medium     75.00
MEETING OF THE WATERS, THE; 1868 .........................Small...   35.00
MEETING OF THE WATERS IN THE VALE OF AVOCA...... Medium     49.50
MELROSE ABBEY     ...............................................Small...   25.00
MERCHANT'S EXCHANGE, NEW YORK, WALL STREET ... Small...   275.00
MERRY CHRISTMAS, A ...............................................Small...   24.50
MERRY, MERRY MAIDEN AND THE TAR; 1879 ...............Small..   22.50
MERRY MONTH OF MAY, THE ....................................Small...   20.00
MEXICAN FANDANGO; N. Currier; 1848  .......................Small...   25.00
MEXICAN GUERILLEROS; N. Currier; 1848  ...................Small...   40.00
MEXICANS EVACUATING VERA CRUZ; N. Currier  .........Small...   45.00
MIDNIGHT — RECORD 2:18¼; 1879 ...............................Small...   65.00
MIDNIGHT RACE ON THE MISSISSIPPI, A; (Natchez and
     Eclipse); 1860     ..................................................... Large..   225.00
MIDNIGHT RACE ON THE MISSISSIPPI, A; (Memphis and
     James Howard); 1875    ..........................................Small...   75.00
MIDSUMMER-NIGHT'S DREAM, A ...............................Large..   60.00
MILITARY COLLEGE OF CHAPULTEPEC; N. Currier.......Small...   45.00
MILITARY RING, THE (Political Cartoon)  ....................Small...   38.50
MILL BOY AND BLONDINE; 1881 ...............................Small...   65.00
MILL-COVE LAKE ...................................................Small...   55.00
MILL DAM AT "SLEEPY HOLLOW," THE .....................Large .   175.00
MILL IN THE HIGHLANDS  ......................................Medium     67.50
MILL RIVER SCENERY     .........................................Large..   95.00
MILL-STREAM, THE ................................................Medium     75.00
```

```
MILLARD FILLMORE — 13TH PRESIDENT; N. Currier
   1856; (very rare) ..................................................... Small..$  265.00
MILLARD FILLMORE — 13TH PRESIDENT; N. Currier; 1856
                                                                Large.    175.00
MILLARD FILLMORE — 13TH PRESIDENT — NATIONAL
   AMERICAN CANDIDATE FOR THE 15TH PRESIDENT
   OF THE UNITED STATES; N. Currier; 1856; (Scarce) ...Small..   100.00
MILLARD FILLMORE — WHIG CANDIDATE FOR VICE-
   PRESIDENT; N. Currier; 1848  ............................. Small..    85.00
MILLER'S HOME  ................................................ Medium    90.00
MINIATURE LANDSCAPES  ...................................... Medium    75.00
MINIATURE SHIP "RED, WHITE, AND BLUE"  ............... Small.    67.50
MIND YOUR LESSON................................................. Small..    21.50
MIND YOUR LESSON, FIDO  ...................................... Small.    21.50
MINK TRAPPING; "PRIME"; 1862 ............................... Large. 3,750.00
MINNEHAHA — "Laughing Water"................................ Small..    40.00
MINNEHAHA FALLS, MINNESOTA................................ Medium    95.00
MINNIE; (Girl's Head)  ............................................ Small..    20.00
MINUTE-MEN OF THE REVOLUTION, THE; 1876............. Small..   165.00
MIRACULOUS MEDAL  ............................................ Small..    15.00
MIRACULOUS IMAGE OF ST. FRANCIS XAVIER............. Small..    15.00
MISCHIEF AND MUSIC  .......................................... Small..    24.50
MISCHIEVOUS LITTLE DOGGIE ................................ Small..    27.50
MISCHIEVOUS LITTLE KITTIE  ................................ Small..    27.50
MISCHIEVOUS LITTLE KITTIES; 1877.......................... Small..    27.50
MISERIES OF A BACHELOR, THE ............................... Small..    30.00
MISERY — HAPPINESS; 1872  ...................................Small..    20.00
MISS ELIZABETH REED — THE LILLIPUTIAN QUEEN ....Small..    40.00
MISS ELIZABETH REED — MISS HANNAH CROUSE; (Midget
   and Giantress); N. Currier........................................ Small..    40.00
MISS JANE CAMPBELL; (Giantress)  .......................... Small..    40.00
MISS MARTHA JONES — THE LILLIPUTIAN QUEEN......... Small..    40.00
MISS SUSAN BARTON; (Mammoth Lady); 1849.................. Small..    40.00
MISS WOODFORD; 1885 ............................................ Small .    40.00
MISSIONARY STONE CHAPEL AT WHEELOCK; C. Currier; Small..    32.50
MISSISSIPPI IN TIME OF PEACE; 1865  ........................ Large.   250.00
MISSISSIPPI IN TIME OF WAR; 1865  ........................... Large.   250.00
MIXED AT THE FINISH; 1880  ..................................... Small..    60.00
MODERN COLLEGE SCULL GRADUATING WITH ALL
   HONORS; 1876; (Comic)  ...................................... Small..    32.50
MODERN COLOSSUS, THE  ...................................... Medium    40.00
MOLLIE McCARTHY, THE RACING QUEEN; 1878 ...........Small..    67.50
MOMENTOUS QUESTION, THE; 1861 ........................... Small..    35.00
MOMENTOUS QUESTION, THE — "Ah, Billy, My Beauty,
   Can't You Give Me An Eye Opener? Yes, Sir-ee"; N. Currier;
   1853  ................................................................ Small..    95.00
MONUMENT; (Virginia).............................................. Small..    55.00
MOONLIGHT  ........................................................ Small..    24.00
MOONLIGHT IN FAIRYLAND  .................................... Small..    22.50
MOONLIGHT IN THE TROPICS  ................................. Small..    24.00
MOONLIGHT ON LAKE CATALPA, VIRGINIA................. Small..    35.00
MOONLIGHT ON THE LAKE  .....................................Small..    35.00
MOONLIGHT ON THE MISSISSIPPI ..............................Small..    90.00
MOONLIGHT PROMENADE, THE  ..............................Small..    22.00
MOONLIGHT — THE CASTLE  ...................................Small..    23.50
MOONLIGHT — THE RUINS  .....................................Small..    25.00
MOOSE AND WOLVES — A NARROW ESCAPE.................. Small..   240.00
MOOSEHEAD LAKE  ............................................. Small..    67.50
```

```
MORE FREE THAN WELCOME ............................ Small..$  40.00
MORE FRIGHTENED THAN HURT; N. Currier .............. Small..   60.00
MORE PLUCKY THAN PRUDENT; 1885; (Comic R. R. Scene)
                                                   Small..   60.00
MORE THAN WELCOME ............................... Small..   25.00
MORGAN LEWIS; C. Currier .......................... Small..   32.50
MORNING .......................................... Small..   20.00
MORNING GLORIES .................................. Small..   20.00
MORNING IN THE WOODS; 1852 ....................... Large.  850.00
MORNING IN THE WOODS; 1865 ....................... Large.  850.00
MORNING OF LIFE, THE; 1874 ....................... Small..   20.00
MORNING OF LOVE, THE ............................. Small..   18.50
MORNING PRAYER, THE; N. Currier .................. Small..   15.00
MORNING RECREATION, THE; N. Currier............... Small..   26.50
MORNING RIDE, THE; N. Currier; 1849............... Small..   42.50
MORNING ROSE, THE; N. Currier; 1849 ..............Small..   20.00
MORNING ROSES .................................... Small..   20.00
MORNING STAR, THE; N. Currier; 1846............... Small..   20.00
MOSS ROSE, THE; N. Currier; 1847 ................. Small..   35.00
MOSS ROSES AND BUDS; 1870 ........................ Small..   30.00
MOST HOLY CATHOLIC FAITH; 1872 ...................Small..   1(.00
MOST HOLY SACRIFICE; 1872 ........................ Small..   10.00
MOST REV. JOHN HUGHES, DD., THE; 1864............. Small..   12.00
MOST REV. M. J. SPALDING, DD., (Oval) ............Small..   12.00
MOTHER AND CHILD; N. Currier; 1846............... Small..   20.00
MOTHERLESS, THE .................................. Small..   15.00
MOTHER'S BLESSING, THE............................ Medium    35.00
MOTHER'S DREAM, THE .............................. Small..   18.50
MOTHER'S JOY; N. Currier; 1846 ................... Small .   18.50
MOTHER'S PET; N. Currier .........................Small..   18.50
MOTHER'S TREASURE, A; N. Currier .................Small..   18.50
MOTHER'S WING; (Birds); 1866 .....................Small..   48.50
MT. HOLYOKE FEMALE SEMINARY, SOUTH HADLEY,
     MASS., N. Currier ............................ Small..   95.00
MT. VESUVIUS, ITALY .............................. Small..   25.00
MOUNT WASHINGTON AND THE WHITE MOUNTAINS; 1860 Large.  400.00
MOUNTAIN PASS, SIERRA NEVADA; 1867 .............. Large.  375.00
MOUNTAIN RAMBLE, A ...............................Small..   32.50
MOUNTAIN SPRING, WEST POINT, NEAR COZZEN'S DOCK,
     THE; 1862 ....................................Medium  125.00
MOUNTAIN STREAM, THE..............................Medium    65.00
MOUNTAINEER'S HOME, THE ..........................Medium  110.00
MR. AUGUST BELMONT'S POTOMAC AND MASHER; 1891.. Large .  200.00
MR. BONNER'S HORSE "JOE ELLIOTT"; 1873 .............. Large .  200.00
MR. PIERRE LORILLARD'S BR. COLT "IROQUOIS" .......Small..   75.00
MR. WILLIAM H. VANDERBILT DRIVING HIS MAGNIFICENT
     TEAM "MAUD S." AND "ALDINE"; 1883 ............. Small..  100.00
MR. WM. H. VANDERVILT'S CELEBRATED ROAD TEAM
     "LYSANDER" AND "LEANDER"; 1879.................. Small..  100.00
MR. WM. H. VANDERBILT'S CELEBRATED ROAD TEAM
     "SMALL HOPES" AND "LADY MAC"; 1877.............. Small..  100.00
MRS. FISK AND THE MISSES FOX; N. Currier ......... Small..   65.00
MRS. GEORGE JONES — THE TRAGIC ACTRESS .......... Small..   35.00
MRS. JAMES K. POLK; N. Currier; 1846 ............. Small..   35.00
MRS. LUCRETIA R. GARFIELD ........................ Medium    35.00
MRS. LUCY I. BLISS ............................... Small..   30.00
MUCKROSS ABBEY, KILLARNEY........................ Small..   27.50
MUD S. — DE GREAT RECORD BUSTER; 1885.............. Small..   35.00
```

```
MULE TRAIN ON A DOWN GRADE, A; 1881 ..................... Small..$  37.50
MULE TRAIN ON AN UP GRADE; 1881......................... Small..    37.50
MURDER OF MISS JANE McCREA, N. Currier ................. Small..    38.50
MUSIC; 1875 ........................................... Small..    55.00
MUSIC; (Chestnut Mare); 1875 .......................... Large.   175.00
MUSIC HATH CHARMS; 1875 ............................... Small..    20.00
MUSTANG TEAM, THE; N. Currier ......................... Small..    48.00
MY ABSENT LOVE; (Oval)................................. Small..    18.50
MY BOYHOOD HOME ....................................... Small..    48.50
MY BROTHER; N. Currier; 1846 .......................... Small..    20.00
MY CHARMING GIRL ...................................... Small..    20.00
MY CHILD; N. Currier; 1849 ............................ Small..    20.00
MY CHILD! MY CHILD! ................................... Small..    20.00
MY CHOICE ............................................. Small..    18.00
MY COTTAGE HOME; 1866.................................. Large   150.00
MY DARLING BOY; N. Currier ............................ Small..    20.00
MY DARLING GIRL; N. Currier............................ Small..    20.00
MY DEAR LITTLE PET; 1877 .............................. Small..    20.00
MY FAVORITE HORSE ..................................... Small..    24.50
MY FAVORITE PONY ...................................... Small..    24.50
MY FAVORITE; (Female Head) ............................ Small..    20.00
MY FIRST LOVE; N. Currier ............................. Small..    20.00
MY FRIEND AND I; N. Currier; 1846 ..................... Small..    20.00
MY GENTLE DOVE; 1871 .................................. Small..    18.50
MY GENTLE LOVE; 1872 .................................. Small..    18.50
MY HEARTS DESIRE ..................................... Small..    20.00
MY HEARTS TREASURE ................................... Small..    20.00
MY HERO ............................................... Small..    20.00
MY HIGHLAND BOY; N. Currier ........................... Small..    20.00
MY HIGHLAND GIRL; N. Currier .......................... Small..    20.00
MY INTENDED; N. Currier; 1847 ......................... Small..    20.00
MY KITTIE AND CANARY; 1871 ............................ Small..    20.00
MY LITTLE DRUMMER BOY ................................. Small..    20.00
MY LITTLE FAVORITE ................................... Small..    20.00
MY LITTLE FAVORITE ................................... Medium    25.00
MY LITTLE FRIEND; N. Currier; 1845 .................... Small..    20.00
MY LITTLE PET; N. Currier; 1845 ...................... Small..    20.00
MY LITTLE PLAYFELLOW; N. Currier; 1847................ Small..    20.00
MY LITTLE WHITE BUNNIES RECEIVING A VISITOR ........ Small..    20.00
MY LITTLE WHITE KITTENS ............................. Small..    20.00
MY LITTLE WHITE KITTIE AFTER THE GOLDFISH ...........Small..    20.00
MY LITTLE WHITE KITTIE — FISHING .................... Small..    20.00
MY LITTLE WHITE KITTIES INTO MISCHIEF ............... Small..    20.00
MY LITTLE WHITE KITTIES LEARNING THEIR ABC'S ...... Small..    20.00
MY LITTLE WHITE KITTIES PLAYING BALL; 1870 .......... Small..    20.00
MY LITTLE WHITE KITTIES PLAYING DOMINOS.............. Small..    20.00
MY LITTLE WHITE KITTIES PLAYING WITH A MINIATURE Small..    20.00
MY LITTLE WHITE KITTIES TAKING THE CAKE ............. Small..    20.00
MY LITTLE WHITE KITTIES — THEIR FIRST MOUSE ........ Small..    20.00
MY LOVE AND I; 1872 .................................. Small..    20.00
MY OWN MAMA ......................................... Small..    20.00
MY OWN SWEET PET .................................... Small..    20.00
MY OWN TRUE LOVE .................................... Small..    20.00
MY PET BIRD ......................................... Medium    27.50
MY PET BIRD ......................................... Small..    20.00
MY PICTURE; N. Currier; 1856 ........................ Small..    20.00
MY PONY AND DOG ..................................... Small..    22.50
MY PRETTY IRISH GIRL................................. Small..    20.00
```

MY SISTER; N. Currier; 1846 .... Small.. $ 20.00
MY SWEETHEART .... Small.. 20.00
MY THREE WHITE KITTENS .... Small.. 20.00
MY THREE WHITE KITTIES LEARNING THEIR A B C........ Small.. 20.00

– N –

NANCY; N. Currier .... Small.. $ 20.00
NANCY HANKS; 1892... Small.. 60.00
NAPOLEON AT ST. HELENA; N. Currier........................... Small.. 35.00
NAPOLEON AT WATERLOO; N. Currier ....Small.. 40.00
NAPOLOEN EMPEROR OF FRANCE.................................Small.. 35.00
NAPOLEON I; N. Currier ....Small.. 40.00
NAPOLEON, THE HERO OF 100 BATTLES......................Small.. 40.00
NAPOLEON; N. Currier ....Small.. 40.00
NAPOLEON'S STRATEGY; 1870 .... Small.. 35.00
NAPOLEON II – DUKE OF REICHSTADT; N. Currier ....Small.. 37.50
NARRAGANSETT S.S. COMFANY'S STEAMER "PROVIDENCE"
OF THE FALL RIVER LINE ....Small.. 60.00
NARROW WAY, THE; N. Currier ....Small.. 35.00
NARROWS FROM FORT HAMILTON; N. Currier .... Small.. 120.00
NARROWS FROM STATEN ISLAND, THE; N. Currier .... Small.. 120.00
NARROWS, NEW YORK BAY FROM STATEN ISLAND .... Small.. 120.00
NAT LANGHAM CHAMPION OF THE MIDDLE WEIGHTS ..... Medium 120.00
NATIONAL CADETS 9TH REGT. NEW YORK STATE
ARTILLERY; N. Currier .... Small.. 37.50
NATIONAL DEMOCRATIC BANNER OF 1860.................... Small.. 35.00
NATIONAL DEMOCRATIC BANNER OF VICTORY; 1868 Small.. 35.00
NATIONAL GAME. THE – THREE "OUTS" AND ONE "RUN"
(Political Cartoon) .... Small.. 60.00
NATIONAL UNION REPUBLICAN BANNER, 1860; (Lincoln
and Hamlin); 1860 .... Small.. 65.00
NATIONAL UNION REPUBLICAN BANNER, 1868; (Grant and
Colfax); 1868 ....Small.. 45.00
NATIONAL WASHINGTON MONUMENT, WASH. D. C..........Small.. 55.00
NATURAL AND THE SPIRITUAL, THE; N. Currier ....Small.. 15.00
NATURAL BRIDGE, VA. ....Small.. 60.00
NAUGHTY CAT; 1874 ....Small.. 22.00
NAVAL BOMBARDMENT OF VERA CRUZ; N. Currier .... Small.. 75.00
NAVAL HEROES OF THE U.S., PLATE I, N. Currier, 1846 .. Small.. 175.00
NAVAL HEROES OF THE U. S., PLATE 2; N. Currier; 1846. Small.. 175.00
NAVAL HEROES OF THE U.S., PLATE 3, N. Currier; 1846 .. Small.. 175.00
NAVAL HEROES OF THE U.S., PLATE 4, N. Currier; 1846.. Small.. 175.00
NAZARETH OF GALLILEE .... Small.. 15.00
NEARER MY GOD TO THEE; (Motto) .... Small.. 16.00
NEAREST WAY IN SUMMER TIME; THE .... Medium 70.00
NEARING THE FINISH LINE; 1888 ....Large . 175.00
NECKER; N. Currier .... Small.. 25.00
NELLIE .... Small.. 20.00
NETTIE; (Race Horse); 1874...................................... Small.. 65.00
NEW BROOD, THE; (Chickens) .... Small.. 25.00
NEW ENGLAND BEAUTY, A .... Small.. 20.00
NEW ENGLAND COAST SCENE, OFF BOSTON LIGHT ...... Small.. 95.00
NEW ENGLAND COAST SCENE .... Small.. 148.00
NEW ENGLAND HOME, A .... Small.. 65.00
NEW ENGLAND HOMESTEAD, A................................... Small.. 65.00
NEW ENGLAND SCENERY; 1866 .... Large . 400.00

```
NEW ENGLAND WINTER SCENE; 1861 ...................... Large....$  1,650.00
NEW EXCURSION STEAMER "COLUMBIA"; 1877 ,........ Large....     200.00
NEW FASHIONED GIRL, THE  .............................. Small....      20.00
NEW JERSEY FOX HUNT; "A Smoking Run"; 1876 ..... Small ....      70.00
NEW JERSEY FOX HUNT; "Taking Breath"; 1876 ....... Small ....      70.00
NEW HAT MAN, THE; 1875 .................................. Small ....      30.00
NEW PALACE STEAMER "PILGRIM" OF THE FALL
    RIVER LINE;................................................... Medium .      75.00
NEW ST. PATRICK'S CATHEDRAL, THE  ................ Small....      60.00
NEW STEAMSHIP "UMBRIA" OF THE CUNARD LINE . Small....      60.00
NEW SUSPENSION BRIDGE, NIAGARA FALLS  ........ Small....     100.00
NEW YORK AND BROOKLYN; 1875  ..................... Large....     375.00
NEW YORK AND BROOKLYN; (Jersey City and Hoboken
    Water Front); 1877 ........................................... Large....     350.00
NEW YORK BAY FROM BAY RIDGE, L. I. 1860 .......... Large....     300.00
NEW YORK BAY FROM BAY RIDGE, L. I.  ................ Small....      95.00
NEW YORK BAY FROM THE TELEGRAPH STATION ... Small....     120.00
NEW YORK BEAUTY, THE  .................................. Small....      20.00
NEW YORK CLIPPER SHIP "CHALLENGE"; N. Currier Small....     275.00
NEW YORK CRYSTAL PALACE; N. Currier; 1853  ...... Large....     250.00
NEW YORK CRYSTAL PALACE; N. Currier  .............. Small....     110.00
NEW YORK FERRY BOAT ...................................... Small....     100.00
NEW YORK FIREMEN'S MONUMENT, GREENWOOD CEME-
    TERY, L. I.; N. Currier ; 1855 .............................Medium..      50.00
NEW YORK FROM WEEHAWKEN; C. Currier; 1835.........Small....     200.00
NEW YORK, LOOKING NORTH FROM THE BATTERY;
    1860  .......................................................Small....     125.00
NEW YORK PILOT'S MONUMENT; N. Currier; 1855 ......Medium..      50.00
NEW YORK YACHT CLUB REGATTA....................... Large....     600.00
NEWFOUNDLAND DOG ............................................Small....      30.00
NEWPORT BEACH ...............................................Small....     150.00
NIAGARA BY MOONLIGHT ................................... Small ....      60.00
NIAGARA FALLS; N. Currier  ................................. Small ....      70.00
NIAGARA FALLS  .............................................. Large....     175.00
NIAGARA FALLS FROM GOAT ISLAND ..................... Medium..      80.00
NIAGARA FALLS FROM GOAT ISLAND  ................... Small ....      60.00
NIAGARA FALLS FROM TABLE ROCK; N. Currier....... Small ....      62.50
NIAGARA FALLS FROM THE CANADA SIDE ..............Small....      60.00
NICE AND TEMPTING OYSTERS ............................Small....      20.00
NICE FAMILY PARTY, A; (Political Cartoon).............Small....      35.00
"NIGGER" IN THE WOODPILE; (Political Cartoon) .....Small....      35.00
NIGH TO BETHANY; N. Currier  .............................Small....      15.00
NIGHT  .............................................................Small....      18.50
NIGHT AFTER THE BATTLE − BURYING THE DEAD. Small....      40.00
NIGHT BEFORE THE BATTLE − THE PATRIOT'S DREAM
                                                                Medium..      40.00
NIGHT BY THE CAMP-FIRE; 1861 ........................... Medium..      95.00
NIGHT EXPRESS, THE; "The Start" ........................ Small ....     525.00
NIGHT ON THE HUDSON, A; "Through At Daylight"; 1864
                                                                Large ....     400.00
NIGHT RACE ON THE MISSISSIPPI .........................Small....     150.00
NIGHT SCENE AT A JUNCTION; 1884 ......................Small ....     400.00
NIGHT SCENE AT AN AMERICAN RAILWAY JUNCTION;
    1876  ........................................................Large....   2,500.00
NIGHTMARE IN THE SLEEPING CAR, A; 1875 .........Small ....      70.00
NINETY AND NINE; 1875  ................................... Small ....      20.00
NIP AND TUCK! 1878; (Comic) ............................. Small ....      40.00
NIPPED IN THE ICE ..........................................Small ....     140.00
```

```
NO MA'AM, I DON'T CARE TO SHOOT BIRDS; 1880 ....Small ....  $    22.50
NO ONE TO LOVE ME; 1880 (Comic) .........................Small ....       20.00
NO ROSE WITHOUT A THORN; N. Currier .................Small ....       30.00
NO TICK HERE ....................................................Small ....       20.00
NO TIME HERE — PLAYED OUT..............................Small ....       25.00
NO YOU DON'T; N. Currier .....................................Small ....       25.00
NOAH'S ARK; N. Currier .......................................Small ....       60.00
NOONTIDE — A SHADY SPOT ...............................Small ....       40.00
NORTH AMERICAN INDIANS ...............................Medium..      120.00
NORTH RIVER FERRY BOAT...................................Small ....       65.00
NORTH SEA WHALE FISHERY; N. Currier ...............Small ....      275.00
NORTH SIDE VIEW ON THE NORTH CHINCHA ISLAND Small ....       40.00
NORTHERN BEAUTY, THE .................................... Small ....       22.00
NOSE OUT OF JOINT, THE; N. Currier ................... Small ....       20.00
NOSEGAY, THE; N. Currier; 1848; (Bouquet) ..............Small ....       50.00
NOT CAUGHT; (Fox and Rabbit); N. Currier ...............Medium..       80.00
NOT CAUGHT YET; (Fox Trap); N. Currier ...............Small ....       65.00
NOTCH HOUSE, WHITE MOUNTAINS, N. H., THE ......Small ....       75.00
NOTHING VENTURED — NOTHING HAVE; (Animals)....Small ....       21.50
NOTICE TO SMOKERS AND CHEWERS; N. Currier .......Small ....       35.00
NOVA SCOTIA SCENERY; 1868 ............................. Medium..      140.00
```

— O —

```
O DAT WATERMILLION; 1882 ................................. Small....  $    25.00
O! THERE'S A MOUSIE .................................... Small....       21.50
OBDURATE MULE — GOING BACK ON THE PARSON;
    1890 ............................................................ Small....       32.50
OCCIDENT; 1876 ...................................... Large ...      200.00
OCCIDENT — Record 2:16¾ ............................. Small....       65.00
OCEAN STEAMER IN A HEAVY GALE, AN ................. Small....       75.00
OCTAVIA; (Head) ................................................ Medium .       20.00
OCTOBER LANDSCAPE ................................... Medium .      175.00
ODD FELLOWS — TWO MEN; N. Currier ................... Small....       20.00
ODD FELLOWS; (Man, full length); N. Currier ............. Small....       18.50
ODD FELLOWS CHART; 1877 .................................Small ...       18.00
ODD FELLOWS CHART; (For Negroes) ..................... Small....       18.00
ODD FELLOWS CHART; 1872 (30 Symbols) ................ Small....       18.00
ODD TRICK, THE; 1884....................................... Small....       25.00
OFF LEE SHORE................................................ Small....      150.00
OFF FOR THE WAR — THE SOLDIER'S ADIEU. 1861 ... Small....       22.50
OFF HIS NUT; 1886 ........................................... Small....       30.00
OFF ON FIRST SCORE; 1891 ................................ Small....       32.50
OFF THE COAST IN A SNOWSTORM — TAKING A PILOT
                                                            Small....      140.00
OH HOW FINE; N. Currier ...................................... Small....       25.00
OH, HOW NICE; N. Currier ..................................... Small....       20.00
OLD BARN FLOOR, THE........................................ Large ...      475.00
OLD BLANFORD CHURCH, PETERSBURG, VA. .......Small....       60.00
OLD BRIDGE, THE ............................................. Small....       28.50
OLD BULL DOG ON THE RIGHT TRACK, THE; (Political
    Cartoon) ......................................................Small....       35.00
OLD CASTLE, THE.............................................. Small....       25.00
OLD CREDIT PLAYED OUT ................................... Small....       22.50
OLD DARBY AND JOAN ....................................... Small....       28.50
OLD FARM GATE, THE; 1864 ................................ Large ...      300.00
OLD FARM HOUSE, THE; N. Currier ...................... Small....       95.00
```

```
OLD FARM HOUSE, THE; 1872 ...................................Medium.. $ 125.00
OLD FEUDAL CASTLE ...........................................Small ....    27.50
OLD FORD BRIDGE, THE .......................................Small ....    30.00
OLD GENERAL READY FOR A MOVEMENT, THE .........Small ....    30.00
OLD HOMESTEAD, THE; N. Currier; 1855 ..................Small ....   130.00
OLD HOMESTEAD, THE ..........................................Medium..   185.00
OLD HOMESTEAD IN WINTER, THE; 1864 .................Large ... 1,650.00
OLD KENTUCKY HOME, DE; 1884 ............................Small ....    25.00
OLD LADY WHO LIVED IN A SHOE, THE ...................Small ....    30.00
OLD MANSE, THE ................................................Small ....    95.00
OLD MANSION HOUSE, GOWANUS ROAD; N. Currier ...... Small ....    90.00
OLD MARE THE BEST HORSE, THE; 1881 ..................Large....   225.00
OLD MASSA'S GRAVE ...........................................Small ....    20.00
OLD MILL IN SUMMER, THE ..................................Small ....    35.00
OLD MILL-DAM AT SLEEPY HOLLOW ......................Small ....    75.00
OLD NORMAN CASTLE, THE; N. Currier ...................Large....    70.00
OLD NORMAN CASTLE, THE ...................................Small ....    30.00
OLD OAKEN BUCKET; 1864 ...................................Large....   225.00
OLD OAKEN BUCKET; 1872 ....................................Small ....    45.00
OLD PLANTATION HOME, THE; 1872.......................Small ....    95.00
OLD RUINED CASTLE ...........................................Small ....    25.00
OLD RUINS, THE...................................................Small ....    24.50
OLD SAW-MILL, L. I., N. Currier...............................Small ....    95.00
OLD SLEDGE ......................................................Small ....    60.00
OLD STONE HOUSE, THE; N. Currier .......................Small ....    75.00
OLD STONE HOUSE, L. I., THE ..............................Small ....    85.00
OLD SUIT AND THE NEW, THE; 1879 .......................Small ....    20.00
OLD TENNENT PARSONAGE ON MONMOUTH BATTLE-
    FIELD, THE; C. Currier; 1859 ............................ Medium..   200.00
OLD VIRGINNY .....................................................Small ....    25.00
OLD WAY, THE — THE NEW WAY; "I Gave Credit — I Sell
    For Cash"; 1870 .............................................Small ....    35.00
OLD WIER BRIDGE, THE — LAKES OF KILLARNEY ......Medium..    24.50
OLD WINDMILL, THE ............................................ Medium..    60.00
ON A POINT; N. Currier; 1855 .................................Medium..   285.00
ON A STRONG SCENT; 1880 ..................................Small ....    35.00
ON DE HAF SHELL; 1886 ......................................Small ....    25.00
ON GUARD; 1876 .................................................Small ....    32.50
ON HIS STYLE; 1886 ............................................Small ....    27.50
ON THE COAST OF CALIFORNIA ............................Small ....    75.00
ON THE DOWNS, AT EPSOM .................................Medium..   125.00
ON THE HOME STRETCH; 1882...............................Small ....    40.00
ON THE HUDSON; 1869 ........................................Small ....    60.00
ON THE JUNIATA; 1869.........................................Medium..   110.00
ON THE LAKE .....................................................Small ....    60.00
ON THE MISSISSIPPI; 1869....................................Small ....    95.00
ON THE MISSISSIPPI, LOADING COTTON; 1870 ...........Small ....   100.00
ON THE OWAGO ..................................................Small ....    48.00
ON THE ST. LAWRENCE — INDIAN ENCAMPMENT .......Small ....    95.00
ONE FOR HIS NOB; 1884 .....................................Small ....    27.50
ONE FOR H IS PET; 1884 .....................................Small ....    22.50
ONE OF THE HEAVYWEIGHTS ...............................Small ....    25.00
ONLY DAUGHTER, THE; N. Currier .........................Small ....    20.00
ONLY SON, THE .................................................Small ....    22.50
ORANGEMENS CHART, O. B. L. .............................Small ....    18.50
"OREGON", (Steamship); N. Currier .........................Small ....    70.00
ORIENTAL LANDSCAPE .......................................Large ...    65.00
ORIGIN OF THE SPECIES; 1874 .............................Small ....    45.00
```

```
ORIGINAL GENERAL TOM THUMB, THE ................. Small ....$    50.00
ORIGINAL GENERAL TOM THUMB; (Queen Victoria); 1860
                                                    Small ....    60.00
ORMONDE; 1882 .................................................... Small ....    65.00
OSCAR J. DUNN, LIEUT. GOV. OF LOUISIANA............ Small....    30.00
O'SULLIVAN'S CASCADE, LAKE OF KILLARNEY ........ Small ....    60.00
OTHELLO ............................................................. Small ....    4 850
"OULD TIMES" AT DONNYBROOK FAIR; (Dance).........Small ....    24.50
OUR CABINET; 1885 ............................................. Small ....    30.00
OUR FATHER WHO ART IN HEAVEN; 1876 ............. Small ....    10.00
OUR LADY OF GUADALUPE; N. Currier; 1848 ......... Small ....    10.00
OUR LADY OF KNOCK ......................................... Small ....    10.00
OUR LADY OF MERCY ......................................... Small ....    10.00
OUR LADY OF MT. CARMEL; N. Currier; 1849 ........... Small ....    10.00
OUR LADY OF REFUGE ...................................... Small ....    10.00
OUR LADY OF THE LIGHT .................................. Small ....    10.00
OUR LADY OF THE ROSARY ............................... Small ....    10.00
OUR LADY OF THE SEVEN SORROWS........................Small ....    10.00
OUR PASTURE; (Sheep); N. Currier ..................... Small ....    24.50
OUR PASTURE; (Cows); N. Currier ........................... Small ....    24.00
OUR PETS − FAST ASLEEP ................................Small ....    24.00
OUR PETS − WIDE AWAKE ...............................Small ....    24.00
OUR REDEEMER .................................................Small ....    10.00
OUR SAVIOUR ....................................................Small ....    10.00
OUR SAVIOUR AT PRAYER ................................ Small ....    10.00
OUR VICTORIOUS FLEETS IN CUBAN WATERS; 1898 ... Large....   150.00
OUT FOR A DAY'S SHOOTING − OFF FOR THE WOODS;
   1869 .............................................................. Large....   450.00
OUTLET OF THE NIAGARA RIVER, THE ............... Small ....    50.00
OUTWARD BOUND; N. Currier; 1845 .......................... Small ....   160.00
OVER THE GARDEN WALL .....................................Small ....    30.00
OYSTER PADDY; 1875 ......................................... Small ....    27.50
OYSTER SUPPER, AN; N. Currier ...............................Small ....    40.00
OYSTERS ........................................................... Small ....    25.00
```

− P −

```
PACIFIC COAST STEAMSHIP CO'S "STATE OF CALIFORNIA"
   1878 ............................................................. Small ....$   65.00
PACIFIC MAIL STEAMSHIP COMPANY'S STEAMER "GREAT
   REPUBLIC" ...................................................... Small ....    65.00
PACING A FAST HEAT; 1892 ............................... Small ....    65.00
PACING FOR A GRAND PURSE; 1890 .................... Large....   225.00
PACING HORSE "BILLY BOYCE," OF ST. LOUIS; 1868 Large....   225.00
PACING IN THE LATEST STYLE; 1893 ............... Small ....    68.50
PACING KING, "HAL POINTER," − Record 2:01½ ...... Small ....    70.00
PACING KING "ROBERT J." − Record 2:02½; 1894...... Large....   225.00
PACING KING "ROBERT J." IN HIS RACE WITH JOE
   PATCHEN." 1894 ........................................... Small ....    75.00
PACING WONDER "LITTLE BROWN JUG" − Record 2:11¾
   1882 .............................................................. Small ....    70.00
PACING WONDER "SLEEPY TOM." THE BLIND HORSE Small ....    70.00
PADDLE WHEEL STEAMSHIP "MASSACHUSETTS," THE
                                                    Large....   195.00
PADDY AND THE PIGS ......................................... Small ....    32.50
PADDY MURPHY'S "JANTIN' CAR." ........................ Small ....    30.00
PADDY RYAN; "The Trojan Giant" ........................... Medium..    85.00
```

```
PAGE, THE; N. Currier; 1846 ............................................. Small ... $ 22.50
PAIR OF NUTCRACKERS; (Squirrels);  .................... Small ...   48.00
PAPAL BENEDICTION, THE  ................................... Small ...   12.50
PAPA'S COMING; 1872  ............................................ Small ..   25.00
PAPA'S DARLINGS; 1877 ........................................ Small ...   20.00
PAPA'S NEW HAT  ................................................... Small ...   20.00
PAPA'S PET  .......................................................... Small ...   20.00
PARLEY, A; "Prepared For An Emergency"  .............. Large ..3500.00
PAROLE; 1877  ....................................................... Small ...   65.00
PARSON'S COLT, THE; 1879 ................................. Small ...   30.00
PARSON'S COLT, THE; 1880  .................................. Large ..   85.00
PARTING HOUR, THE; N. Currier; 1849 .................... Small ...   20.00
PARTRIDGE SHOOTING; 1852; N. Currier .............. Large ..2750.00
PARTRIDGE SHOOTING; 1885; N. Currier  .............. Small ...  225.00
PARTRIDGE SHOOTING; 1865; (C. & I.)  .............. Large ..  750.00
PARTRIDGE SHOOTING; 1870  ............................... Small ...  140.00
PAST AND THE FUTURE, THE; (Oval) ...................... Large ..   45.00
PASTURE IN SUMMER, THE — THE DRINKING TROUGH;
   1867 ................................................................. Large ..  295.00
PASTURE — NOONTIDE  ........................................ Medium   75.00
PATH THROUGH THE FIELDS, THE  ...................... Small ...   45.00
PATRIOT OF 1776, A; "Defending His Homestead"; 1876 ...Small ...  135.00
PATTERN IN CONNEMARA, A; (Dance)  .................. Small ...   22.50
PAUL  ................................................................. Small ...   22.50
PAUL AND VIRGINIA; N. Currier  ........................ Small ...   30.00
PAUL AND VIRGINIA'S DEPARTURE FOR FRANCE;
   N. Currier  ....................................................... Small ...   30.00
PAUL AND VIRGINIA; "Lost in the Woods," N. Currier ..... Small ...   30.00
PEACE  ................................................................ Small ...   25.00
PEACE AND PLENTY; 1871  ................................... Medium   75.00
PEACE BE TO THIS HOUSE; 1872 ........................... Small ...   20.00
PEACEFUL RIVER, THE ......................................... Small ...   40.00
PEACHES AND GRAPES — FIRST PRIZE; 1870 .............. Small ...   35.00
PEEK-A-BOO .......................................................... Small ...   22.50
PEERLESS BEAUTY, THE  ...................................... Small ...   20.00
PEERLESS GOLDSMITH MAID, THE; 1871  .............. Small ...   65.00
PELHAM; N. Currier; 1850 ...................................... Medium 185.00
PENITENT MULE, A; "The Parson On Deck"; 1890 ........ Small ...   30.00
PENNSYLVANIA RAILROAD SCENERY  ...................... Small ...  125.00
PEOPLE IN THE TUILERIES, THE; N. Currier .............. Small ...   30.00
PEOPLES LINE, HUDSON RIVER; 1877  .................. Small ...   65.00
PEOPLES LINE, HUDSON RIVER — THE PALACE STEAMERS
   OF THE WORLD; 1877 .......................................... Large ..  225.00
PERFECT BLISS; 1879  ........................................... Small ...   27.50
PERMANENT FAIR GROUNDS OF THE QUEENS COUNTY
   AGRICULTURAL SOCIETY, MINEOLA, L. I.; C. Currier;
   1867 ................................................................. Large ..  235.00
PERRY'S VICTORY ON LAKE ERIE; N. Currier .............. Small ...  125.00
PERSIAN BEAUTY  ................................................. Small ...   20.00
PET OF THE FAMILY, THE........................................ Small ...   20.00
PET OF THE FANCY, THE; 1879 (Comic)  .................. Small ...   20.00
PET OF THE LADIES, THE  ..................................... Small ...   20.00
PETS IN SPRINGTIME  ........................................... Small ...   20.00
"PEYTONA" AND "FASHION"; N. Currier .................. Large ..4250.00
PHALLAS — Record 2:13¾; 1883  ........................... Small ...   65.00
PHEBE; N. Currier; 1846  ....................................... Small ...   20.00
PHILOSOPHER IN ECSTASY, A  .............................. Small ...   32.50
PHILOSOPHY OF TOBACCO, THE............................. Small ...   35.00
```

```
PHOEBE; N. Currier; 1846 ............................................... Small...$  20.00
PHOTOGRAPH MARRIAGE CERTIFICATE  .................. Small ...  10.00
PIC-NIC PARTY, THE  ..................................................... Medium  85.00
PIC-NIC PARTY, THE; 1858 ........................................ Small...  50.00
PICADOR; 1883  ............................................................. Small...  35.00
PICADOR .......................................................................... Medium  55.00
PICKEREL; 1872 .......................................................... Small...  40.00
PIEDMONT; 1882 ........................................................ Small...  65.00
PIGEON SHOOTING — PLAYING THE DECOY; 1862  ...... Large..  675.00
"PILGRIM"; 1883  ....................................................... Small...  60.00
PILGRIMS AT THE SHRINE OF OUR LADY OF LOURDES; Small...  15.00
PILOT BOAT IN A STORM  ........................................... Small...  95.0 0
PINCH TAKEN, THE; N. Currier  ................................ Small...  35.00
PIONEER CABIN OF THE YO-SE-MITE VALLEY  ............ Small...  95.00
PIONEER'S HOME ON THE WESTERN FRONTIER, THE;
   1867  ......................................................................Large..  300.00
PLACID LAKE, ADIRONDACKS.......................................Small...  60.00
PLAN OF GILBERT'S BALANCE FLOATING DRY DOCK....Large..  80.00
PLAN OF NEW HAVEN, CONNECTICUT; C. Currier  ........ Medium  80.00
PLAN OF THE SCHOOL HOUSE ....................................Small...  15.00
PLAN OF THE CITY OF NEW YORK; (Bradford Map);
   N. Currier; 1849  ...................................................Medium  200.00
PLAYED OUT; 1871.....................................................Small...  35.00
PLAYFUL .....................................................................Small...  27.50
PLAYFUL FAMILY; N. Currier  ....................................Small...  20.00
PLAYFUL PETS, THE; N. Currier  ...............................Small...  20.00
PLAYING DOMINOS  ....................................................Small...  20.00
PLAYMATES, THE; N. Currier  ...................................Small...  20.00
PLAYMATES, THE; (C. & I.)  ......................................Small...  20.00
PLEASE GIVE ME A LIGHT, SIR; 1879 ...........................Small...  25.00
PLEASURE  ..................................................................Small...  20.00
PLEASURES OF THE COUNTRY, THE; "Sweet Home"......Medium  75.00
PLEASURES OF THE COUNTRY, THE; "Winter"............. Small...  125.00
PLUCK — ONE OF THE RIGHT SORT; N. Currier .............Small...  50.00
PO-CAN-TECO FROM IRVING PARK, THE; (Oval).............Small...  27.50
POCAHONTAS BOY — Record 2:31  ............................ Large..  200.00
POCAHONTAS SAVING THE LIFE OF CAPTAIN JOHN SMITH;
   N. Currier  ............................................................. Small...  35.00
POINT OF THE JOKE, THE; 1879  ............................. Small...  12.50
POINTER, THE; N. Currier; 1848  ............................. Small...  110.00
POINTERS; N. Currier; 1846  ..................................... Small...  125.00
POINTING A BEVY; 1866 ............................................ Large..  225.00
POLISHED OFF; 1888 ................................................ Small...  27.50
POLITICAL ARENA, THE ............................................. Small...  32.50
POLITICAL "BLONDINS" CROSSING SALT RIVER; 1860. Small...  40.00
POLITICAL DEBATE IN THE DARKTOWN CLUB  .......... Small...  30.00
POLITICAL GYMNASIUM, THE  ................................. Small...  40.00
POLITICAL SIAMESE TWINS, THE  ........................... Small...  36.00
POLKA, THE, NO. 1; N. Currier  ............................... Small...  20.00
POLKA, THE, NO. 2; N. Currier  ............................... Small...  20.00
POLKA, THE, NO. 3; N. Currier  ............................... Small...  20.00
POLKA, THE, NO. 4; N. Currier  ............................... Small...  20.00
POLLY AND KITTY, ROSES AND THORNS  .................. Small...  25.00
POMONA'S TREASURES .............................................. Small...  27.50
POND IN THE WOODS, THE  ..................................... Medium  80.00
PONTO; (Boy and dog) ............................................... Small...  25.00
PONY TEAM, THE  ...................................................... Small...  27.50
PONY WAGON, THE  .................................................. Small...  27.50
```

```
POOL, THE.................................................. Small ...$  30.00
POOL OF SILOAM, THE; N. Currier ...................... Small ...   25.00
POOR DOLLY .............................................. Small ...   24.50
POOR TRUST IS DEAD; (Bad Pay Killed Him) ...............Small ...   30.00
POPE LEO XIIITH; 1878 ................................... Small ...   25.00
POPE PIUS IX, A.D.; 1846; N. Currier .................. Small ...   25.00
POPE PIUS IXTH, LYING IN STATE; 1878 ............... Small ...   25.00
POPPING THE QUESTION; N. Currier; 1847 ............. Small ...   22.50
PORT OF NEW YORK, THE; 1872 .......................... Large...  650.00
PORT OF NEW YORK, THE; 1892 .......................... Large...  500.00
PORTRAIT OF A GIRL; N. Currier; 1846 ................. Small ...   20.00
POSITIVE PROCESS, FROM A NEGATIVE RESULT ......... Small ...   25.00
POST OFFICE, NEW YORK, THE; N. Currier  ............. Small ...  375.00
POT LUCK; N. Currier ..................................... Small ...   20.00
POULTRY SHOW ON THE BUST; 1883 .......................Small ...   20.00
POULTRY SHOW ON THE ROAD; 1883 ....................Small ...   20.00
POULTRY YARD, THE; 1870 ...............................Small ...   25.00
POWER OF MUSIC, THE; N. Currier .....................Small ...   30.00
PRAIRIE FIRES OF THE GREAT WEST; 1871................. Small ...  185.00
PRAIRIE HENS ............................................ Small ...  120.00
PRAIRIE HUNTER, THE; N. Currier; 1852 ................. Medium.  750.00
PRAIRIE ON FIRE; N. Currier  ...........................Small ...  190.00
PRAISE THE LORD; 1875 ..................................Small ...   10.00
PRAISE THE LORD – O MY SOUL .........................Small ...   10.00
PRAY "GOD BLESS PAPA AND MAMA" .......................Small ...   10.00
PREMIUM FRUIT; 1875 .................................... Small ...   35.00
PREMIUM POULTRY ....................................... Small ...   30.00
PREPARING FOR MARKET; N. Currier; 1856 ............. Large ...  600.00
PRESIDENT CLEVELAND AND HIS CABINET; 1893........ Small ...   35.00
PRESIDENT CLEVELAND AND HIS CABINET; 1884 ....... Small ...   35.00
PRESIDENT HARRISON AND HIS CABINET; 1889 .......... Small ...   35.00
PRESIDENT HAYES AND CABINET; 1877...................... Small ...   35.00
PRESIDENT LINCOLN AND HIS CABINET; 1876............. Small ...   50.00
PRESIDENT LINCOLN AND SECRETARY SEWARD; 1865
    (Oval) ................................................. Small ...   50.00
PRESIDENT LINCOLN AT GENERAL GRANT'S HEADQUARTERS;
    1865 .................................................Small ...   60.00
PRESIDENT LINCOLN AT HOME; 1863; (Oval).............Small ...   60.00
PRESIDENTIAL FISHING PARTY OF 1848, THE .............Medium.   45.00
PRESIDENTIAL RECEPTION IN 1789 BY GEN. WASHINGTON
    AND MRS. WASHINGTON; 1876 ............................Small ...   90.00
PRESIDENTS OF THE UNITED STATES; (Washington to
    Harrison); N. Currier; 1842 .......................Small ...   50.00
PRESIDENTS OF THE UNITED STATES; N. Currier; 1845; Small ...   48.50
PRESIDENTS OF THE UNITED STATES; N. Currier; 1846; Small ...   48.50
PRESIDENTS OF THE UNITED STATES; N. Currier; 1847..Small ...   48.50
PRESIDENTS OF THE UNITED STATES; N. Currier; 1848..Small ...   48.50
PRESIDENTS OF THE UNITED STATES; N. Currier; 1850;
    (Washington to Fillmore) .......................... Small ...   48.50
PRESS GANG, THE; N. Currier ........................Small ...   35.00
PRETTY AMERICAN, THE....................................Small ...   20.00
PRETTY DOLLY; 1873 ....................................Small ...   20.00
PRETTY POLL; N. Currier ...............................Small ...   20.00
PRETTY STORY, THE ....................................Small ...   20.00
PRIDE OF AMERICA, THE....................................Small ...   24.00
PRIDE OF KENTUCKY ....................................Small ...   24.00
PRIDE OF KILDARE, THE  ................................ Small ...   18.00
PRIDE OF THE GARDEN; 1873 ..............................Small ...   45.00
```

```
PRIDE OF THE SOUTH, THE; 1870 ........................... Small ... $ 20.00
PRIDE OF THE WEST, THE; (Girl on horse); 1847............ Small ...   20.00
PRIME TOBACCO..................................................... Small ...   35.00
PRINCE ALBERT; (Mounted on horse); N. Currier .......... Small ...   25.00
PRINCE ALBERT; (Portrait); N. Currier ....................... Small ...   25.00
PRINCE ALBERT; (In uniform); N. Currier .................... Small ...   25.00
"PRINCE" AND "LANTERN"; N. Currier; 1847............... Large ...  225.00
PRINCE AND PRINCESS OF WALES ......................... Small ...   25.00
PRINCE OF ORANGE ........................................... Small ...   20.00
PRINCE OF THE BLOOD; 1893 ................................. Small ...   45.00
PRINCE OF WALES AND FAMILY.............................. Small ...   25.00
PRINCE OF WALES AT THE TOMB OF WASHINGTON ...... Small ...   30.00
PRIZE BLACK HAMBURG GRAPES........................... Medium.   60.00
PRIZE BOY, THE; 1857........................................... Small ...   25.00
PRIZE BOY, THE  ............................................... Large ...   80.00
PRIZE FAT CATTLE ............................................. Small ...   40.00
PRIZE FIGHTER, THE; (Oval)................................... Small ...   40.00
PRIZE GRAPES — A FOUR POUND BUNCH; 1865 .......... Small ...   50.00
PRIZE HERD ..................................................... Small ...   50.00
PRIZE JERSEY LITCHFIELD BULL............................ Small ...   30.00
PRIZE JERSEY "NIOBE"; (Cattle) ........................... Small ...   30.00
PRIZE SETTER, A .............................................. Medium.   70.00
PRIZE SETTER, A .............................................. Small ...   48.00
PRIZE TROTTER, A; 1873 ..................................... Small ...   65.00
PROCTOR KNOTT; 1888 ........................................ Small ...   48.50
PRODIGAL SON IN MISERY, THE; N. Currier ................ Small ...   30.00
PRODIGAL SON RECEIVING HIS PATRIMONY... ........... Small ...   30.00
PRODIGAL SON RETURNS TO HIS FATHER; N. Currier .. Small ...   35.00
PRODIGAL SON WASTING HIS SUBSTANCE; N. Currier  .. Small ...   30.00
PROFIT AND LOSS; 1880 ....................................... Small ...   25.00
PROGRESS OF INTEMPERANCE; PLATE I; "The Invitation
  to Drink"; N. Currier; 1841 ................................. Small ...   65.00
PROGRESS OF INTEMPERANCE, PLATE 2; "Sick and Re-
  pentant"; N. Currier; 1841 ................................. Small ...   65.00
PROGRESS OF INTEMPERANCE, PLATE 3; "The Relapse"
  N. Currier; 1841 ............................................. Small ...   65.00
PROGRESS OF INTEMPERANCE, PLATE 4; "The Ruined
  Family"; N. Currier; 1841; ................................. Small ...   65.00
PROGRESS OF INTEMPERANCE, PLATE 5; "The Expec-
  tant Wife"; N. Currier; 1841 ............................... Small ...   65.00
PROGRESS OF INTEMPERANCE, PLATE 6; "The Robber"
  N. Currier; 1841............................................... Small ...   65.00
PROGRESS OF THE CENTURY, THE; 1876 ................... Small ...  175.00
PROGRESSIVE DEMOCRACY — PROSPECT OF A SMASH UP;
  (Political Cartoon) ........................................... Small ...   32.50
PROMISING FAMILY, A; "Black and Tan"; 1868............. Small ...   32.50
PROPAGATION SOCIETY — MORE FREEDOM THAN WELCOME;
  1853 ........................................................... Small ...   32.50
PROPOSAL, THE; N. Currier ................................. Small ...   20.00
PROTEINE — Record 2:18; 1878 .............................. Small ...   65.00
PROVIDENCE AND STONINGTON STEAMSHIP CO.'s
  STEAMERS, "MASSACHUSETTS" AND "RHODE ISLAND";
  1877 ........................................................... Large ...  225.00
PROVISIONS DOWN ........................................... Small ...  115.00
PUBLIC PARK OF MEXICO, THE; N. Currier; 1848 ........ Small ...   25.00
PUPPIES NURSERY, THE ..................................... Small ...   25.00
"PURITAN" AND "GENESTA" ON THE HOMESTRETCH..Large ...  225.00
PURSUIT, THE; N. Currier; 1856 ............................ Large ...1500.00
```

PURSUIT, THE; (Elopement); N. Currier ....Small ...$ 25.00
PURSUIT OF THE MEXICANS BY THE U.S. DRAGOONS;
   N. Currier; 1847 ....Small ... 50.00
PUSS IN BOOTS ....Small ... 20.00
PUSSY'S RETURN ....Small ... 20.00
PUT UP JOB, A; 1883 ....Small ... 29.50
PUTTING ON HIS AIRS ....Small ... 22.50
PUZZLE FOR A WINTER'S EVENING, A ....Small ... 35.00
PUZZLE PICTURE — OLD SWISS MILL; 1872 ....Small ... 35.00
PUZZLED FOX, THE; 1872 ....Small ... 40.00

- Q -

QUAIL; 1865 .... Small ...$120.00
QUAIL OR VIRGINIA PARTRIDGE; 1871 .... Small ... 115.00
QUAIL SHOOTING; N. Currier; 1852 .... Large ...1450.00
QUAIL SHOOTING .... Small ... 200.00
QUAILS; N. Currier; 1849 .... Small ... 90.00
QUARREL, THE; N. Currier.. Small ... 20.00
QUEEN OF ANGELS; N. Currier .... Small ... 15.00
QUEEN OF BEAUTY, THE .... Small ... 20.00
QUEEN OF CATTLE; 1886 .... Small ... 27.50
QUEEN OF HEARTS; 1857 .... Small ... 27.50
QUEEN OF LOVE, THE .... Small ... 20.00
QUEEN OF LOVE AND BEAUTY; 1870 .... Small ... 20.00
QUEEN OF THE AMAZONS ATTACKED BY A LION ...... Small ... 24.50
QUEEN OF THE BALL, THE; 1870 .... Small ... 20.00
QUEEN OF THE BLONDES .... Small ... 20.00
QUEEN OF THE BRUNETTES; 1870 .... Small ... 20.00
QUEEN OF THE FLOWERS .... Small ... 22.50
QUEEN OF THE GARDEN; 1872 .... Small ... 37.50
QUEEN OF THE HOUSE; 1875 .... Small ... 20.00
QUEEN OF THE SOUTH .... Small ... 20.00
QUEEN OF THE TURF, "MAUD S." Record 2:10; 1880 ..... Large ... 225.00
QUEEN OF THE WEST, THE .... Small ... 125.00
QUEEN OF THE WOODS, THE ....Medium. 35.00
QUEEN VICTORIA; C. Currier ....Small ... 30.00
QUEEN VICTORIA AND EMPRESS EUGENIE ....:Small ... 29.50
QUEEN'S OWN, THE; 1875 .... Medium. 40.00
QUEENSTOWN HARBOR, COVE OF CORK, IRELAND....... Small ... 35.00

- R -

R. B. CONKLING'S BAY GELDING "RARUS," THE "KING
   OF THE TROTTERS"; 1878.....................................Large ...$225.00
R. CORNELL WHITE'S NEW PALATIAL EXCURSION
   STEAMER "COLUMBIA"; 1877 ....Large ... 175.00
R. T. Y. C. SCHOONER "CAMBRIA,"; 1870 ....Large ... 175.00
RAAL CONVANIENCE, A .... Small ... 27.50
RABBIT CATCHING — THE TRAP SPRING ....Small ... 95.00
RABBIT HUNT, THE — ALL BUT CAUGHT; N. Currier; 1849
                                 Small ... 110.00
RABBITS IN THE WOODS ....Small ... 85.00
RACE FOR THE AMERICAN DERBY; 1878 ....Small ... 200.00
RACE FOR THE BLOOD, A; 1890 ....Large ... 200.00
RACE FOR THE QUEEN'S CUP, THE .... Small ... 125.00

RACE FROM THE WORD "GO"; 1890 ....Small ... 65.00
RACE ON THE MISSISSIPPI, A; The "Eagle" and "Diana",
    1870 ....Small ... 90.00
RACE TO THE WIRE; 1891 ....Small ... 65.00
RACHEL; N. Currier ....Small ... 20.00
RACING CHAMPIONS ON THEIR METTLE; 1889 ....Small ... 65.00
RACING CRACKS; 1886 ....Small ... 70.00
RACING KING SALVATOR, THE — Record 1:35½; 1890......Small ... 65.00
RACING KING — SALVATOR; 1891 .... Large ... 225.00
RADICAL PARTY ON A HEAVY GRADE, THE .... Small ... 30.00
RAFTING ON THE ST. LAWRENCE ....Small ... 95.00
RAIL CANDIDATE, THE ....Small ... 70.00
RAIL SHOOTING ....Small ... 450.00
RAIL SHOOTING ON THE DELAWARE; N. Currier; 1852....Large ...1950.00
RAIL SPLITTER AT WORK REPAIRING THE UNION ....Small ... 60.00
RAILROAD SUSPENSION BRIDGE NEAR NIAGARA FALLS,
    THE; N. Currier; 1856 ....Small ... 85.00
RALLY ROUND THE FLAG BOYS; 1861........................Medium. 50.00
RAPIDS OF DUNAS ON THE SHANNON ....Small ... 35.00
RAQUET RIVER — ADIRONDACKS ....Small ... 75.00
RARUS — Record 2:20¾; 1876 ....Small ... 65.00
"RARUS" AND "GREAT EASTERN"; 1877.....................Small ... 70.00
RASPBERRIES; 1870 .... Small ... 32.50
RASPBERRIES; 1863 .... Small ... 32.50
RATHGALLAN HEAD .... Small ... 20.00
RATTLING HEAT, A; 1891 ....Small ... 65.00
READING THE BIBLE; N. Currier; 1848....................... Small ... 12.00
READING THE SCRIPTURES; N. Currier .... Small ... 12.00
READY FOR A BATTLE: (DEER)............................... Small ... 40.00
READY FOR A FROLIC; 1874 ....Small ... 22.50
READY FOR AN OFFER ....Small ... 25.00
READY FOR THE RACE ; 1891 ....Small ... 60.00
READY FOR THE SIGNAL — THE CELEBRATED RUNNING
    HORSE HARRY BASSETT; 1872 ....Large ... 225.00
READY FOR THE START ....Small ... 60.00
READY FOR THE TROT — BRING UP YOUR HORSES; 1877
                                                                    Large ... 225.00
REBECCA; N. Currier; 1846 ....Small ... 20.00
RECHABITE; N. Currier; 1849 ....Small ... 20.00
RECONCILIATION , THE; N. Currier .... Small ... 21.50
RE-CONSTRUCTION .... Small ... 30.00
RECORD OF BIRTH AND BAPTISM ....Small ... 10.00
RED CLOUD — Record 2:18; 1874 .... Small ... 70.00
RED CLOUD — WINNER OF THE FIRST PRIZE ETC. 1876 Large ... 200.00
RED HOT REPUBLICANS ON THE DEMOCRATIC GRIDIRON;
    (Political Cartoon) .... Small ... 35.00
REDEEMER; N. Currier .... Small ... 12.00
REDEEMER, THE; (C. & I.) .... Small ... 12.00
REDEMPTION — REPUDIATION; 1875 .... Small ... 12.00
REDPATH; 1875 ....Small ... 60.00
REDPATH; 1882 ....Small ... 60.00
REDPATH; 1885 ....Small ... 50.00
REFRESHING FOUNTAIN; 1879.................................Small ... 22.50
REGATTA OF THE NEW YORK YACHT CLUB, "COMING
    In", 1854 ....Large ...1000.00
REGULAR HUMMER; 1879 ....Small ... 40.00
REJECTED, THE ....Small ... 21.50
REMEMBER THE SABBATH-DAY TO KEEP IT HOLY ....Small ... 12.00

```
REPUBLICAN BANNER FOR 1860 ............................Small ... $ 55.00
RESCUE; 1876 ...............................................Small ...   25.00
RESCUE, THE; (Soldiers) ................................Small ...  110.00
RESCUED; (Dog and Children)...........................Small ...   30.00
RESCUED; (Dog and Boy) ...............................Small ...   30.00
RESIDENCE OF LORD BYRON, THE...........................Small ...   27.50
RESIGNATION; N. Currier; 1847........................Small ...   20.00
RESULT IN DOUBT, THE ..................................Small ...   28.00
RESURRECTION, THE; N. Currier; 1849...................Small ...   12.00
RETURN, THE; (Oval) ....................................Small ...   20.00
RETURN FROM EGYPT, THE; N. Currier ...................Small ...   15.00
RETURN FROM ELBA; (Napoleon); N. Currier ............Large ...   75.00
RETURN FROM THE PASTURE, THE..........................Large ...  195.00
RETURN FROM THE WOODS, THE ..........................Medium.  185.00
RE-UNION ON THE SECESH-DEMOCRATIC PLAN ..........Small ...   35.00
REVENGE; (Dogs); N. Currier ..........................Small ...   32.50
REVD. CHARLES WESLEY, A. M. .........................Small ...   30.00
REVD. FATHER THOMAS N. BURKE .......................Small ...   25.00
REVD. JOHN WESLEY .....................................Small ...   25.00
REV. WILLIAM McALLISTER; C. Currier; (Oval) ..........Medium.   24.50
RIDE TO SCHOOL, A .....................................Small ...   70.00
RIGHT MAN FOR THE RIGHT PLACE, THE ................Small ...   40.00
RIGHT REVEREND T. HOLLY, D. D.; 1875 ...............Small ...   20.00
RIP VAN WINKLE'S COTTAGE IN THE CATSKILLS ........Small ...   65.00
RIPE CHERRIES; 1870 ...................................Small ...   37.50
RIPE FRUIT; 1875 .......................................Small ...   30.00
RIPE STARWBERRIES ....................................Small ...   30.00
RIPTON; N. Currier; '1850 .............................Medium.  275.00
RISING FAMILY, A; 1857 ...............................Large ... 2500.00
RIVAL QUEENS, THE .....................................Small ...   25.00
RIVAL ROSES; 1873 .....................................Small ...   55.00
RIVER BOAT PASSING THE PALISADES; 1867 .............Small ...   70.00
RIVERROAD, THE .......................................Medium.  225.00
RIVER SHANNON, THE ...................................Small ...   24.00
RIVER-SIDE, THE; N. Currier ..........................Small ...   40.00
ROAD — SUMMER, THE; N. Currier; 1853.................Large ...  650.00
ROAD TEAM; 1882 .......................................Small ...   65.00
ROAD TO THE HOLY CROSS, THE; N. Currier ...........Small ...   12.00
ROAD TO THE VILLAGE, THE .............................Medium.   75.00
ROAD — WINTER, THE; N.Currier ; 1853 ...............Large ... 2000.00
ROAD-SIDE, THE; N. Currier ...........................Small ...   60.00
ROADSIDE COTTAGE ......................................Medium.  100.00
ROADSIDE MILL, THE; 1870 .............................Small ...   60.00
ROBERT BLUM; N. Currier; 1849 .......................Small ...   20.00
ROBERT BROWN ELLIOTT ................................Small ...   20.00
ROBERT BURNS ..........................................Medium.   25.00
ROBERT BURNS AND HIS HIGHLAND MARY; N. Currier; 1846
                                                     Small ...   25.00
ROBERT EMMET ON TRIAL ...............................Small ...   25.00
ROBERT EMMET, DUBLIN, 1803 .........................Small ...   25.00
ROBERT EMMET — IRELAND'S "MARTYR OF FREEDOM"
                                                     Small ...   20.00
ROBERT McGREGOR; Record 2:18; 1882 ................Small ...   60.00
ROBINSON CRUSOE AND HIS MAN FRIDAY; 1874 ........Small ...   35.00
ROBINSON CRUSOE AND HIS PETS; 1874 ...............Small ...   35.00
ROCHESTER UNION GRAY'S QUICK STEP, THE ..........Small ...   15.00
ROCK OF AGES; 1873 ...................................Small ...   12.00
ROCKY MOUNTAINS, THE; (Buffalo in foreground) ........Small ...  125.00
```

```
ROCKY MOUNTAINS, THE — EMIGRANTS CROSSING THE
    PLAINS; 1866 ................................................... Large .$ 3500.00
ROLL OF HONOR; 1874 ........................................... Small ...    10.00
ROMEO AND JULIET; N. Currier .............................. Small ...    20.00
ROSANNA; N. Currier; 1849 ..................................... Small ...    20.00
ROSE ............................................................... Small ...    20.00
ROSE, THE; N. Currier............................................. Small ...    37.50
ROSE, THE ( 1 Rose, 5 Buds) .. ............................. Small ...    37.50
ROSE, THE (2 Roses, 3 Buds) ................................. Small ...    38.00
ROSE AND LILY; (Heads) ...................................... Small ...    20.00
ROSE OF BEAUTY, THE; N. Currier............................ Small ...    22.00
ROSE OF KILLARNEY ........................................... Small ...    18.00
ROSE OF MAY, THE; N. Currier; 1848......................... Small ...    25.00
ROSEBUD AND EGLANTINE; (Heads) ...................... Small ...    20.00
ROSES AND ROSEBUDS; 1862 ................................. Small ...    48.50
ROSES OF MAY, THE ............................................ Small ...    50.00
ROSIE ................................................................Small ...    24.00
ROSS CASTLE, LAKE OF KILLARNEY .....................Medium.    39.50
ROSS TREVOR .....................................................Small ...    25.00
ROUNDING A BEND ON THE MISSISSIPPI — THE PARTING
    SALUTE; (Ships) 1866 ......................................Large ...  325.00
ROUNDING THE LIGHT SHIP; 1870 ..........................Large ...  335.00
ROUTE TO CALIFORNIA, THE; 1871 ..........................Small ...  350.00
ROWDY BOY — Record 2:13¾; 1879............................Small ...    65.00
ROY WILKES — Record 2:12¾; 1890 ..........................Small ...    65.00
ROY WILKES — Record 2:12¼; 1889 ..........................Small ...    65.00
ROYAL BEAUTY, THE ........................................... Small ...    22.50
ROYAL FAMILY OF ENGLAND, THE ........................ Small ...    27.50
ROYAL MAIL STEAMSHIP "AMSTERDAM" OF THE NETHER-
    LANDS LINE ................................................... Small ...    75.00
ROYAL MAIL STEAMSHIP "ARABIA"; N. Currier; 1853 ... Small ...    75.00
ROYAL MAIL STEAMSHIP "ASIA"; N. Currier; 1851 ....... Small ...    75.00
ROYAL MAIL STEAMSHIP "AUSTRALIAN"; 1861 .......... Small ...    75.00
ROYAL MAIL STEAMSHIP "EUROPA"; N. Currier .......... Small ...    75.00
ROYAL MAIL STEAMSHIP "PERSIA"; N. Currier ........ Large ...  225.00
ROYAL MAIL STEAMSHIP "SCOTIA"............................. Large ...  225.00
ROYAL MAIL STEAMSHIP "SCOTIA" ........................... Small ...    80.00
ROYAL MAIL STEAMSHIP "VEENDAM" ...................... Small ...    75.00
RUBBER, THE ...................................................... Small ...    85.00
RUBBER, THE; "Put To His Trumps" N. Currier ..... Medium.  400.00
RUFFED GROUSE — PHEASANT OR PARTRIDGE; 1871.. Small ...    20.00
RUINS, THE — THE CASTLE .................................... Small ...    20.00
RUINS OF CHEPSTOW CASTLE; (Oval) .................... Small ...    20.00
RUINS OF THE ABBEY ........................................... Small ...    20.00
RUINS OF THE MERCHANT'S EXCHANGE, N. Y.; 1835 ..Small ...  150.00
RUINS OF THE PLANTER'S HOTEL, NEW ORLEANS;
    N. Currier ...................................................Small ...  140.00
RUN DOWN; 1877 .................................................Small ...    32.00
RUN OF LUCK, A; 1871 ...........................................Small ...    30.00
RUNNING THE "MACHINE",(Political Cartoon) ............ Small ...    30.00
RURAL LAKE, THE ...............................................Small ...    60.00
RURAL SCENERY .................................................Small ...    35.00
RUSH FOR THE HEAT; 1884 .................................... Small ...    65.00
RUSH FOR THE POLE; 1887 .....................................Small ...    65.00
RUSTIC BRIDGE, CENTRAL PARK, N.Y. ..................... Small ...  150.00
RUSTIC STAND OF FLOWERS; 1875 .........................Small ...    37.50
RUTHERFORD B. HAYES; 19TH PRESIDENT ...............Small ...    35.00
```

RYSDYK'S HAMBLETONIAN — "The Great Sire of Trotters";
1880 .... Large . $ 225.00
RYE AND ROCK; 1884... Small ..   30.00

— S —

SACRAMENT OF ST. JAMES; N. Currier .... Small .. $ 10.00
SACRED HEART OF JESUS; N. Currier; 1848.................. Small ..   10.00
SACRED HEART OF MARY; N. Currier; 1848 .... Small ..   10.00
SACRED MOTTO TOKENS; 1874 .... Small .   10.00
SACRED TO THE MEMORY OF; N. Currier; 1847............. Small ..   10.00
SACRED TOMB OF THE BLESSED REDEEMER .... Small ..   10.00
S ACRED TOMB OF THE BLESSED VIRGIN .... Small ..   10.00
SAFE SAILING .... Small ..   21.50
SAGE OLD SMOKER; 1888 .... Small ..   27.50
SAILOR BOY, THE; N. Currier .... Small ..   30.00
S AILOR FAR-FAR-AT SEA, THE; N. Currier .... Small ..   30.00
SAILOR'S ADIEU, THE; N. Currier; (Ship left)............... Small ..   30.00
SAILOR'S ADIEU, THE; N. Currier; (Ship right) .... Small ..   30.00
SAILOR'S BRIDE, THE; N. Currier; 1849 .... Small ..   30.00
SAILOR'S RETURN, THE; N. Currier; 1847 .... Small ..   30.00
SAINT ANNE .... Small ..   10.00
ST. ANTHONY OF PADUA; N. Currier; 1849 .... Small ..   10.00
ST. BENEDICT THE MOOR .... Small ..   10.00
ST. BRIDGET, ABBESS OF KILDARE; N. Currier ; 1848... Small ..   10.00
S T. CATHERINE...... .... Small ..   10.00
ST. CECELIA .... Small ..   10.00
S T. CHARLES BORROMEO .... Small ..   10.00
ST. CLOTILDE .... Small ..   10.00
ST. ELIZABETH .... Small ..   10.00
SANTA EMELLIA; N. Currier; 1846 .... Small ..   10.00
S T. EMILY; N. Currier; 1846.................................. Small ..   10.00
ST. FERDINAND, THE KING; N. Currier .... Small ..   10.00
ST. FINEEN'S WELL, IRELAND................................ Small ..   25.00
ST. FRANCIS OF ASSISI .... Small ..   10.00
ST. FRANCIS OF PAUL .... Small ..   10.00
ST. FRANCIS XAVIER; N. Currier; 1849 .... Small ..   10.00
ST. IGNATIUS OF LOYOLA .... Small ..   10.00
ST. JAMES .... Small ..   10.00
ST. JOHN, N. B., RIVER INDIAN TOWN .... Small ..   70.00
ST. JOHN THE BAPTIST .... Small ..   10.00
ST. JOSEPH; N. Currier; 1846 .... Small ..   10.00
ST. JOSEPH .... Small ..   10.00
ST. JUAN BATTISTA .... Small ..   10.00
ST. JULIEN; (Horse); 1879 .... Small ..   60.00
ST. JULIEN — "King of the Turf"; 1880 .... Large.. 225.00
ST. LAWRENCE .... Small ...   60.00
ST. LAWRENCE; N. Currier; 1850............................. Medium   250.00
ST. LOUIS, THE KING; N. Currier .... Small ..   18.50
ST. LOUIS ROI; N. Currier; 1849 .... Small ..   10.00
ST. A. MADALENA .... Small ..   10.00
ST. MARGARET .... Small ..   10.00
ST. MARY; N. Currier; 1857.................................... Small ..   10.00
ST. MARY'S ABBEY — HIGHLAND FALLS; (Oval) .... Small ..   20.00
ST. MICHAEL... Small ..   10.00
ST. MICHAEL; N. Currier .... Small ..   10.00
ST. NICHOLAS; N. Currier .... Small ..   10.00

```
ST. PATRICK; N. Currier ....................................... Small.. $  20.00
ST. PAUL.............................................................. Small..     10.00
ST. PETER; N. Currier........................................... Small..     10.00
ST. PETER RECEIVING THE KEYS ..................... Small..     10.00
ST. PHILOMENA; N. Currier 1845............................ Small..     10.00
ST. RAMON NO NACIDO; N. Currier; 1849............... Small..     10.00
ST. RAPHAEL ......................................................... Small..     10.00
ST. RITA DE CASIA; N. Currier; 1849 .................... Small..     10.00
ST. ROSE OF LIMA .............................................Small..     10.00
ST. THERESA ......................................................... Small..     10.00
ST. VINCENT DE PAUL ....................................... Small..     10.00
SALE OF BLOODED STOCK, A; 1880 ..................... Small..     29.50
SALE OF THE PET LAMB; N. Currier ...................... Large.     95.00
SALE OF THE PET LAMB ......................................Small..     50.00
SALMON FISHING; 1872............................................ Small..    375.00
"SALVATOR" AND "TENNY"; 1890 ........................ Small..     65.00
SAM PURDY; (Stallion) ........................................Small..     65.00
SAN ANTONIO; (Saint Anthony)................................. Small..     10.00
SAN LUIS REY; N. Currier; 1849 .............................. Small..     10.00
"SANCHO"; (Hunting dog); N. Currier .....................Small..    195.00
SANCTUARY OF OUR LADY OF GUADALUPE ..............Small..     12.00
SANTA ANNA'S MESSENGERS ETC., N. Currier; 1847 .....Small..     38.50
SANTA CLAUS; 1882 ..........................................Small..     40.00
SANTIAGO, CUBA ................................................ Small..     39.50
SAPPHO ................................................................ Small..     12.00
SARAH; C. Currier ................................................ Small..     20.00
SARAH ANN; N. Currier; 1846.................................... Small..     20.00
SARAH BERNHARDT ............................................ Small..     30.00
SARATOGA LAKE ................................................ Small..     55.00
SARATOGA SPRINGS ............................................ Small..     70.00
SATISFACTION ...................................................... Small..     33.50
SAUCY KATE ........................................................ Small..     20.00
SAVED; (Girl and Dog) ........................................... Small..     25.00
SAVIOUR OF THE WORLD; N. Currier; 1845 ............. Small..     10.00
SAVIOUR'S INVITATION, THE; 1866 ....................... Small..     10.00
SCALES OF JUSTICE, THE; N. Currier...................... Small..     35.00
SCAPULAR, THE; N. Currier ................................... Small..     15.00
SCENE IN FAIRYLAND, A ..................................... Small..     21.50
SCENE IN OLD ENGLAND, A ................................. Small..     35.00
SCENE IN OLD IRELAND, A .................................Small..     35.00
SCENE OFF NEWPORT, A .....................................Small..    175.00
SCENE ON THE LOWER MISSISSIPPI, A ..................... Small..     95.00
SCENE ON THE SUSQUEHANNA, A ............................ Small..     90.00
SCENERY OF IRELAND, THE; "Upper Lake Killarney"; 1869
                                                                             Medium    37.50
SCENERY OF THE CATTSKILLS; "Mountain House".......Small..     65.00
SCENERY OF THE CATTSKILLS; "The Cattskill Falls of
    the Cattskill Mountains"; N. Currier......................... Small..     65.00
SCENERY OF THE HUDSON NEAR "ANTHONY'S NOSE". Large.    235.00
SCENERY ON THE HUDSON; "The Mountain House"...... Small..     70.00
SCENERY OF THE UPPER MISSISSIPPI ....................... Small..     72.50
SCENERY OF THE WISSAHICKON NEAR PHILADELPHIA
                                                                             Small..     67.50
SCHOLAR'S REWARDS; 1874.......................................Small..     27.50
SCHOOL REWARDS; 1874 ....................................Small..     20.00
SCHOOL'S IN .......................................................Small..     25.00
SCHOOLS OUT ...................................................Small..     25.00
```

```
SCHOONER; N. Currier; 1846 .........................................Small..$  140.00
SCHOONER YACHT "CAMBRIA," ...........................Small..     100.00
SCIENTIFIC SHAVING ON THE DARKTOWN PLAN; 1890...Small..      28.50
SCORING — COMING UP FOR THE WORD; 1869 ............. Large.     210.00
SCORING FOR THE FIRST HEAT; 1878........................ Large.     220.00
SCOTCH BEAUTY, THE ......................................... Small..      21.50
SCOTCH CUTTER "MADGE"; 1881.............................. Small..      70.00
SCOTCH LADDIE, THE ................................................Small..      20.00
SEA OF TIBERIAS, THE .........................................Small..      21.50
SEAL OF AFFECTION; N. Currier ....................................Small..      18.50
SEARCH THE SCRIPTURES; N. Currier ........................Small..      10.00
SEASON OF BLOSSOMS, THE.........................................Small..      67.50
SEASON OF BLOSSOMS, THE; 1865...............................Large .     360.00
SEASON OF JOY, THE; 1872 .....................................Small..      45.00
SECESSION MOVEMENT, THE .................................. Small..      40.00
SECOND BATTLE OF BULL RUN  ........................... Small..      50.00
SECOND SMOKE — ALL WRONG; 1870 ........................... Small..      42.50
SEE MY DOGGIE? N. Currier ........................................Small..      20.00
SEE MY NEW BOOTS? N. Currier; 1856     ........................ Small..      20.00
SEE-SAW ..................................................................... Small..      25.00
SELLING OUT CHEAP; (Political Cartoon)  .................. Small..      32.50
SENSATION — Record 2:22¼; 1876  ............................. Small..      65.00
SERENADE; 1866          .................................................: Small..      22.50
SERGEANT JASPER OF CHARLESTON; 1876 .............,...... Small..     165.00
SERVICEABLE GARMENT, A  ................................... S mall..      32.00
SET OF EIGHT, A .................................................... Small..      25.00
SETTER AND WOODCOCK............................................. Small..     135.00
SETTERS; N. Currier; 1846 ........................................... Small..     160.00
SETTLING THE QUESTION; 1884  .......................... Small..      30.00
SEVEN CHURCHES OF CLONMACNOISE, ON THE RIVER
      SHANNON ....................................................... Small..      32.50
SEVEN STAGES OF MATRIMONY; N. Currier .................. Small..      37.50
SHADE AND TOMB OF NAPOLEON, THE  ..................... Small..      37.50
SHADE AND TOMB OF WASHINGTON, THE; 1876 .......... Small..      45.00
SHAKERS NEAR LEBANON; N. Currier  ......................... Small..     250.00
SHALL I? — THROW IF YOU DARE; (On one folio)  .......... Small..      68.50
SHARP BRUSH ON THE LAST QUARTER; 1874 .............. Small..      70.00
SHARP PACE,  A; 1884         ......................................... Small..      65.00
SHARP PACE, A; 1886   ............................................ Small..      65.00
SHARP RIFLE, A; 1882     ........................................ Small..      35.00
SHARPSHOOTER, A; 1882    ....................................... Small..      35.00
SHAUGHRAUN; Act II, Scene I  ................................... Medium      30.00
SHEEP PASTURE, THE .............................................. Small..      35.00
SHEEP PASTURE, THE ............................................. Medium      40.00
SHERIDAN'S CAVALRY AT THE BATTLE OF FISHER'S
      HILL; .................................................................. Small..      49.50
SHERMAN AND HIS GENERALS; 1865 ......................... Medium      50.00
SHING-GAA-BA-W'OSIN — OR THE FIGURED STONE;
      (Indian Chief) ...................................................... Small..      40.00
SHIPS "ANTARCTIC" OF NEW YORK, CAPT. STOUFFER,
      AND "THREE BELLS" OF GLASGOW, CAPT. CREIGH-
      TON RESCUING THE PASSENGERS AND CREW FROM
      THE WRECK OF THE STEAMSHIP "SAN FRANCISCO";
      N. Currier  .........................................................Large . 1850.00
SHOEING THE HORSE; N. Currier .................................. Small..      80.00
SHOEMAKER, THE ...................................................... Small..      40.00
SHOEMAKER'S CIRCUS, THE; 1882 ............................. Small..      32.50
SHOOTING ON THE BAY SHORE; 1883 ....................... Small..     475.00
```

```
SHOOTING ON THE BEACH ........................................Small.. $ 400.00
SHOOTING ON THE PRAIRIE  ....................................Small..   295.00
SHORT STOP AT A WAY STATION, A; 1875 ...................Small..    75.00
SHRINE OF OUR LADY OF LOURDES  ..........................Small..    12.50
SHUT THE DOOR; 1880  ..........................................Small..    33.50
SICKNESS AND HEALTH; N. Currier   .......................... Medium    32.50
SIDE-WHEELER, THE                            ................ Small..    40.00
SIEGE AND CAPTURE OF VICKSBURG, MISS.  .............. Small..    50.00
SIEGE OF CHARLESTON, THE ...................................Small..    55.00
SIEGE OF CONSTANTINE  .......................................Small..    24.00
SIEGE OF LIMERICK, THE; N. Currier; 1848  ................ Small..    25.00
SIEGE OF VERA CURZ; N. Currier; 1847 ...................... Small..    50.00
SIGHTS AT THE FAIR GROUNDS; 1888 .........................Small..    80.00
SIGN OF THE CROSS, THE ......................................Small..    10.00
SIGNAL FIRES ON THE SHEVANAMON MOUNTAINS, IRE-
    LAND; N. Currier; 1848  ...................................... Small..    40.00
SILVER CASCADE, NEAR ST. ANTHONY, MINN.  ......... Small..    70.00
SILVER CASCADE, WHITE MOUNTAINS   ..................... Small..    70.00
SILVER CREEK — CALIFORNIA  ............................. Small..   150.00
SIMPLY TO THE CROSS I CLING; 1872 ....................... Small..    10.00
SINGLE; N. Currier; 1845   ..................................... Small..    24.00
SINKING OF THE BRITISH BATTLESHIP "VICTORIA 1893 Small..    60.00
SINKING OF THE "CUMBERLAND"BY THE IRON CLAD
    "MERRIMAC," 1862  ......................................... Small..    75.00
SINKING OF THE STEAMSHIP "ELBE".......................... Small..    60.00
SINKING OF THE STEAMSHIP "OREGON", OF THE CUNARD
    LINE; 1888 ................................................... Small..    60.00
SINKING OF THE STEAMSHIP "VILLE DU HAVRE,"; 1873
                                                                   Small..    60.00
SISTER JENNIE  ................................................ Small..    20.00
SISTERS, THE; N. Currier; 1845 ................................. Small..    20.00
SISTERS PRAYER, THE ............................................. Small..    20.00
SIX MORAL SENTENCES; 1875 .................................. Small..    25.00
SKATING CARNIVAL, THE ......................................... Small..    95.00
SKATING SCENE — MOONLIGHT; 1868  ...................... Small..    95.00
SKIN GAME, A; 1884 ............................................... Small..    24.50
SKINNER SKINNED, A; 1884 ...................................... Small..    24.50
SLEEPING BEAUTY, THE ......................................... Small..    24.00
SLEEPY HOLLOW BRIDGE, TARRYTOWN, N.Y.  ......... Small..    70.00
SLEEPY HOLLOW CHURCH NEAR TARRYTOWN, N.Y. ... Medium   185.00
SLEIGH RACE, THE; N. Currier; 1848 .......................... Small..   200.00
SLEIGH RACE, THE; 1859   ..................................... Large .   400.00
SLOOP YACHT "MAYFLOWER"; 1886 .......................... Small..    75.00
SLOOP YACHT "POCAHONTAS" OF NEW YORK; 1881 .... Large.    225.00
SLOOP YACHT "VOLUNTEER"; 1887 ........................... Small..    95.00
SLOOP YACHTS "MISCHIEF" AND "ATLANTA"; 1882 ... Large .   215.00
SLUGGED OUT — BETTER LUCK NEXT TIME; 1883   .... Small..    45.00
SLUICE GATE. THE  ........................................... Small..    65.00
"SMALL HOPES" AND "LADY MAC"; 1878   .............. Large .   200.00
SMALL PROFITS AND QUICK SALES; 1870   ................ Small..    32.50
SMELLING COMMITTEE, THE  .................................. Small..    32.50
SMOKER'S PROMENADE; 1876 ................................... Small..    35.00
SMUGGLER; (Horse); 1874   .................................. Small..    65.00
"SMUGGLER" AND "JUDGE FULLERTON"; 1876 ......... Small..    65.00
SNAKE IN THE GRASS  ........................................ Small..    18.00
SNAP APPLE NIGHT — ALL HALLOW EVE .................. Medium   275.00
SNIPE SHOOTING   ............................................. Large .   950.00
```

```
SNIPE SHOOTING ...................................................Small..$ 300.00
SNOW-SHOE DANCE, THE ............................................Medium   135.00
SNOW STORM, THE..................................................Small..  350.00
SNOWED UP – RUFFED GROUSE IN WINTER; 1867.......... Large.  1000.00
SNOWY MORNING, A; 1864   .......................................Medium   300.00
SOCIABLE SMOKE, A; 1880  .......................................Small..   18.50
SOCIAL CUP; 1883 ...............................................Small..   22.50
SOFIA; N. Currier; 1846   ......................................Small..   22.50
SOFT THING ON SNIPE, A; 1880....................................Small..   55.00
SOLDIER BOY, THE; "Off Duty"; 1864  ......................... Small..   30.00
SOLDIER BOY, THE; "On Duty"; 1864 ........................... Small..   30.00
SOLDIER BOYS, THE  ............................................ Small..   30.00
SOLDIER'S ADIEU, THE; C. Currier..............................Small..   32.50
SOLDIER'S BRIDE, THE  ........................................ Small..   30.00
SOLDIER'S DREAM OF HOME, THE   ............................ Small..   30.00
SOLDIER'S DREAM OF HONOR    ............................... Small..   30.00
SOLDIER'S GRAVE, THE; 1862  ..................................Small..   15.00
SOLDIER'S HOME; "The Vision"; 1862 ..........................Small..   22.50
SOLDIER'S MEMORIAL, THE  ..................................... Small..   20.00
SOLDIER'S MEMORIAL, 3RD REGT., CO. B. "DELAWARE
   VOLUNTEERS"  .............................................. Small..   32.50
SOLDIER'S RECORD, THE: 5TH. REGT., CO. E., NEW YORK
   VOLUNTEER ARTILLERY; 1862  .............................Medium   27.50
SOLDIER'S RETURN; C. Currier  ............................... Small..   30.00
SOME PUMPKINS; (Oval) .........................................Small..   42.50
SON AND DAUGHTER OF TEMPERANCE; N. Currier ........Small..   24.50
SON OF TEMPERANCE; N. Currier; 1848 ........................ Small..   24.50
SONS OF TEMPERANCE; N. Currier ............................. Small..   24.50
"SONTAG" AND "FLORA TEMPLE"; N. Currier; 1855   ... Large.  300.00
SOPHIA; N. Currier; 1846 ...................................... Small..   20.00
SOPHIA ......................................................... Medium   20.00
SORREL DAN; 1881  ............................................. Small..   60.00
SORRY DOG, A; 1888  .......................................... Small..   24.00
SORRY HER LOT WHO LOVES TOO WELL; 1879 ............. Small..   22.50
SOURCE OF THE HUDSON, THE.................................... Small..  100.00
SOUTH CAROLINA'S "ULTIMATUM"; (Political Cartoon) .. Small..   35.00
SOUTH SEA WHALE FISHERY; N. Currier  ................... Small..  300.00
SOUTHERN BEAUTY, THE  ....................................... Small..   22.00
SOUTHERN BELLE, THE .......................................... Small..   22.00
SOUTHERN CROSS; 1873  ........................................ Small..   15.00
SOUTHERN RIVER SCENERY; 1870............................... Small..   37.50
SOUTHERN ROSE, THE  ..........................................Small..   25.00
SOUTHERN VOLUNTEERS, THE ...................................Small..   27.50
SPANIEL, THE; N. Currier; 1848  ............................ Small..   75.00
SPANISH DANCE, THE; N. Currier  ............................ Small..   22.50
SPANISH DANCE, THE; (C. & I.) ................................ Small..   22.50
SPEAK MY DARLING...............................................Small..   20.00
SPEAK QUICK...................................................... Small..   20.00
SPEAKING LIKENESS, A  ........................................ Small..   20.00
SPEARING BLACK BASS – MOONLIGHT  ..................... Medium  750.00
SPEEDING ON DARKTOWN TRACK; 1892 ...................... Small..   27.50
SPEEDING ON THE AVENUE; 1870  ............................ Large.  950.00
SPEEDING TO THE "BIKE"; 1893 ............................... Small..   60.00
SPENDTHRIFT; 1880 ............................................. Small..   60.00
SPENDTHRIFT; 1881 ............................................. Small..   60.00
SPERM WHALE "IN A FLURRY"; N. Currier  ............... Small..  300.00
SPICE OF THE TROTTING TURF, THE; 1876   ............. Small..   65.00
SPILLOUT ON THE SNOW; 1870  ............................... Small..  120.00
```

```
SPILLOUT ON THE SNOW, A  .................................... Large .  $ 500.00
SPIRIT OF '61, THE; 1861  ...............................Small..     22.50
SPIRIT OF '76 — STAND BY THE FLAG  ....................Small..     22.50
SPIRIT OF THE UNION; 1860  ................................ Small..     22.50
SPIRITS FLIGHT; 1874  ......................................... Small..     22.50
SPIRITS FLIGHT, THE; 1893 ................................. Small..     22.50
SPLENDID NAVAL TRIUMPH ON THE MISSISSIPPI; 1862... Large.    200.00
SPLENDID NEW IRON STEAMER "ALBANY"  ................ Small..     65.00
SPLENDID TEA; 1881  ............................................. Small..     21.50
SPLIT ROCK, ST. JOHNS, N. B. .. ............................ Small..     67.50
SPLITTING THE PARTY; (Political Cartoon)  ................ Small..     35.00
SPOILING A SENSATION; 1881 .................................. Small..     27.50
SPONGING; 1880  ................................................... Small..     27.50
SPORTS WHO CAME TO GRIEF, THE; 1881 ................... Small..     37.50
SPORTS WHO LOST THEIR TIN; 1878  ....................... Small..     45.00
SPORTSMAN'S SOLACE; 1879  .................................. Small..     40.00
SPRING; N. Currier; 1849  ..................................... Small..     38.50
SPRING; 1870  ..................................................... Medium     95.00
SPRING FLOWERS; 1861  ........................................ Small..     65.00
SQUALL OFF CAPE HORN, A; N. Currier  .................. Small..    120.00
SQUIRREL SHOOTING  ............................................. Small..     95.00
STABLE, THE — NO. 1; N. Currier  ........................... Medium     75.00
STABLE  THE — NO. 2; N. Currier  ........................... Medium     75.00
STABLE SCENES, NO. 1; N. Currier ............................. Small..     60.00
STABLE SCENES, NO. 2; N. Currier  ........................... Small..     60.00
STAG AT BAY, THE  ............................................... Small..     65.00
STAG AT BAY, THE  ............................................... Medium     95.00
STAG HOUNDS; N. Currier; 1846.................................. Small..    125.00
STAG HUNT AT KILLARNEY  ................................... Small..     35.00
STAGES OF MAN'S LIFE  ........................................Small..     35.00
STAGES OF WOMAN'S LIFE..........................................Small..     35.00
STANCH POINTER, A ;1871  ..................................... Small..     95.00
STAR LAMP; 1885  ................................................Small..     25.00
STAR OF BEAUTY  ................................................Small..     21.50
STAR OF LOVE, THE; N. Currier; 1847  .......................Small..     21.50
STAR OF THE EAST, THE; N. Currier 1846 .....................Small..     20.00
STAR OF THE NIGHT, THE; (Head)  ........................... Small..     20.00
STAR OF THE ROAD, THE; N. Currier; 1849 ................... Small..     75.00
STAR OF THE SOUTH, THE; N. Currier; 1847.................. Small..     20.00
STAR OF THE WEST; N. Currier; 1846  ........................Small..     20.00
STAR POINTER — Record 1:59¼  ............................Small..     65.00
STAR SPANGLED BANNER, THE  ............................. Small..     25.00
STARS OF THE TROTTING TRACK  .......................... Large .    225.00
STARS OF THE TURF — NO. 1; 1885  ......................... Small..     65.00
STARS OF THE TURF — NO. 2; 1885  ......................... Small..     65.00
STARTING OUT ON HIS METTLE; 1876........................ Small..     50.00
STARTLING ANNOUNCEMENT, A  ............................. Small..     35.00
STARUCCA VALE  ................................................. Medium     60.00
STATE STREET, BOSTON MASS., N. Currier; 1849  ......... Small..    225.00
STATEN ISLAND AND THE NARROWS FROM FORT HAMIL-
   TON; 1861 .....................................................Large .    250.00
STATUE UNVEILED; (Cartoon).....................................Small..     60.00
STAUNCH POINTER, A; 1870  .....................................Small..     65.00
STEADFAST IN THE FAITH  ....................................Small..     10.00
STEAM CATAMARAN — H. W. LONGFELLOW  ............. Small..     65.00
STEAM YACHT "ANTHRACITE" THE  ....................... Small..     75.00
STEAM YACHT "CORSAIR"; 1881  ........................... Medium     90.00
```

STEAM YACHT "NAMOUNA" 1882 ....Small....$ 95.00
STEAM YACHT "POLYNIA"; 1880 ....Small.... 80.00
STEAMBOAT "EMPIRE": N. Currier; 1843 ....Small.... 115.00
STEAMBOAT "ISAAC NEWTON"; N. Currier; 1848 ....Small.... 85.00
STEAMBOAT "KNICKERBOCKER"; N. Currier................Small.... 120.00
STEAMBOAT "PEERLESS" OF LAKE SUPERIOR LINE....Large ... 135.00
STEAMBOAT "PRISCILLA" ....Small.... 75.00
STEAMBOATS PASSING AT MIDNIGHT ON LONG ISLAND
    SOUND .... Small.... 225.00
STEAMER "DREW"; 1883 .... Small.... 75.00
STEAMER "MASSACHUSETTS"; 1882......................... Small.... 70.00
STEAMER "MESSENGER" NO. 2; N. Currier .... Small.... 75.00
STEAMER "PENOBSCOT"; 1883 .... Large ... 200.00
STEAMER "TEMPEST"; 1882 .... Small.... 70.00
STEAMSHIP "ADRIATIC"; 1860 .... Large ... 180.00
STEAMSHIP "ADRIATIC" – WHITE STAR LINE ....Small.... 70.00
STEAMSHIP "ALASKA" OF THE GUION LINE .... Small.... 70.00
STEAMSHIP ALLER" ....Small.... 70.00
STEAMSHIP "AMERICA" ....Small.... 70.00
STEAMSHIP "ANTHRACITE" .... Small.... 70.00
STEAMSHIP "ASSYRIAN MONARCH" OF THE MONARCH
    LINE ....Small.... 70.00
STEAMSHIP "AUGUSTA VICTORIA"; 1873....................Small.... 70.00
STEAMSHIP "BELGENLAND" OF RED STAR LINE.........Small.... 70.00
STEAMSHIP "BOTHNIA" OF THE CUNARD LINE.......... Small.... 70.00
STEAMSHIP "CALIFORNIA" OF THE ANCHOR LINE...... Small.... 70.00
STEAMSHIP "CEPHALONIA" ....Small.... 70.00
STEAMSHIP "CITY OF BERLIN" OF THE INMAN LINE ...Small.... 70.00
STEAMSHIP "CITY OF MONTREAL" OF THE INMAN LINE
                                                                        Small.... 70.00
STEAMSHIP "CITY OF WASHINGTON" ....Small.... 70.00
STEAMSHIP "DENMARK" ....Small.... 70.00
STEAMSHIP "EGYPT" OF THE NATIONAL LINE ....Small.... 70.00
STEAMSHIP "EGYPTIAN MONARCH" OF WILSON LINE...Small....: 70.00
STEAMSHIP "EIDER" ....Small.... 65.00
STEAMSHIP "ETRURIA" .... Small.... 70.00
STEAMSHIP "FLORIDA" ....Small.... 70.00
STEAMSHIP "FRANKLIN"...Small.... 70.00
STEAMSHIP "FRIESLAND" ....Small.... 65.00
STEAMSHIP "GAANDAM" ....Small.... 65.00
STEAMSHIP "GALILEO" OF WILSON LINE ....Small.... 65.00
STEAMSHIP "GREAT NORTHERN" ....Small.... 70.00
STEAMSHIP "HAMMONIA" ....Small.... 65.00
STEAMSHIP "HERMAN" ....Small.... 70.00
STEAMSHIP "HERMANN" ....Small.... 70.00
STEAMSHIP IN A GALE...Small.... 70.00
STEAMSHIP "LAHN" ....Small.... 65.00
STEAMSHIP "MAJESTIC" OF WHITE STAR LINE .... Small.... 65.00
STEAMSHIP "MINNESOTA" .... Small.... 65.00
STEAMSHIP "MISSISSIPPI"; N. Currier .... Small ... 70.00
STEAMSHIP "NOORDLAND" ....Small.... 70.00
STEAMSHIP "OCEANIC" OF WHITE STAR LINE .... Small.... 65.00
STEAMSHIP "OREGON" OF THE GUION LINE .... Small.... 70.00
STEAMSHIP "PAVONIA" .... Small.... 67.50
STEAMSHIP "PEREIRE" .... Small.... 67.50
STEAMSHIP "PERSIAN MONARCH"............................. Small.... 67.50
STEAMSHIP "PRESIDENT"; N. Currier .... Small.... 80.00
STEAMSHIP "PURITAN" OF FALL RIVER LINE .... Small.... 65.00

```
STEAMSHIP "RHODE ISLAND"; 1882 ...................... Small....    65.00
STEAMSHIP "RHODE ISLAND" .............................. Large ...  165.00
STEAMSHIP "ROTTERDAM" ................................ Small....    65.00
STEAMSHIP "SAALE" ..................................... Small....    65.00
STEAMSHIP "ST. PAUL"................................... Small....    65.00
STEAMSHIP "SCYTHIA" OF CUNARD LINE.................. Small....     65.00
STEAMSHIP "SERVIA"....................................Small....    65.00
STEAMSHIP "SPAIN" OF THE NATIONAL LINE.............Small ...     65.00
STEAMSHIP "SPREE" .................................... Small....    65.00
STEAMSHIP "TEUTONIC" OF THE WHITE STAR LINE ... Small....       67.50
STEAMSHIP "TRAAVE"....................................Small....    70.00
STEAMSHIP "VANDERBILT"; 1857 ........................Large ...  195.00
STEAMSHIP "VILLE DE PARIS" ...........................Small....    70.00
STEAMSHIP "WASHINGTON"; N. Currier; 1847 ............... Small....    75.00
STEAMSHIP "WASHINGTON" FIRST AMERICAN OCEAN
   MAIL STEAMER; N. Currier ............................ Small....    75.0 0
STEAMSHIP "WASHINGTON" RESCUING THE PASSENGERS
   OF THE "WINCHESTER" OF BOSTON ....................Small....   120.00
STEAMSHIP "WESTERNLAND" .............................Small....    70.00
STEAMSHIP "WILLIAM PENN"..............................Small....    70.00
STEAM.     "ZEENDAM" ................................. Small....    70.00
STEEL CRUISER "PHILADELPHIA"; 1893 .................. Small....    75.00
STEEPLE CHASE CRACKS; (Dogs and Monkeys)    .........Small....    37.50
STEEPLE CHASER, A; 1880  ...............................Small....    40.00
STELLA; 1872 ...........................................Small....    22.50
STELLA AND ALICE GREY - LANTERN AND WHALEBONE;
   N. Currier; 1855 .....................................Large ...   200.00
STEPHEN FINDING HIS MOTHER; (Political Cartoon) .....Small....    35.00
STEPPING STONES, THE  ....................................... Medium.   85.00
STOCK FARM, THE  ...................................... Small....    48.50
STOCKS DOWN; N. Currier; 1849 .............................. Small....    95.00
STOCKS UP; N. Currier; 1849  ...........................Small....    95.00
STOLEN INTERVIEW; 1872 ................................Small....    24.50
STOPPING PLACE ON THE ROAD — THE HORSE SHED;
   1868 ..................................................Large ...   200.00
STORMING OF CHAPULTEPEC; N. Currier; 1847 ...........Small....    45.00
STORMING OF FORT DONELSON, THE; 1862 ...............Small....    48.50
STORMING OF THE BISHOP'S PALACE; 1847 ............. Small....    45.00
STORMING OF THE FORTRESS OF CHAPULTEPEC BY
   GENL. PILLOW; N. Currier ............................ Small....    48.50
STORMING THE HEIGHTS OF CERRO GORDO; 1847  ..... Small....    45.00
STORMING THE HEIGHTS OF MONTEREY; 1846 ........... Small....    45.00
STORY OF THE FIGHT, THE  ................................. Medium.   49.50
STORY OF THE GREAT KING  .............................. Small....    18.00
STORY OF THE REVOLUTION; 1876 ......................... Small....    45.00
STRATFORD ON AVON ................................... Small....    35.00
STRAW-YARD, WINTER, THE  ................................. Medium.   80.00
STRAWBERRIES; 1863  .................................... Small....    35.00
STRAWBERRIES; 1870  ....................................Small....    35.00
STRAWBERRY FEAST, A  ..................................Small....    30.00
STRAWBERRY SEASON, THE; 1870 ......................... Small....    30.00
STRICTLY CONFIDENTIAL  ...............................Small....    20.0 0
STRIDE OF A CENTURY; 1876  ...........................Small....    45.00
STRIPED BASS; 1872  ....................................Small....    42.50
STYLE OB DE ROAD, DE; 1884 ...........................Small....    30.00
SUBURBAN GOTHIC VILLA, MURRAY HILL; N. Currier
   1846 ................................................. Small....    35.00
SUBURBAN RETREAT, A  ................................. Small....    38.50
```

```
SUFFER LITTLE CHILDREN TO COME UNTO ME ..........Small... $ 12.00
SUMMER; 1871 ....................................................Medium    50.00
SUMMER; N. Currier ...........................................Small...    45.00
SUMMER AFTERNOON  ......................................Small...    40.00
SUMMER EVENING  ............................................Small...    40.00
SUMMER FLOWERS; 1861 ...................................Small....   45.00
SUMMER FLOWERS; 1861 ...................................Large..   100.00
SUMMER FRUITS; 1861 .....................................Small...    40.00
SUMMER GIFT; 1870  ..........................................Small...    35.00
SUMMER IN THE COUNTRY.................................. Small...    40.00
SUMMER IN THE COUNTRY; 1866................................ Large..  200.00
SUMMER IN THE HIGHLANDS  ...............................Large..  175.00
SUMMER IN THE WOODS  ....................................Medium    48.00
SUMMER LANDSCAPE, A; (Haymaking)  ......................... Medium    75.00
SUMMER MORNING ............................................. Small...    55.00
SUMMER MORNING  ............................................ Medium    75.00
SUMMER NIGHT, THE .........................................  Small...    40.00
SUMMER NOON  ................................................ Small...    40.00
SUMMER RAMBLE, A  ......................................... Small...    45.00
SUMMER RETREAT, A; 1869 .................................. Medium    55.00
SUMMER SCENES IN NEW YORK HARBOR .................... Medium   675.00
SUMMER SHADES; 1859  ......................................Large..  150.00
SUMMER TIME  ................................................Medium    95.00
SUMMER TIME  ................................................. Small...    35.00
SUMMIT OF HAPPINESS, THE  ............................... Small...    35.00
SUNBEAM, THE ............................................... Small...    18.00
SUNDAY IN THE OLDEN TIME  ............................... Small...    37.50
SUNDAY MORNING – IN THE OLDEN TIME; N. Currier .....Medium   125.00
SUNDAY SCHOOL EMBLEMS; 1874 .............................Small...    10.00
SUNLIGHT  ....................................................Small...    20.00
SUNNY HOUR, THE  .......................................... Small...    30.00
SUNNY MORNING ............................................. Small...    34 .50
SUNNY SOUTH, THE; 1870  ................................. Small...    32.50
SUNNY SIDE – THE RESIDENCE OF THE LATE WASHINGTON
   IRVING, NEAR TARRYTOWN, N. Y. .........................Large..   165.00
SUNNYSIDE – ON THE HUDSON  ...............................Small...    60.00
SUNRISE ON LAKE SARANAC; 1860  ......................... Large..   700.00
SUNSET TREE, THE .........................................Medium    75.00
SURE HORSE FOR FIRST MONEY, THE; 1886  ..............Small...    65.00
SURE OF A BITE; 1881 ....................................Small...    30.00
SURE THING, A; 1884 ....................................... Small...    25.00
SURPRISE, THE; 1858 .....................................Large ..1500.00
SURRENDER OF CORNWALLIS; N. Currier  .................. Small...    95.00
SURRENDER OF GENL. BURGOYNE AT SARATOGA, N.Y.;
   N. Currier; 1852 ......................................Large ..1500.00
SURRENDER OF GENL. JOE JOHNSTON NEAR GREENSBORO,
   N.C., 1865 ............................................. Small...    50.00
SURRENDER OF GENL. LEE AT APPOMATTOX C. H., VA.,
   1865  ....................................................Small...    55.00
SURRENDER OF GENL. LEE AT APPOMATTOX C. H., VA.,
   1868  ....................................................Small...    55.00
SURRENDER OF LORD CORNWALLIS; 1876 ...................Small...    95.00
SURRENDER OF NAPOLEON III .................................. Large..    50.00
SURRENDER OF PORT HUDSON, LA., 1863  ................ Small...    45.00
SURROUNDING THE HERO  ....................................... Medium   175.00
SUSAN; N. Currier; 1844  ...................................Small...    20.00
SUSANNA; N. Currier; 1849  ................................Small...    20.00
SUSIE  ........................................................Small...    20.00
```

```
SUSSEX VALE — NEW BRUNSWICK ........................... Small... $ 65.00
SWEET SIXTEEN ......................................Small...   22.50
SWEET SPRING TIME..................................Medium    60.00
SWEETSER; 1877 .....................................Small...   60.00
SWEETSER — SLEEPY GEORGE AND LUCY SWEETSER ....Small...       70.00
SWELL SMOKER — GETTING THE SHORT END; 1888 .......Small...   28.50
SWELL SMOKER — GIVING LONG ODDS; 1888 ..............Small...   28.50
SWELL SPORT ON A BUFFALO HUNT, A; 1882 ..............Small...   45.00
SWELL SPORT STAMPEDED, A; 1882 .....................Small...   45.00
SWIFT PACER "ARROW", — Record 2:13¼; 1888 .........Small...   65.00
SWING OF THE FIRST HEAT, THE; 1877 ...................Small...   65.00
SYBIL'S TEMPLE, THE ............................... Small...   24.00
SYLVAN LAKE; 1868 ................................. Small...   45.00
```

— T —

```
"TACONY," N. Currier; 1853 ...............................Large ..$ 300.00
"TACONY" AND "MAC,"; N. Currier; 1853 ...............Large ..  300.00
TAGLIONI; N. Currier ...................................Small...    20.00
TAKE A PEACH .........................................Small...    22.50
TAKE A PINCH; N. Currier ..............................Small...    35.00
TAKE BACK THE HEART THAT THOU GAVEST; 1875 ....Small...    20.00
TAKE CARE; (Girl's Head) ..............................Small...    20.00
TAKE YOUR CHOICE; (Three Girls) .....................Small...    22.50
TAKING A BREATH ......................................Small...    20.00
TAKING A REST; 1894 ..................................Small...    21.50
TAKING A SMASH; (Comic) ..............................Small...    50.00
TAKING A SMILE; N. Currier; 1854......................Small...    50.00
TAKING COMFORT; 1879 ................................Small...    27.50
TAKING OFF HIS AIRS ..................................Small...    25.00
TAKING THE BACK TRACK — A DANGEROUS NEIGHBORHOOD;
  1866 ................................................Large ..2450.00
"TAKING THE STUMP", OR, STEPHEN IN SEARCH OF HIS
  MOTHER; (Political Cartoon).......................... Small...    35.00
TALKED TO DEATH; 1873 ............................... Small...    25.00
TALLEYRAND (Letter) ................................. Small...    10.00
TALLULAH FALLS, GEORGIA ............................ Small...    75.00
TANTALLON CASTLE, COAST OF SCOTLAND ........... Medium    40.00
TASTE FOR THE FINE ARTS, A ......................... Small...    50.00
TEA PARTY, THE ...................................... Small...    25.00
TEA WITH DOLLY ...................................... Small...    25.00
TEAM FAST ON THE POLE, A; 1883 .................... Small...    60.00
TEAM FAST ON THE SNOW, A; 1853 ................... Small...    65.00
TEAM ON THE SNOW, A; 1883 ......................... Medium   150.00
TEAM THAT TAKES NO DUST, A; 1875 ................. Small...    60.00
TEE-TO-TAL SOCIETY, THE; N. Currier.................. Small...    24.50
TELASCO AND AMARILLI; N. Currier ................... Small...    27.50
TEMPLE OF JUPITER, THE .............................. Small...    15.00
TEMPLE OF SOLOMON, THE; N. Currier; 1846.......... Small...    15.00
TEMPTATION OF CHRIST, THE ......................... Small...    12.00
TEMPTED ............................................. Small...    95.00
TEMPTING FRUIT; 1870 ............................... Small...    50.00
TEMPTING LUNCH; 1870 .............................. Small...    40.00
TEN BROECK; 1877 .................................... Small...    85.00
TEN COMMANDMENTS, THE; N. Currier ............... Small...    18.50
TEN VIRGINS, THE ....................................Small...    21.50
```

```
"TENNY"; 1891 .................................................. Small.....$ 65.00
TERRA COTTA; 1888 ........................................... Small..... 65.00
TERRIBLE COLLISION; 1880 .................................. Small... 65.00
TERRIBLE COLLISION BETWEEN THE STEAMBOATS
   "DEAN RICHMOND" AND "C. VANDERBILT" ......... Small..... 95.00
TERRIBLE COLLISION BETWEEN THE STEAMBOATS
   "STONINGTON" AND "NARRAGANSETT"; 1880 ..... Small..... 95.00
TERRIFIC COMBAT BETWEEN THE "MONITOR" 2 GUNS,
   AND "MERRIMAC" 10 GUNS, 1864 ..................... Small..... 125.00
TERRIFIC ENGAGEMENT BETWEEN "MONITOR" 2 GUNS,
   AND "MERRIMAC" 10 GUNS; 1862 ....................... Large .... 375.00
THAT BLESSED BABY ...................................... Small..... 15.00
THAT'S SO ..................................................... Small..... 85.00
THATCHED COTTAGE, THE ............................. Small..... 35.00
THATCHED ROOF, THE .................................. Small..... 35.00
THAT'S WHAT'S THE MATTER; 1882...................... Small..... 32.50
THEODORE FRELINGHUYSEN; N. Currier ............... Small..... 30.00
THEY'RE SAVED! THEY'RE SAVED! ..................... Small..... 20.00
THIRD HEAT IN TWO SIXTEEN, A; 1874 ............... Large .... 220.00
THIS CERTIFIES . . . HAS BEEN A MEMBER; 1889........Small..... 9.50
THIS CERTIFIES . . . IS A MEMBER; 1889 ................ Small..... 9.50
THIS CERTIFIES THAT . . . IS A MEMBER OF THE SUNDAY
   SCHOOL OF . . . . ........................................Small..... 9.50
THIS MAN FORGOT TO SHUT THE DOOR; 1880 ...........Small..... 28.50
THIS MAN WAS TALKED TO DEATH ..................... Small.... 25.00
THISTLE (YACHT); 1887 ...................................Large .... 200.00
THOMAS CORWIN; N. Currier; 1847 ...................Small..... 27.50
THOMAS F. MEAGHER; N. Currier; 1852 ...............Small..... 22.50
THOMAS JEFFERSON - 3RD PRESIDENT; N. Currier.....Small..... 40.00
THOMAS JEFFERSON - THE BLACK WHIRLWIND OF THE
   EAST; 1875 ..............................................Large .... 175.00
THOMAS W. DORR - GOVERNOR OF RHODE ISLAND.....Small..... 25.00
THOMAS WILDEY; N. Currier ............................ Small..... 20.00
THOU GAV'ST ME A BRIGHT SWORD, LADY............... Small..... 18.50
THOU HAST LEARNED TO LOVE ANOTHER; 1875 ....... Small..... 18.50
THOU SHALT NOT STEAL ................................Small..... 15.00
THREE FAVORITES, THE; N. Currier ...................Small..... 45.00
THREE GRACES, THE; N. Currier ....................... Small..... 20.00
THREE GREEDY KITTIES - AT THE FEAST ............. Small..... 29.50
THREE GREEDY KITTIES - AFTER THE FEAST ........ Small..... 29.50
THREE HOLY WOMEN, THE .............................Small..... 12.50
THREE JOLLY KITTENS - AFTER THE FEAST; 1871 ...Small..... 29.50
THREE JOLLY KITTENS - AT THE FEAST; 1871 .........Small..... 29.50
THREE LITTLE WHITE KITTENS - FIRST MOUSE ........Small..... 29.50
THREE LITTLE WHITE KITTENS - FISHING; 1871 ........Small..... 29.50
THREE SISTERS, THE ....................................Small..... 20.00
THREE SORRY KITTIES - AFTER THE FEAST ..........Small..... 29.50
THREE WHITE KITTENS, THE; PEACE ................... Small..... 29.50
THREE WHITE KITTENS, THE; THE WAR ............... Small..... 29.50
THROUGH EXPRESS, THE ............................... Small..... 500.00
THROUGH THE BAYOU BY TORCHLIGHT................... Small..... 100.00
THROUGH TO THE PACIFIC; 1870 ...................... Small..... 175.00
THROW IF YOU DARE ..................................... Small..... 70.00
THY KINGDOM COME; 1872 .............................Small..... 12.00
THY WILL BE DONE; 1872 ...............................Small..... 12.00
THY WORD IS A LIGHT; 1872 ...........................Small..... 12.00
TICK, TICK, TICKLE; 1873 ...............................Small..... 27.50
TICKLE! TICKLE! ......................................... Small..... 27.50
```

```
TIME IS MONEY; 1873 ...............................................Small.....$ 30.00
TIME IS PRECIOUS; 1872 ........................................Small.....  20.00
TIME WORN ABBEY, THE .......................................Small.....  20.00
TIP-TOP; 1879 ........................................................Small.....  20.00
TIRED SOLDIER, THE ............................................Small.....; 21.50
TO AVOID A SMASH, WE SELL FOR CASH; 1875 .........Small.....  30.00
TO THE MEMORY OF; N. Currier; 1845 ......................Small.....  10.00
TO THE MEMORY OF; (St. Paul's Churchyard); N. Currier;
   1846 ...................................................................Small.....  14.50
TO THE MEMORY OF WM. H. HARRISON ..................Small.....  60.00
TO THE RESCUE ...................................................Small.....  20.00
TO THY CROSS I CLING ........................................Small.....  10.00
TOBOGGANING IN THE ALPS ...............................Medium.. 225.00
TOBOGANNING ON DARKTOWN HILL − GETTING A HIST;
   1890 ...................................................................Small.....  32.50
TOBOGANNING ON DARKTOWN HILL − AN UNTIMELY
   MOVE; 1890 .........................................................Small.....  32.50
TOCSIN OF LIBERTY, THE; 1876 ............................Small.....  75.00
TOILETTE, THE; (Oval) .........................................Small.....  20.00
TOLL-GATE, JAMAICA PLANK ROAD; N. Currier .......... Small..... 160.00
TOLL-GATE, JAMAICA, L. I., N. Currier ....................Small..... 150.00
TOM BOWLING; 1873 ............................................. Small.....  60.00
TOM OCHILTREE; 1877 ........................................... Small.....  67.50
TOM PADDOCK ..................................................... Small.....  95.00
TOM SAYERS; (Boxing Champion); 1860 ....................... Small.....  95.00
TOMB AND SHADE OF NAPOLEON, THE...................Small.....  30.00
TOMB AND SHADE OF WASHINGTON, THE; 1842 .........Small.....  37.50
TOMB OF GENL. W. H. HARRISON, THE; N. Currier; 1842 Small.....  57.50
TOMB OF KOSCIUSKO, THE − WEST POINT .............. Small.....  45.00
TOMB OF LINCOLN, SPRINGFIELD, ILLINOIS ............. Small.....  70.00
TOMB OF NAPOLEON, ST. HELENA; N. Currier .......... Small.....  40.00
TOMB OF WASHINGTON, MOUNT VERNON, VA., N. Currier
                                                    Small.....  35.00
TOMB OF WASHINGTON, MOUNT VERNON, VA. ...........Medium.. 100.00
TOMMY ................................................................ Small.....  24.50
TONSORIAL ART IN THE DARKTOWN STYLE; 1890 .......Small.....  32.50
TOO SWEET FOR ANYTHING ...................................Small.....  21.50
TOP OF THE HEAP; 1880 ........................................Small.....  25.00
TORONTO CHIEF, GENL. BUTLER AND DEXTER; 1866..Large .... 225.00
TOY BRIDGE, THE .............................................Small.....  20.00
TRANSFIGURATION; N. Currier .............................Small.....  15.00
TRAPPER'S CAMP-FIRE, THE; 1866 .......................Large .... 475.00
TRAPPER'S LAST SHOT, THE ...............................Medium.. 175.00
TRAPPERS ON THE PRAIRIE − PEACE OR WAR? 1866..Large ....2800.00
TRAVELING ON HIS BEAUTY .................................. Small.....  28.50
TREE OF EVIL, THE; N. Currier ...........................Small.....  40.00
TREE OF GOOD, THE; N. Currier ..............................Small.....  40.00
TREE OF INTEMPERANCE; N. Currier; 1849 .................Small.....  50.00
TREE OF LIFE, THE; C. Currier ............................ Small.....  50.00
TREE OF LIFE, THE CHRISTIAN; N. Currier ........... Small.....  50.00
TREE OF TEMPERANCE; N. Currier; 1849 .................Small.....  50.00
TRENTON FALLS, NEW YORK ............................... Small.....  65.00
TRENTON HIGH FALLS, NEW JERSEY ...................... Small.....  65.00
TRIAL OF EFFIE DEANS, THE .............................Large ....  90.00
TRIAL OF PATIENCE, THE ...................................Small.....  48.50
TRIAL OF THE IRISH PATRIOTS AT CLONMEL; 1848 ...Small.....  28.50
TRIBUTE MONEY; N. Currier ................................. Small.....  20.00
TRIBUTE OF AUTUMN, THE; 1870 ......................... Small.....  42.50
```

```
TRINKET; 1881 ..............................................................Small.... $ 65.00
"TRINKET", — Record 2:14; 1879 ...............................Small....   65.00
"TRINKET", — Record 2:14; 1884 ...............................Large ...  220.00
TRIUMPH OF FAITH; 1874 .....................................Small....   10.00
TRIUMPH OF THE CROSS; 1874 ............................Small....   10.00
TROJAN QUICK STEP; N. Currier .........................Small....   18.50
TROLLING FOR BLUE FISH; 1866 .........................Large ... 1000.00
TROPICAL AND SUMMER FRUITS; 1867 ................Small....   50.00
TROPICAL SUMMER FRUITS; 1867 .........................Medium.  135,00
TROT FOR THE GATE MONEY, A; 1869 .................Large ...  220.00
TROT WITH MODERN IMPROVEMENTS, A; 1881 ...........Small....   60.00
"TROTTERS" ............................................................Large ...  400.00
TROTTER'S BURIAL, THE; 1878 ..............................Small....   35.00
TROTTERS ON THE GRAND CIRCUIT — WARMING UP;
    1877 ................................................................ Large ...  200.00
"TROTTING CRACKS" AT HOME; 1868 .............. Large ...  500.00
"TROTTING CRACKS" AT THE FORGE; 1868 ........... Large ...  850.00
"TROTTING CRACKS" ON THE SNOW; 1858 ............. Large ...  400.00
TROTTING FOR A GREAT STAKE; 1890 .................Large ...  200.00
TROTTING GELDING "BILLY D." WITH "RUNNING MATE"
                                                                     Large ...  200.00
TROTTING GELDING "FRANK"; 1853 ......................Large ...  200.00)
TROTTING GELDING "HARRY WILKES," — Record 2:13½
    1885 ...............................................................Small....   65.00
TROTTING GELDING "PRINCE WILKES" — Record 2:14¾;
    1882 ................................................................ Small....   65.00
TROTTING GELDING "ST. JULIEN" — Record 2:11¼ ...... Small....   65.00
TROTTING GELDING "STEVE MAXWELL" .................. Small....   65.00
TROTTING HORSE "DARBY" — Record 2:16½; 1879 ...... Small....   60.00
TROTTING HORSE "JUDGE FULLERTON"; 1874 .......... Medium.  125.00
TROTTING MARE "AMERICAN GIRL" ........................ Large ...  200.00
TROTTING MARE "AMERICAN GIRL"; 1871.................. Small....   60.00
TROTTING MARE "BELLE HAMLIN" — Record 2:12¾; 1889
                                                                     Small....   60.00
TROTTING MARE "MARTHA WILKES" — Record 2:08 ..... Small....   60.00
TROTTING MARE "NANCY HANKS" — Record 2:04; 1892. Small....   60.00
TROTTING MARE "SUNOL"; 1889 ............................ Small....   60.00
TROTTING ON THE ROAD ...................................... Small....   60.00
TROTTING QUEEN "MAUD S." — Record 2:08¾ ............. Small....   65.00
TROTTING QUEEN "NANCY HANKS" — Record 2:04 ...... Large ...  200.00
TROTTING STALLION "ALCRYON"; 1889 ................. Small....   60.00
TROTTING STALLION "COMMODORE VANDERBILT"
    1866 ............................................................... Large ...  200.00
TROTTING STALLION "DAN RICE"; 1866 ................Large ...  220.00
TROTTING STALLION "DIRECTUM" — Record 2:05¼ ..... Large ...  225.00
TROTTING STALLION "GEORGE M. PATCHEN, JR. OF
    CALIFORNIA .......................................................Large ...  225.00
TROTTING STALLION "GRAY EAGLE," OF KENTUCKY. Small....   70.00
TROTTING STALLION "HAMBLETONIAN MAMBRINO"....Small....   70.00
TROTTING STALLION "HANNIS"; 1877 ...................Small....   60.00
TROTTING STALLION "MAMBRINO CHAMPION"; 1867 ..Large ...  200.00
TROTTING STALLION "MONROE CHIEF" — Record 2:18¼;
    1881 ............................................................... Small....   60.00
TROTTING STALLION "NELSON" — Record 2:14¼ ........Small....   60.00
TROTTING STALLION PALO ALTO; 1890 ................. Small....   60.00
TROTTING STALLION "PATRON" — Record 2:14¼ ....... Small....   60.00
TROTTING STALLION "PHALLAS"; 1883 ................. Large ..  200.00
TROTTING STALLION "SANTA CLAUS" — Record 2:17½. Small....   65.00
```

TROTTING STALLION "STAMBOUL" — Record 2:12¼ ..... Small.... $ 65.00
TROTTING STALLION "STEAMBOAT"; 1890 .... Small.... 65.00
TROTTING STALLION "TOM MOORE"; 1870 ....Large... 200.00
TROUT BROOK, THE; 1862 .... Medium. 160.00
TROUT FISHING .... Large ... 875.00
TROUT POOL, THE .... Small.... 300.00
TROUT STEAM, THE; 1852 .... Large... 900.00
TROUT VERSUS GOUT .... Small.... 70.00
TRUE DAUGHTER OF THE NORTH; 1870 .... Small.... 20.00
TRUE DAUGHTER OF THE SOUTH, THE; 1870 .... Small.... 20.00
TRUE FRIEND, THE .... Small.... 20.00
TRUE ISSUE OR "THAT'S WHAT'S THE MATTER" (Political
    Cartoon) ....Small.... 35.00
TRUE PEACE COMMISSIONER, THE .... Small.... 32.50
TRUE PORTRAIT OF OUR BLESSED SAVIOUR .... Small.... 10.00
TRUE PORTRAIT OF OUR VIRGIN MARY ....Small.... 10.00
TRUE YANKEE SAILOR, THE; N. Currier ....Small.... 37.50
TRUST IN THE LORD; 1872 ....Small.... 10.00
TRUST ME TILL I SELL MY DOG; 1873 ....Medium. 100.00
TRY OUR CLAMS; 1875 .... Small.... 35.00
TRYING IT ON; 1874 .... Small.... 35.00
TSHU-GUE-GA; (Indian Chief); C. Currier .... Small.... 37.50
TUG OF WAR, DE; 1883 ....Small.... 25.00
TUMBLED TO IT; 1881 ....Small.... 32.50
TURN OF THE TUNE, THE ....Small.... 50.00
'TWAS A CALM STILL NIGHT; 1875 ....Small.... 20.00
'TWERE VAIN I TELL THEE ALL I FEEL ....Small.... 16.50
TWILIGHT HOUR, THE .... Medium 42.50
TWIN BROTHERS, THE .... Small.... 18.50
TWIN MONKEYS, THE ....Small.... 30.00
TWIN-SCREW S. S. "KENSINGTON" OF THE RED STAR LINE;
                                                             Small.... 65.00
TWIN-SCREW STEAMER "DEUTSCHLAND" OF THE HAMBURG
    AMERICAN LINE .... Small.... 65.00
TWIN-SCREW STEAMER "LUCANIA" OF THE CUNARD LINE;
                                                             Small.... 65.00
TWO BEAUTIES, THE ....Small.... 18.00
TWO LITTLE FRAID CATS ....Small.... 18.00
TWO MINUTE CLIP, A; 1893 .... Small.... 65.00
TWO PETS, THE; N. Currier; 1848............................. Small.... 22.50
TWO PETS, THE; (C. & I.).......................................Small.... 21.50
TWO SISTERS, THE; N. Currier; 1845.......................... Small.... 18.50
TWO SOULS WITH BUT A SINGLE THOUGHT; 1889 .... Small.... 30.00
TWO TO GO; 1882 .... Small.... 25.00
TWO TWENTY ON THE ROAD; 1875 .... Small.... 65.00
TWO WATCHERS, THE ....Small.... 18.50

— U —

UNBOLTED ....Small.... $ 55.00
UNCLE SAM MAKING NEW ARRANGEMENTS; (Political Car-
    toon) ....Small.... 60.00
UNCLE TOM AND LITTLE EVA; N. Currier ....Small.... 42.50
UNCONSCIOUS SLEEPER, THE ....Small.... 15.00
UNDER CLIFF — ON THE HUDSON .... Small.... 55.00
UNDER THE ROSE; 1872 ....Small.... 18.75

```
UNION IRON CLAD MONITOR "MONTAUK" DESTROYING THE
  REBEL STEAMSHIP "NASHVILLE" ........................Small....$  70.00
UNION LEAGUE OF AMERICA CERTIFICATE; 1863 ......Small....   22.50
UNION PLACE HOTEL, UNION SQUARE, N.Y., N. Currier.Small....  425.00
UNION SOLDIER'S DISCHARGE CERTIFICATE; 1865 .....Small....   22.50
UNION VOLUNTEER, THE ...................................Small....   22.50
UNION VOLUNTEER, THE — HOME FROM THE WAR; 1863
                                                     Large...   45.00
UNION VOLUNTEER, THE — OFF FOR THE WAR; 1863...Large...   45.00
U. S. ARMY LEAVING THE GULF SQUADRON; 1847 ......Small....   85.00
U. S. BRIG OF WAR "SOMERS"; N. Currier .................Small..... 200.00
U. S. BRIG "PORPOISE" IN A SQUALL; N. Currier .......Small....  125.00
UNITED STATES CAPITOL, WASHINGTON, D.C. ........Small....   65.00
UNITED STATES CAPITOL ON CAPITOL HILL, WASHING-
  TON, D.C.. EAST FRONT ...............................Small....   60.00
U. S. CRUISER "NEW YORK"" ...................Large...   85.00
U. S. DRAGOONS, N. Currier 1846 ...........................Small....   50.00
U. S. FRIGATE "CONSTITUTION"; N. Currier ...............Small....  210.00
U. S. FRIGATE "CUMBERLAND"; N. Currier; 1848 .......Small....  200.00
U. S. FRIGATE "INDEPENDENCE"; N. Currier; 1841 ......Small....  200.00
U. S. FRIGATE "ST. LAWRENCE"; N. Currier ...............Small....  190.00
U. S. FRIGATE "SAVANNAH"; N. Currier; 1843.............Small....  195.00
U. S. FRIGATE "UNITED STATES" CAPTURING H. M.
  FRIGATE "MACEDONIAN"; N. Currier .................Small....  175.00
U. S. MAIL STEAMSHIP "ADRIATIC"; N. Currier ........... Small....  120.00
U. S. MAIL STEAMSHIP "ARCTIC"; N. Currier; 1850....... Medium.  200.00
U. S. M. STEAMSHIP "ARCTIC" OF COLLINS LINE; ..... Medium.  210.00
U. S. M. STEAMSHIP "ATLANTIC" OF COLLINS LINE;
  N. Currier; 1852 .....................................Medium.  200.00
U. S. MAIL STEAMSHIP "BALTIC" ........................Large ...  225.00
U. S. MAIL STEAMSHIP "CALIFORNIA" ..................Small....   95.00
U. S. MAIL STEAMSHI P "PACIFIC"; N. Currier ...........Medium.  200.00
U. S. MILITARY ACADEMY, WEST POINT; 1862 .............Medium.  250.00
U. S. POST OFFICE, NEW YORK ...........................Small....  125.00
U. S. SHIP "NORTH CAROLINA"; N. Currier; 1843 ........Small....  200.00
U. S. SHIP "NORTH CAROLINA"; N. Currier; 1844 ........Small....  200.00
U. S. SHIP OF THE LINE "DELAWARE"; N. Currier .....Small....  200.00
U. S. SHIP OF THE LINE IN A GALE; N. Currier ..........Small....  125.00
U. S. SHIP OF THE LINE "OHIO"; N. Currier ..............Small....  200.00
U. S. SHI P OF THE LINE "PENNSYLVANIA"; N. Currier.Small....  150.00
U. S. SLOOP OF WAR "ALBANY"; N. Currier ..............Small....  145.00
U. S. SLOOP OF WAR IN A GALE; N. Currier .............Small....  145.00
U. S. SLOOP OF WAR "KEARSARGE"; 1864 ................Small....  125.00
U. S. SLOOP OF WAR "VINCENNES"; N. Currier; 1845.....Small....  195.00
U. S. STEAM FRIGATE "MISSISSIPPI"; N. Currier; 1848...Small....  150.00
U. S. STEAM FRIGATE "MISSISSIPPI" IN A TYPHOON; ..Large ...  450.00
U. S. STEAM FRIGATE "MISSOURI"; N. Currier .........Small....  150.00
U. S. STEAM FRIGATE "NIAGARA"; 1857 .................Large ...  225.00
U. S. STEAM FRIGATE "NIAGARA" .........................Small....  150.00
U. S. STEAM FRIGATE "PRINCETON"; N. Currier; 1844..Small....  150.00
U. S. STEAM FRIGATE "WABASH" .........................Small....  125.00
"UNSER KARL" .........................................Small....   21.50
UP IN A BALLOON; 1876 ............................. ......Small....   45.00
UP THE HUDSON .......................................... Small....  125.00
UPPPER AND LOWER BAY OF NEW YORK FROM THE
  BATTERY LOOKING SOUTHWEST ......................... Small....  200.00
UPPER LAKE OF KILLARNEY, KERRY COUNTY, IRELAND
                                                     Small....   30.00
```

VALE OF AVOCA, IRELAND ....Small.... $ 30.00
VALKYRIE ....Small.... 55.00
VALLEY FALLS — VIRGINIA ....Small.... 70.00
VALLEY OF THE BLACK WATER, IRELAND ....Small.... 30.00
VALLEY OF THE SHENANDOAH, THE; 1864 .... Large ... 225.00
VALLEY OF THE SUSQUEHANNA ....:Large ... 225.00
VAN AMBURG & CO.'S TRIUMPHAL CAR PASSING THE
    ASTOR HOUSE; N. Currier; 1846 ....Small.... 200.00
VASE OF FLOWERS, THE; N. Currier; 1847 ....Small.... 65.00
VASE OF FRUIT; 1864 ....Small.... 50.00
VELOCIPEDE, THE; 1869 ....Small.... 85.00
VENICE FROM THE CANAL OF THE GUIDECCA — MOON-
    LIGHT; ....Medium. 50.00
VENICE FROM THE CANAL OF THE GUIDECCA — DAY-
    LIGHT .... Medium. 50.00
VERA CRUZ, FROM THE ROAD TO MEXICO; N. Currier;
    1847 ....Small.... 37.50
VERY REVEREND FATHER THEOBOLD MATHEW ....Small.... 22.50
VERY WARM CORNER, A; 1883 ....Small.... 30.00
VICTORIOUS ATTACK ON FORT FISHER, N. C., 1865 ....Large ... 165.00
VICTORIOUS BOMBARDMENT OF PORT ROYAL, S.C. ....Small.... 60.00
VICTORY DOUBTFUL ....Small.... 30.00
VICTORY OF ROANOKE, THE ....Small.... 55.00
VIEW DOWN THE RAVINE AT TRENTON FALLS, N. Y. ...Medium. 125.00
VIEW FROM FORT PUTNAM, N. Y. ....Small.... 65.00
VIEW FROM PEEKSKILL, HUDSON RIVER, N. Y.; 1862... Medium. 225.00
VIEW FROM WEST POINT; C. Currier ....Small.... 125.00
VIEW IN DUTCHESS COUNTY, N.Y. ....Large ... 450.00
VIEW NEAR SALISBURY, ENGLAND ....Small.... 24.50
VIEW OF BALTIMORE; N. Currier; 1848 ....Small.... 200.00
VIEW OF BOSTON; N. Currier; 1848 ....Small.... 225.00
VIEW OF BUNKER HILL AND MONUMENT; N. Currier..... Small ... 90.00
VIEW OF CHAPULTEPEC AFTER THE BATTLE; N.Currier; 1847
                                                                    Small.... 45.00
VIEW OF CHAPULTEPEC AND MOLINO DEL REY ....Small.... 45.00
VIEW OF ESOPUS CREEK ....Medium. 70.00
VIEW OF HARPERS FERRY, VA. ....Large ... 275.00
VIEW OF KING STREET, CITY OF TORONTO, N.C. .....Medium. 175.00
VIEW OF NEW YORK 1859 ....Small.... 165.00
VIEW OF NEW YORK FROM BROOKLYN HEIGHTS; N. Currier;
    1849 ....Medium. 350.0 0
VIEW OF NEW YORK FROM WEEHAWKEN; N. Currier; 1848
                                                                    Small.... 285.00
VIEW OF NEW YORK, JERSEY CITY, HOBOKEN AND BROOKLYN;
                                                                    Large ... 375.00
VIEW OF NEW YORK BAY FROM STATEN ISLAND ....Small.... 150.00
VIEW OF PHILADELPHIA; 1875....................................Small.... 125.00
VIEW OF SAN FRANCISCO. CALIFORNIA; N. Currier ......Large ... 1850.00
VIEW OF THE DISTRIBUTING RESERVOIR ON MURRAYS
    HILL — CITY OF NEW YORK; N. Currier; 1842 ....Small.... 250.00
VIEW OF THE FEDERAL HALL OF THE CITY OF NEW
    YORK; C. Currier ....Medium. 225.00
VIEW OF THE GREAT CONFLAGRATION OF DEC. 16TH
    AND 17TH; 1835 ....Small.... 250.00
VIEW OF THE GREAT CONFLAGRATION AT NEW YORK,
    JULY 19TH, 1845; N. Currier; 1845 ....Small.... 235.00
VIEW OF THE GREAT RECEIVING RESERVOIR, YORK-
    VILLE, CITY OF NEW YORK; N. Currier; 1841 ....Small.... 200.00

VIEW OF THE HOUSES OF PARLIAMENT AND GOVERNMENT
   OFFICES, CITY OF TORONTO, N. C. .... Medium....$ 150.00
VIEW OF THE HUDSON .... Large...... 350.00
VIEW OF THE HUDSON RIVER FROM RUGGLES HOUSE;
   N. Currier .... Small...... 200.00
VIEW OF THE PARK FOUNTAIN AND CITY HALL, N.Y.;
   N. Currier; 1846 .... Small...... 165.00
VIEW OF THE TERRIFIC EXPLOSION; N. Currier; 1845.Small...... 350.00
VIEW OF WATERBURY, CONN; N. Currier ....Large...... 375.00
VIEW OF WEST END, ST. CROIX, (West Indies) ....Small...... 100.00
VIEW OF WEST ROCK, NEAR NEW HAVEN, CONN. ......Large...... 350.00
VIEW ON ESOPUS CREEK ....Medium.... 100.00
VIEW ON FULTON AVENUE, BROOKLYN; N. Currier....Small...... 125.00
VIEW ON LAKE GEORGE, N. Y.; 1866 .... Large 225.00
VIEW ON LAKE GEORGE, N.Y. ....Medium.... 145.00
VIEW ON LONG ISLAND, N. Y.; 1857 .... Large...... 500.00
VIEW ON MONTGOMERY CREEK NEAR THE HUDSON.. Small...... 85.00
VIEW ON THE DELAWARE, NEAR EASTON, PENNA. .. Small...... 100.00
VIEW ON THE HARLEM RIVER, N. Y. – THE HIGHBRIDGE
   IN THE DISTANCE ....Large...... 475.00
VIEW ON THE HOUSATONIC; 1867 ....Medium.... 300.00
VIEW ON THE HUDSON ....Mednüm.... 335.00
VIEW ON THE HUDSON – CROW'S NEST ....Small...... 90.00
VIEW ON THE HUDSON FROM RUGGLES HOUSE, NEW-
   BURGH .... Small...... 95.00
VIEW ON THE POTOMAC NEAR HARPERS FERRY; 1866
   Large...... 210.00
VIEW ON THE RHINE ....Small...... 24.50
VIEW ON THE RONDOUT..........................Medium.... 85.00
VIEW ON THE ST. LAWRENCE – INDIAN ENCAMPMENT
   Small...... 60.00
"VIGILANT" ....Small...... 65.00
VIGILANT AND VALKYRIE IN A "THRASH TO WINDWARD";
   1893 ....Large.... 200.00
VILLA ON THE HUDSON; 1869 .... Medium.... 120.00
VILLA ON THE HUDSON .... Small...... 67.50
VILLAGE BEAUTY, THE .... Small...... 20.00
VILLAGE BLACKSMITH, THE; N. Currier .... Medium.... 125.00
VILLAGE BLACKSMITH, THE; 1864 .... Large...... 275.00
VILLAGE STREET, THE; N. Currier; 1855 .... Small...... 100.00
VIOLET AND DAISY .... Small...... 18.50
VIRGIN AND CHILD .... Small...... 12.00
VIRGIN MARY, THE; N. Currier; 1848 .... Small...... 12.00
VIRGINIA; N. Currier .... Small...... 20.00
VIRGINIA HOME IN THE OLDEN TIME, A; 1872 .... Small...... 90.00
VIRGINIA WATER, WINDSOR PARK .... Small...... 35.00
VIRTUE, LOVE AND TEMPERANCE, LOVE, PURITY AND
   FIDELITY; N. Currier; 1851 ....Small...... 48.50
VISION, THE; N. Currier ....Small...... 15.00
VOLTAIRE – Record 2:20¼; 1879 ....Small...... 60.00
VOLUNTEER, 1880 ....Small...... 65.00
VOLUNTEER CROSSING THE FINISH LINE; 1887 ....Small...... 65.00
VOLUNTEERING MANNER IN WHICH SOME OF THE
   SOUTHERN VOLUNTEERS ENLIST, THE .... Small...... 35.00

WAA-NA-TAA OR THE FOREMOST IN BATTLE; C. Currier
```
                                              Small......$   35.00
WACHT AM DEM RHEIN, DIE  .............................. Small......   20.00
WAIT FOR ME  ................................................. Small......   21.50
WAIT YOUR TURN ............................................ Small......   21.50
WAITING FOR A BITE; N. Currier........................ Small......   70.00
WAITING FOR A DRINK; N. Currier ..................... Small......   55.00
WAKING UP THE OLD MARE; 1881 .......................... Large......  225.00
WAKING UP THE WRONG PASSENGER; 1875 .............. Small......   60.00
WALKED HOME ON HIS EAR; 1878  ..................... Small......   32.50
WAR ........................................................... Small......   20.00
WAR PRESIDENT, A; (Political Cartoon) ................. Small......   32.50
WARMING UP; 1884  ......................................... Small......   50.00
WARREN MILLER  ............................................. Medium....  35.00
WARWICK CASTLE ON THE AVON  .......................... Medium....  40.00
WASHINGTON; (Bust Portrait); N. Currier ................. Large.....  125.00
WASHINGTON: (Full length Portrait); N. Currier  ........ Small......   65.00
WASHINGTON: (Three-quarter length)  ...................... Medium....  65.00
WASHINGTON: (Standing by horse); N. Currier ............. Small......   60.00
WASHINGTON: (Resting on rock); N. Currier  .............Small......   60.00
WASHINGTON — CINCINNATUS OF THE WEST ...........Small......   60.00
WASHINGTON — FIRST IN WAR, FIRST IN PEACE;
    C. Currier  ...............................................Small......   50.00
WASHINGTON FROM THE PRESIDENT'S HOUSE; N. Currier
    1848  .....................................................Small......   50.00
"WASHINGTON" —(Race Horse); N. Currier; 1853 ........Large......  250.00
WASHINGTON AND HIS CABINET; 1876 ..................... Small......   60.00
WASHINGTON AND LINCOLN; 1865  .........................Medium....  75.00
WASHINGTON APPOINTED COMMANDER-IN-CHIEF; 1876
                                              Small......   60.00
WASHINGTON AS A MASON; 1868 ........................... Small......   42.50
WASHINGTON AT HOME; 1867  .............................Large......  145.00
WASHINGTON AT MOUNT VERNON; N. Currier; 1852 ...Small......  125.00
WASHINGTON AT PRAYER; C. Currier  ...............Small......   42.50
WASHINGTON AT PRINCETON; N. Currier; 1846  ........ Small......  360.00
WASHINGTON AT VALLEY FORGE; N. Currier .......... Small......   85.00
WASHINGTON COLUMNS, THE — YOSEMITE VALLEY . Small......   60.00
WASHINGTON CROSSING THE DELAWARE; N. Currier.. Small......  120.00
WASHINGTON FAMILY, THE  ................................ Small......   55.00
WASHINGTON IN THE FIELD; N. Currier  ................. Small......   48.50
WASHINGTON, McCLELLAN AND SCOTT  ............ Small.......  135.00
WASHINGTON'S DREAM  ...................................Medium....  75.00
WASHINGTON, SHERMAN AND GRANT ................... Small......  165.00
WASHINGTON TAKING LEAVE OF THE OFFICERS OF
    HIS ARMY AT FRAUNCE'S TAVERN; N. Y., N. Currier
                                              Small......  100.00
WASHINGTON'S ENTRY INTO NEW YORK; 1857 .......... Medium....  600.00
WASHINGTON'S FAREWELL TO THE OFFICERS OF HIS
    ARMY; 1876  .............................................Small......  110.00
WASHINGTON'S HEADQUARTERS, AT NEWBURGH, ON
    THE HUDSON  .............................................Small......  100.00
WASHINGTON'S RECEPTION ON THE BRIDGE AT TREN-
    TON IN 1789 ..............................................Small......  100.00
WASHINGTON'S RECEPTION BY THE LADIES; N. Currier;
    1845  .....................................................Small......   85.00
WATCH ON THE RHINE, THE  ...........................Small......   29.50
WATCHERS, THE  ............................................Small......   21.50
WATER FOWL SHOOTING; N. Currier ......................Small......  135.00
```

```
WATER JUMP, THE; 1884 ................................................ Small.. $  145.00
WATER JUMP AT JEROME PARK, THE  ..................... Small..     150.00
WATER LILY, THE; N. Currier  ...................................Medium       37.50
WATER NYMPH, THE  ...............................................Small..       18.00
WATER RAIL SHOOTING; N. Currier; 1855  ..................Small..      360.00
WATERFALL — TIVOLI, ITALY  .................................Small..       20.00
WATKIN'S GLEN, NEW YORK  ..................................  Small..       75.00
WAVERLY HOUSE; N. Currier ................................... Medium      575.00
WAY THEY CAME FROM CALIFORNIA, THE; N. Currier;
    1849  ......................................................................Medium      300.00
WAY THEY CROSS THE ISTHMUS, THE; N. Currier; 1849...Medium      300.00
WAY THEY GET MARRIED IN CALIFORNIA, THE; N. Currier
                                                    Small..      225.00
WAY THEY GO TO CALIFORNIA; N. Currier; 1849  ..........Medium      425.00
WAY THEY RAISE A CALIFORNIA OUTFIT; N. Currier; 1849
                                                    Medium      225.00
WAY THEY WAIT FOR THE "STEAMER" AT PANAMA; N.
    Currier; 1849  .....................................................Medium      220.00
WAY TO GROW POOR, THE; 1875  ............................Small..       55.00
WAY TO HAPPINESS, THE; N. Currier  .........................Small..       20.00
WAYSIDE INN, THE; 1864  ........................................ Large .     285.00
WE MET BY CHANCE; 1875  ..................................... Small..       30.00
WE PARTED ON THE HILLSIDE; 1880  ..................... Small..       45.00
WE PRAISE THEE, O LORD  ..................................... Small..       12.50
WE TRUST. OVER THE LEFT; (Comic)  ..................... Small..       27.50
WEARING OF THE GREEN, THE .............................. Small..       25.00
WEDDING, THE; N. Currier  ..................................... Small..       28.50
WEDDING DAY, THE; N. Currier; 1846  ..................... Small..       28.50
WEDDING EVENING, THE  ....................................... Small..       28.50
WEDDING MORNING, THE; N. Currier  ..................... Small..       28.50
WEDGEWOOD, 1881 ...............................................Small..       65.00
WEIR BRIDGE, LAKES OF KILLARNEY  .....................Medium       30.00
WELCOME; 1873  ...................................................Small..       25.00
WELCOME HOME  ..................................................Small..       21.50
WELCOME TO OUR HOME; 1874.............................Small..       20.00
WELL-BRED SETTER, A; 1871  .................................Small..       75.00
WELL BROKEN RETRIEVER, A; 1870  .......................Small..       75.00
WELL BUNCHED AT THE LAST HURDLE; 1887  ..........Large .     225.00
WELL — I'M BLOWED; 1883  ....................................Small..       75.00
WELL TOGETHER; 1886  .........................................Small..       57.50
WELL TOGETHER AT THE FIRST TURN; 1873 .............. Large .     225.00
WEST POINT FOUNDRY — COLD SPRING, HUDSON RIVER,
    N.Y.  ....................................................................Medium      215.00
WESTERN BEAUTY, THE  ........................................ Small..       22.50
WESTERN FARMER'S HOME, THE; 1871  ..................... Small..       75.00¦
WESTERN RIVER SCENERY; 1866  ........................... Medium      140.00
WE'VE HAD A HEALTHY TIME; 1880  ...................... Small..       27.50
WHALE FISHERY — ATTACKING A RIGHT WHALE ......... Small..      400.00
WHALE FISHERY — ATTACKING A SPERM WHALE — AND
    "CUTTING IN"  .................................................. Large . 2,500.00
WHALE FISHERY — IN A FLURRY; N. Currier; 1852 ....... Small..      400.00
WHALE FISHERY — CUTTING IN  .......................... Small..      400.00
WHALE FISHERY — LAYING ON; N. Currier; 1852 .......... Small..      400.00
WHAT SHALL THE HARVEST BE; 1886 ....................... Small..       20.00
WHAT'S SAUCE FOR THE GOOSE IS SAUCE FOR THE
    GANDER; N. Currier; 1851  ............................... Small..       60.00
WHEAT FIELD, THE; N. Currier  .............................. Small..       45.00
WHEELMAN IN RED HOT FINISH; 1894  ..................... Small..      140.00
```

```
WHEN SHALL WE THREE MEET AGAIN?  ..................... Small.. $  27.50
WHEN THE FLOWING TIDE COMES IN; 1879  ................ Small..   37.50
WHERE DO YOU BUY YOUR CIGARS? 1879.................... Small..   25.00
WHICH DONKEY SHALL I TAKE? 1881  .................... Small..   40.00
WHICH OF US WILL YOU MARRY? N. Currier; 1846  ........ Small..   22.50
WHITE DOGGIES INTO MISCHIEF  .........................Small..   30.00
WHITE DOG'S GOT HIM, DE; 1889  ............................Small..   27.50
WHITE FAWN, THE; 1868  ...........................................Small..   40.00
WHITE SQUADRON, U.S. NAVY; 1893  ..........................Small..   75.00
WHO COMES HERE! N. Currier  ...............................Small..   32.50
WHO GOES THERE! N. Currier  ..................................Small..   32.50
WHO SPEAKS FIRST  ...............................................Small..   18.00
WHO'S AFRAID OF YOU? 1868  ..................................Small..   30.00
WHOSE CHICKS ARE YOU?  .....................................Small..   20.00
WHY DON'T HE COME?  ........................................ Small..   20.00
WHY DON'T YER COME ALONG; 1883  .......................... Small..   45.00
WHY DON'T YOU TAKE IT?  ......................................Small..   25.00
WICKLOW — IRELAND  .............................................Medium   40.00
WIDE AWAKE  .......................................................Small..   18.00
WIDE PATH, THE; N. Currier  .....................................Small..   38.50
"WIDOW McCHREE" AND "HAMBLETONIAN"; 1867 ........Small..   75.00
WIDOW'S SON, THE  .............................................. Small..   20.00
WIDOW'S TREASURE, THE; N. Currier  ......................... Small..   22.50
WIDOWER'S TREASURE, THE; N. Currier ...................... Small..   22.50
WI-JUN-JON — THE PIGEON'S EGG HEAD  .................. Small..   65.00
WILD CAT BANKER, A; N. Currier; 1853  ................. Small..   49.50
WILD CAT TRAIN, A — NO STOP OVERS  .................. Small..   70.00
WILD DUCK SHOOTING; C. Currier  ........................ Small..  250.00
WILD DUCK SHOOTING; N. Currier  .........................Small..  250.00
WILD DUCK SHOOTING; N. Currier; 1852 ......................Large. 1,500.00
WILD DUCK SHOOTING — A GOOD DAY'S SPORT; N. Currier;
    1854  ..............................................................Large. 1,500.00
WILD DUCK SHOOTING — ON THE WING; 1870  ..............Small..  150.00
WILD FLOWERS  ................................................... Small..   40.00
WILD HORSES AT PLAY ON THE AMERICAN PRAIRIES  . Medium  150.00
"WILD IRISHMAN" (Race Horse); (RARE); N. Currier  .......Large. 1,200.00
WILD TURKEY SHOOTING; 1871.................................. Small..  135.00
WILD WEST IN DARKTOWN, THE — ATTACK ON THE DEAD-
    HEAD COACH; 1893  ..........................................Small..   35.00
WILD WEST IN DARKTOWN, THE — THE BUFFALO CHASE;
    1893  ..............................................................Small..   35.00
WILHELM I  ....................................................... Small..   21.50
WILL YOU BE TRUE? (Oval) ...................................... Small..   18.50
WILLIAM A. GRAHAM; (V. Pres. Candidate); N. Currier; 1852
                                                              Small..   27.50
WILLIAM AND SUSAN; N. Currier  ............................Small..   22.50
WILLIAM BIGLER, GOVERNOR OF PENNSYLVANIA  ...... Small..   30.00
WILLIAM F. JOHNSTON, GOVERNOR OF PENNA.  ......... Small..   30.00
WILLIAM HENRY HARRISON; N. Currier  .....................Small..   37.50
WILLIAM O. BUTLER; (V. Pres. Candidate); N. Currier; 1848
                                                              Small..   27.50
WILLIAM P. DEWEES, M.D., N. Currier; 1834; (Earliest known
    Currier print)  ..............................................Small..   60.00
WILLIAM PENN'S TREATY WITH THE INDIANS; N. Currier Small..   55.00
WILLIAM PRINCE OF ORANGE LANDING AT TORBAY,
    ENGLAND .......................................................... Small..   25.00
WILLIAM R. KING; (V. Pres. Candidate)  ..................... Small..   27.50
WILLIAM SHAKESPEARE  ........................................Medium   42.00
```

WILLIAM SMITH O'BRIEN, IRELAND'S PATRIOT; N. Currier;
  1848 ....Small...$ 30.00
WILLIAM STEDDING ....Small... 25.00
WILLIAM TELL — DEATH OF GESSLER ....Small... 25.00
WILLIAM TELL — ESCAPING FROM THE TYRANT ....Small... 25.00
WILLIAM TELL -REPLYING TO GESSLER .... Small... 25.00
WILLIAM TELL — REPLYING TO THE GOVERNOR .... Small... 25.00
WILLIAM TELL — SHOOTING THE APPLE ON HIS SON'S
  HEAD; N. Currier ....Small... 40.00
WILLIAM TELL'S CHAPEL ....Small... 20.00
WILLIAM TILLMAN ....Small... 35.00
WILLIAM W. BROWN; (Colored Orator) ....Small... 20.00
WILLIE AND MARY ....Small... 24.50
WILLIE AND ROVER ....Small... 27.50
WILLIE'S LITTLE PETS ....Small... 25.00
WINDMILL, THE ....Small... 21.50
WINDSOR CASTLE AND THE PARK .... Medium 40.00
WINE TASTERS, THE; N. Currier .... Small... 32.50
WINFIELD SCOTT — PEOPLE'S CHOICE FOR 13TH PRESI-
  DENT; N. Currier; 1847 .... Small... 37.50
WINFIELD SCOTT — WHIG CANDIDATE; N. Currier; 1852... Small... 37.50
WINNING "HANDS DOWN," WITH A GOOD SECOND; 1887 .. Large .. 200.00
WINNING IN STYLE; 1893 .... Small... 45.00
WINTER; N. Currier .... Small... 75.00
WINTER; 1870; (Female head) .... Small... 20.00
WINTER EVENING; N. Currier; 1854 .... Medium 300.00
WINTER IN THE COUNTRY — A COLD MORNING; 1864..... Large ..1600.00
WINTER IN THE COUNTRY — GETTING ICE; 1864 .... Large ..2200.00
WINTER IN THE COUNTRY — THE OLD GRIST MILL; 1864 Small... 600.00
WINTER MOONLIGHT; 1866 ....Large.. 650.00
WINTER MORNING; 1861 ....Medium 600.00
WINTER MORNING — FEEDING THE CHICKENS; 1863 ......Large ..1000.00
WINTER MORNING IN THE COUNTRY; 1873 ....Small... 225.00
WINTER PASTIME; N. Currier; 1855 ....Small... 500.00
WINTER SCENE ....Small... 60.00
WINTER SPORTS — PICKEREL FISHING; 1872 ....Small... 275.00
WISE CHILD; 1884 ....Small... 20.00
WITH MALICE TOWARD NONE; 1865..............................Small... 40.00
WIZARD'S GLEN, THE; 1868ı .... Medium 55.00
WOMAN TAKEN IN ADULTERY, THE; N. Currier .... Small... 18.50
WOMAN'S HOLY WAR; (On Liquor); 1874 .... Small... 125.00
WOMEN OF '76; N. Currier; 1848 .... Small... 95.00
WON! N. Currier .... Small... 25.00
WON BY A DASH .... Small... 65.00
WON BY A FOOT; 1883 .... Small... 25.00
WON BY A NECK; 1869 ....Large.. 250.00
WONDERFUL MARE "MAUD S." — Record 2:10¾; 1890 ......Small... 75.00
WONDERFUL MARE "MAUD S." — PROPERTY OF WM. H.
  VANDERBILT, ESQ., 1878 .... Small... 75.00
WONDERFUL STORY, THE .... Small... 25.00
WOOD-DUCKS .... Small... 125.00
WOODCOCK; 1871 .... Small... 125.00
WOODCOCK SHOOTING; N. Currier .... Small... 24 0.00
WOODCOCK SHOOTING; N. Currier 1852 .... Large .. 900.00
WOODCOCK SHOOTING; N. Currier; 1855 .... Small... 225.00
"WOODING UP" ON THE MISSISSIPPI; 1863 .... Large .. 750.00
WOODLAND GATE, THE; N. Currier .... Medium 65.00
WOODLANDS IN SUMMER ....Small... 50.00

```
WOODLANDS IN WINTER     ..........................Small...$135.00
WOODS IN AUTUMN, THE    ..........................Medium   75.00
WORD AND THE SIGN, THE; 1887   ...................Small...  20.00
WORKING MAN'S BANNER; 1872 .......................Small...  30.00
WOUND UP; 1877 ...................................Small...  25.00
WOUNDED BITTERN, THE; N. Currier .................Small...  35.00
WREATH OF FLOWERS, A   ...........................Small...  45.00
WRECK OF THE "ATLANTIC"; 1873   ..................Small...  80.00
WRECK OF THE SHIP "JOHN MINTURN"; N. Currier; 1846 Small...250.00
WRECK OF THE STEAMSHIP "CAMBRIA"; 1883 ...........Small...  75.00
WRECK OF THE STEAMSHIP "SCHILLER"; 1875 .......... Small... 75.00
WRECK OF THE U. S. M. STEAMSHI P "ARCTIC"; N. Currier;
   1854 ..........................................Large..  260.00
WRECKED BY A COW CATCHER; 1885 ...................Small...  40.00
WRONG WAY — RIGHT WAY ............................Small...  35.00


                         — X —


                         — Y —

YACHT "COUNTESS OF DUFFERIN," THE  ............... Small... $ 85.00
YACHT "DAUNTLESS," OF NEW YORK   ................. Small...  87.50
YACHT "DAUNTLESS," OF NEW YORK ................... Large .. 250.00
YACHT "FLEETWING", OF NEW YORK ................... Small... 100.00
YACHT "HAZE," THE   ..............................Large.. 300.00
YACHT "HENRIETTA," 1861   ........................Large.. 225.00
YACHT "JEANETTE," 1881  ..........................Large.. 250.00
YACHT "MADELEINE"................................. Small...  85.00
YACHT "MAGIC" 1871  ..............................Small...  80.00
YACHT "MALLORY," 1861 ............................Large.. 275.00
YACHT "MARIA," 1852  .............................Large.. 275.00
YACHT "METEOR",  .................................Small...  85.00
YACHT "METEOR," 1869 .............................Large.. 225.00
YACHT "MOHAWK," OF NEW YORK; 1877 ................Large.. 225.00
YACHT "NORSEMAN," 1882  ..........................Small...  85.00
YACHT "PURITAN" OF BOSTON ........................ Small... 115.00
YACHT "PURITAN," OF BOSTON  ......................Large.. 275.00
YACHT "REBECCA," 1861 ............................Small...  95.00
YACHT "SAPPHO," OF NEW YORK, 1869.................Large.. 225.00
YACHT "SAPPHO," OF NEW YORK  .....................Small...  85.00
YACHT SQUADRON AT NEWPORT, THE; 1872  ............Large.. 500.00
YACHT "VESTA"  ................................... Small...  85.00
YACHT "VOLUNTEER," 1887........................... Large .. 300.00
YACHTING SOLACE; 1883 ............................ Small...  85.00
YACHTS ON A SUMMER CRUISE  ....................... Large .. 700.00
YANKEE DOODLE ON HIS MUSCLE   ....................Small...  70.00
YANKEE LOCKE; (Comedian) .........................Large..  60.00
YEAR AFTER MARRIAGE, A; N. Currier; 1847 .........Small...  20.00
YEAR AFTER MARRIAGE, A — THE MOTHER'S JEWEL .... Small...  20.00
YEAR AFTER MARRIAGE, A — THE BRIDE'S JEWEL .......Small...  20.00
YES OR NO?  ......................................Small...  24.00
YO-SEMITE FALLS, CALIFORNIA  ..................... Small... 120.00
YOSEMITE VALLEY — CALIFORNIA, "THE BRIDAL VEIL"
   FALL; 1866 ....................................Large.. 500.00
YOU DON'T MEAN IT; 1872  .........................Small...  20.00
```

```
YOU WILL! WILL YOU? 1868 ......................................... Small. $ 21.50
YOUNG AMERICA; 1876 ................................................. Small..  30.00
YOUNG AMERICA – CELEBRATING THE FOURTH; 1867 ... Small..  50.00
YOUNG AMERICA IN ARMOR ....................................... Small..  75.00
YOUNG BLOOD IN AN OLD BODY; 1874 ...................... Small..  60.00
YOUNG BROOD, THE; 1860 .................................... Large. 100.00
YOUNG BROOD, THE; 1870 ....................................... Small..  60.00
YOUNG CAVALIER, THE ........................................... Small..  24.50
YOUNG CHIEFTAIN; N. Currier 1848 .............................. Small..  25.00
YOUNG CIRCASSIAN; N. Currier ................................. Small..  24.00
YOUNG COMPANIONS, THE ....................................... Small..  24.00
YOUNG CONTINENTAL, THE; N. Currier ................... Small..  30.00
YOUNG ENGLAND ..................................................... Small..  18.00
YOUNG FULLERTON; 1888 ...................................... Large. 175.00
YOUNG GEORGIAN; 1886 .......................................... Small..  21.00 -
YOUNG HOPEFUL; 1874 ............................................ Small..  20.00
YOUNG HOUSEKEEPERS, THE; N. Currier ..................... Small..  27.50
YOUNG HOUSEKEEPERS, THE; (Year After Marriage) ........ Small..  27.50
YOUNG MOTHER; N. Currier ...................................Small..  22.50
YOUNG NAPOLEON; N. Currier ...................................Small..  25.00
YOUNG NAPOLEON CONTEMPLATING HIS FATHER'S
   SWORD ..........................................................Small..  32.50
YOUNG NAVIGATOR; 1858 ....................................Small..  30.00
YOUNG RUFFED GROUSE; 1865 .............................. Small.. 110.00
YOUNG SAILOR, THE; N. Currier; 1849 .......................... Small..  30.00
·YOUNG SCOTLAND ...............................................Small..  20.00
YOUNG SHEPHERDESS, THE ....................................Small..  20.00
YOUNG SOLDIER, THE ...........................................Small..  24.50
YOUNG STUDENTS, THE .........................................Small..  27.50
YOUNG VOLUNTEER, THE; N. Currier ..........................Small..  25.00
"YOUR PLAN AND MINE" ........................................ Small..  45.00
```

– Z –

```
ZACHARY TAYLOR – NATION'S CHOICE FOR 12TH PRESIDENT;
   N. Currier; 1847 ............................................. Small..$ 40.00
ZACHARY TAYLOR; N. Currier; 1848...............................Small..  40.00
ZACHARY TAYLOR – 12TH PRESIDENT OF THE UNITED
   STATES; N. Currier; 1849 ....................................Small..  60.00
```

ADDENDA

```
EXTRA COOL LAGER BEER ................................Small... $  30.00
FAMILY DEVOTION; (C & I.); 1871      .....................Small...    12.00
FAMILY REGISTER (4 small views); C. Currier ............Small...    10.00
FANCIED SECURITY, OR, THE RATS ON A BENDER  .....Small...    32.50
FAREWELL A'WHILE MY NATIVE ISLE; N. Currier ....... Small...    18.50
FARMER'S HOUSE; (Plans for building); N. Currier ......... Small...    15.00
FATE OF THE RADICAL PARTY   ...........................Small...    35.00
FATHER'S PRIDE; (Oval)    ....................................Small...    20.00
FEDERAL PAP!    ................................................ Medium    35.00
FIRST RIDE, THE; (C. & I.)   .................................. Small...    25.00
FIRST SMOKE, THE − ALL WRONG  ..........................Small...    32.50
FLORAL GIFT  ........................................................Minature    27.50
FLOWER BASKET, A ...............................................Small...    40.00
FLOWERS; (3 roses, 10 Buds); N. Currier .......................Small...    42.50
FLOWERS; (4 Roses, 6 Buds); N. Currier   ...................Medium    70.00
FLOWERS; (3 Roses, 7 Buds, Sweet Peas, Daises, Orchid) .Small...    55.00
FLOWERS NO. 1; N. Currier   .................................. Small...    48.50
FLOWERS NO.2 ; N. Currier   ...................................Small...    48.50
FLOWERS − ROSES AND BLUEBELLS; 1870 .................. Small...    48.50
FLOWERS − ROSES AND BLUEBELLS ......................... Medium    75.00
FOX WITHOUT A TAIL − OR, THE SOUTHERN CONFEDERACY;
    1861  ............................................................. Small...    32.00
FREDERICK DOUGLASS; (Colored Champion of Freedom) . Small...    40.00
FRENCH REVOLUTION, THE; ''SCENE IN THE THRONE
    ROOM OF THE TUILERIES; N. Currier; 1848  ............. Small...    32.50
FRUIT; (Peaches, Grapes, and Butterflies)  ................... Medium    75.00
FRUIT; (Apples,. Plums, Grapes, and Butterflies)  .......... Medium    70.00
FRUIT AND FLOWERS; 1870; (Vase of bleeding hearts, 3 roses,
    nasturtiums, grapes, 3 peaches  ............................Small...    50.00
FRUIT AND FLOWERS; 1870; (Basket of strawberries, sur-
    rounded by roses, hydrangea, etc.)   ....................... Small...    50.00
FRUIT PIECE, THE; N. Currier; 1845   ........................ Small...    40.00
FRUIT PIECE; 1859   ............................................. Small...    40.00
FRUIT PIECE; 1867  ............................................. Small...    40.00
FRUIT PIECE; (3 pears, 4 blackberries, peach, 2 plums,
    2 apples, grapes)   .............................................. Small...    40.00
FRUIT VASE, THE; (Vase of hanging cherries, pears, grapes,
    etc.)  ............................................................. Small...    40.00
FRUITS AND FLOWERS OF AUTUMN   ......................... Small...    50.00
GAME COCK, THE − TRIMMED; N. Currier ................... Small...    95.00
GENL. ANDREW JACKSON AT NEW ORLEANS; N. Currier. Small...    45.00
GENL. ANDREW JACKSON − ''We Mourn Our Loss'' ......... Small...    30.00
GENL. CHESTER A. ARTHUR − 21ST PRESIDENT; 1880 . Medium    65.00
GENERAL GRANT − IN UNIFORM  ............................ Large ..  100.00
GENERAL GRANT; 1885  ...........................................Small...    40.00
GENERAL JAMES A. GARFIELD − 20TH PRESIDENT ......Medium    60.00
GENERAL U.S. GRANT; 1885  .................................... Small...    40.00
GENERAL WILLIAM H. HARRISON; N. Currier; (With Sword)
                                                                     Small...    40.00
GENERAL WILLIAM H. HARRISON AT THE BATTLE OF
    TIPPECANOE; N. Currier  .................................... Small...    45.00
GEORGE M. DALLAS; ''The People's Candidate;'' N. Currier;
                                                                     Small...    32.50
GEORGE M. DALLAS; ''Vice-President of the U.S.'' N. Currier;
    1844  ............................................................. Small...    32.50
GEORGIANA; (C. & I.); (Oval)   ............................... Small...    20.00
GHOST, THE; (Cartoon) ......................................... Small...    30.00
GIVE US THIS DAY OUR DAILY BREAD; 1878   ............ Small...    12.00
```

```
GLIMPSE OF THE HOMESTEAD, A; 1859 ..................... Medium $ 120.00
GOLDEN MORNING, THE ......................................... Medium    60.00
GOOD SEND OFF, A — GO! 1889 ........................... Small...   65.00
GRAND FIGHT FOR THE CHAMPION'S BELT — BETWEEN
   GRANITE PIERCE AND OLD CHAPULTEPEC .......... Small...   70.00
GRAND NATIONAL DEMOCRATIC BANNER; McCLELLAN
   AND PENDLETON ........................................... Small...   40.00
GRAND NATIONAL REPUBLICAN BANNER; 1880 .......... Small...   40.00
GRAND PATENT INDIA-RUBBER AIRLINE RAILWAY TO
   CALIFORNIA; (Cartoon) .................................. Small...  175.00
GREAT AMERICAN BUCK HUNT OF 1856; THE .............. Small...   40.00
GREAT AMERICAN TANNER; (Cartoon) ..................... Small...   37.50
GREAT BARTHOLDI STATUE; (Statue of Liberty) ........... Medium   65.00
GREAT EAST RIVER BRIDGE. NO. 1; 1883 ................... Small...  100.00
GREAT EAST RIVER BRIDGE, NO. 2; 1883 ................... Small...  100.00
GREAT EAST RIVER BRIDGE, NO. 3; 1883 ................... Small...  100.00
GREAT EAST RIVER BRIDGE; 1885 ......................... Small...  100.00
GREAT EAST RIVER SUSPENSION BRIDGE; (Between New
   York and Brooklyn); 1886...................................... Large ..  850.00
GREAT MATCH AT BALTIMORE, THE; (Political Cartoon)
                                                      Small...   35.00
GREAT SCULLERS RACE ON THE ST. LAWRENCE; (RARE)
                                                      Small...  650.00
HAPPY MOTHER; N. Currier .................................. Small...   22.50
HAPPY MOTHER, THE; (C. & I.) ................................ Small...   22.50
HAPPY NEW YEAR, A ......................................... Small...   55.00
HENRY BIBB; (Slave) ......................................... Small...   35.00
HENRY CLAY; N. Currier; 1853 .............................. Small...   40.00
HERCULES OF THE NATION SLAYING THE GREAT
   DRAGON OF SECESSION; (Political Cartoon) ............ Small...   35.00
HOLY FAMILY; N. Currier ..................................... Small...   12.00
HONEST ABE TAKING THEM ON THE HALF SHELL  .... Small...   60.00
HON. HANNIBAL HAMLIN — OUR NEXT VICE-PRESIDENT;
   1860 .......................................................... Small...   40.00
HON. SCHUYLER COLFAX ................................... Small...   32.50
HON. STEPHEN A. DOUGLAS — SENATOR ................. Small...   42.50
HOUSEHOLD PETS; (C. & I.) ................................. Small...   24.00
IN AND OUT OF CONDITION; 1880 ......................... Small...   25.00
IN MEMORY OF; (Couple and Child) ......................... Small...   10.00
IN MEMORY OF: (Woman and Boy) ......................... Small...   10.00
IN MEMORY OF; (Young Couple) ............................ Small...   10.00
INDEPENDENCE HALL, PHILADELFHIA, 1776 .............. Small...  125.00
INDIAN HUNTER; N. Currier; 1845 ......................... Small...   60.00
IRREPRESSIBLE CONFLICT, THE; (Political Cartoon) ..... Small...   35.00
JACK ROSSITER; N. Currier; 1850 .......................... Large ..  220.00
JAMES; (Hudson River in background); N. Currier; 1848 ...... Small...   60.00
JAMES BUCHANAN — DEMOCRATIC CANDIDATE FOR
   15TH PRESIDENT; N. Currier; 1856 ...................... Large ..   40.00
JAMES K. POLK — PRESIDENT-ELECT; N. Currier ........ Small...   39.50
JAMES K. POLK; (On Horseback); N. Currier ............... Small...   37.50
JAMES MYERS, SAMUEL LEWIS — CHAS. C. MERCHANT;
   N. Currier ................................................... Small...   57.50
JEFF. D. HUNG ON A "SOUR APPLE TREE," OR,
   TREASON MADE ODIOUS .................................. Small...   35.00
JOHN BULL AND HIS FRIEND CLEVELAND  ............... Small...   36.50
JOHNSON'S HOTEL; C. Currier; 1854 ..................... Medium  650.00
JULIA — I SHOULD LIKE TO BE TREATED LIKE A DOG;
   N. Currier; 1848 ........................................... Small...   20.00
```

LADY SUTTON; N. Currier; 1850 ....Small ...$ 65.00
LEVEE; 1884 ....Small ... 67.50
LIEUT. GENL. WINFIELD SCOTT; (Bust); 1861 ....Small ... 35.00
LITTLE BOUQUETS; (Group of Four) ....Small ... 35.00
LITTLE BROTHERS, THE; 1863 ....Small ... 22.50
LITTLE KITTIE ....Small ... 20.00
LITTLE LIZZY; N. Currier ....Small ... 20.00
LITTLE MARY AND THE LAMB; 1877 ....Small ... 20.00
LITTLE SISTERS, THE; 1862 .... Small ... 20.00
LOVE ONE ANOTHER ....Small ... 20.00
LUCY — Record 2:18¼; 1871 ....Small ... 65.00
MAC (Race horse); N. Currier; 1853 .... Large ... 285.00
MAJ. GENL. BENJ. F. BUTLER OF MASS. .... Small ... 32.50
MARIA ....Small ... 20.00
MARY ....Small ... 20.00
NAPOLEON AT ST. HELENA; C. Currier ....Small ... 35.00
NAPOLEON EUGENE LOUIS — PRINCE IMPERIAL OF
    FRANCE... Small ... 30.00
NATIONAL WASHINGTON MONUMENT IN THE CITY OF
    WASHINGTON, D.C., N. Currier .... Small ... 37.50
NETTIE; (Girl's Head); 1874 ....Small ... 22.50
NEW FOUNTAIN OF DEMOCRACY, THE; (Political Car-
    toon) ....Small ... 35.00
NEW YORK LIGHT GUARD'S QUICK STEP; N. Currier;
    1839; ....Sheet Music ... 15.00
NO SLATE HERE: (Cartoon) ....Small ... 35.00
ONLY SON, THE; N. Currier .... Small ... 20.00
PAP, SOUP, AND CHOWDER; (Political Cartoon) ....Small ... 32.50
PARTHENON OF ATHENS ....Small ... 16.50
PARTING HOUR, THE ....Small ... 20.00
PATH THROUGH THE WOODS, THE ....Small ... 48.50
PEERLESS GOLDSMITH MAID, THE; "The Queen of
    Trotters,"; 1871 ....Small ... 70.00
PREPARING FOR CONGRESS; 1863 ....Small ... 35.00
PRESIDENT LINCOLN AT HOME; (Reading Scriptures to
    Wife and Son) .... Small ... 35.00
PRESIDENTS OF THE U. S. FROM 1789 to 1850 ....Small ... 35.00
PRESIDENTS OF THE U. S. — WASHINGTON TO POLK
                                        Small ... 35.00
PRESIDENTS OF THE U. S. — WASHINGTON TO TYLER
                                        Small ... 35.00
PRESIDENTS OF THE U. S. — WASH. TO BUCHANAN..Small ... 35.00
PRINCE ALBERT; (Full-length portrait); N. Currier .....Small ... 27.50
RAVENSWOOD, L. I. ....Large... 500.00
REGATTA OF THE N. Y. YACHT CLUB; "Rounding the
    S. W. Spit"; N. Currier; 1854 ....Large ... 950.00
REGATTA OF THE N. Y. YACHT CLUB; "The Start";
    N. Currier; 1854 ....Large ... 950.00
RESURRECTION OF CHRIST, THE; N. Currier ....Small ... 15.00
ROADSIDE, THE ....Small ... 55.00
RURAL ARCHITECTURE NO. 1; N. Currier; 1856 .... Small ... 30.00
RURAL ARCHITECTURE NO. 2; N. Currier; 1856 .... Small ... 30.00
SACRED TO THE MEMORY OF; N. Currier; 1859 ....Small ... 10.00
SONS OF TEMPERANCE ....Small ... 22.00
SPRING; (English Scene); N. Currier ....Small ... 28.50
STAR OF THE NORTH, THE; N. Currier; 1847 ....Small ... 30.00
STORMING THE CASTLE; (Political Cartoon) ....Small ... 35.00
SUMMER FRUITS AND FLOWERS ....Small ... 37.50

```
SUMMER LANDSCAPE; 1869 ...............................Small ..$ 40.00
SURPRISE PARTY, A; 1883..................................Small ..  30.00
SUSIE ...................................................Medium    22.00
T. J. JACKSON...............................................Small ..  30.00
"TABLE D'HOTE" THE; N. Currier .......................Small ..  27.50
TAKE YOUR CHOICE: (Girl's Heads) .......................Small ..  20.00
THOMAS F. MEAGHER; (In uniform) .......................Small ..  3 0.00
TROTTERS ON THE SNOW ...............................Small ..  135.00
TROTTING MARE "GOLDSMITH MAID," 1870 .........Large..  225.00
TROY FIRE COMPANY; N. Currier .......................Small ..  40.00
TWILIGHT HOUR − "WHEN THE KYE CAME HAME".. Small ..  35.00
U .S. M. STEAMSHIP "BALTIC," N. Currier; 1852 .....Medium  150.00
UPPER CANADA COLLEGE; N. Currier ...................Medium  200.00
VIEW NEAR HIGHBRIDGE. HARLEM RIVER, N. Y......Medium  800.00
VIEW ON THE RONDOUT ' ...............................Small ...  45.00
WATERFALL, THE ...............................Small ..  25.00
WE SELL FOR CASH; 1875...................................Small ..  30.00
WHITE HALL, BRISTOL COLLEGE, PA; 1835 .........Small ..  25.00
WILL HE BITE? 1868 ...............................Small ..  20.00
WINTER EVENING; N. Currier; 1856 .......................Small ..  125.00
WONDERFUL ELIOPHOBUS FAMILY; 1870 ............ Small ..  40.00
WOODCOCK, SCOLOPAX MINOR; N. Currier; 1849 ..... Small ..  75.00
YOUNG CHIEFTAIN; (Highlander); N. Currier .......... Small ..  22.50
YOUNG MOTHER, THE; (Oval) ...............................Small ..  25 .00
```

CURRIER & IVES REPRODUCTIONS

Reproductions are bound to appear when any-
thing becomes scarce and valuable. They emerge
for two reasons. First and foremost, because un-
principled individuals seek an opportunity to
make a "fast" dollar. Second, a desire of some
individual to "bring back" the charm and style
of yesteryear.

Reproductions began appearing within   ten
years after the firm of Currier & Ives closed
its doors. Around thirty-five years ago a dealer
discovered several stones of Clipper Ships and
had restrikes made. They include "Flying Cloud"
and "Great Republic" in the large folio.

In the ordinary run of reproductions, the
average collector --if he is observant--can dis-
tinquish the old from the new by the type of
paper used. The majority of new prints have a
thinner and lighter colored paper. Reproductions
can also be distinguished from the originals by
the coloring process. Colors were hand-applied
to the old prints while the new are inexpensive-
ly processed by machine.

Still another way by which to determine a
reproduction is the folio size. Many of the reproductions are copies of large folio prints   in
the small size. For example, if a collector
comes across a small folio and finds that it is
catalogued only in the large size in a check-
list, it is a general indication that the print
is a fake. In a rare instance an original which
is catalogued in one size could be uncovered in

another size, for some subjects were originally made in two folio sizes.

The prints "Snipe Shooting," " Woodcock Shooting," "The Star of the Road," "The Flower Vase," "The Express Train," "American Homestead-Winter," "Winter Pastime," "The Old Farm House" and "The Steamship Washington" have been reproduced in the small size on paper that is thinner than that used for the originals.

The reproductions below are listed with the measurements of the printed area only:

"Trotting Cracks at the Forge." This print is 9½" by 14½" and has margins.

"Woodcock Shooting." This print is 9½" by 14½" and has margins.

American Hunting Scenes: "A Good Chance." This print is 11-5/8" by 16-5/8" and does not have margins.

"The Rocky Mountains." This print is 11-5/8 by 16-5/8" and does not have margins.

"A Midnight Race on the Mississippi."This print is 11-5/8" by 16-5/8" and does not have margins.

"The Road -- Winter." This print is 11-5/8" by 16-5/8" and does not have margins.

"The Lightning Express Trains." This print is also 11-5/8" by 16-5/8" and does not have margins.

The name of the reproducer, Einson-Freeman Co., Inc., L. I. City, N. Y., appears in fine type in the lower left corner, below the title, on the preceding group of prints.

The following group is reproduced in the small folio size. The originals were issued only in the large folio. These new prints are on ivory colored paper with fine ribs running horizontally. The imprinted border area of about one-fourth to one-half inch outside the picture area is cream colored. Measurements on these are of the picture area only, without the title:

"Arctic" of New York and "Three Bells" rescuing passengers and crew from "The Steamship San Francisco." 8" by 12".

Central Park, Winter -- "The Skating Pond". 8-1/8" by 12".

Clipper Ship "Dreadnaught" off Tuskar Light. 7-7/8" by 12".

Clipper Ship "Nightengale." 8¼" by 12" .

Lightning Express Trains, the. "Leaving the Junction." 7-7/8" by 12".

"Happy Family, The." (Grouse). 8½" by 12".

American Fireman, The. "Metropolitan System." 7-7/8" by 12".

"On the Coast of the Pacific." 8¼" by 12".

"The Road -- Winter." 8" by 12".

Rocky Mountains, The. "Emigrants Crossing the Plains." 8-1/8" by 12".

"Trotting Cracks at the Forge." 7-7/8" by 12".

The next group is reproduced on a heavy poster cardboard. Measurements are for the printed area only and do not include the title or margins.

"Catching a Trout." 10¼" by 14½". The original was issued in the large folio only.

"Peytona and Fashion." 9" by 14½". The original was issued in the large folio only.

"The Rubber." 9-1/8" by 11¼". The original was published in the medium folio only.

"Trotting Cracks at the Forge." 9-3/8" by 14-5/8". The original was issued in the large folio only.

"Woodcock Shooting." 9-3/8" by 14-5/8".The original was issued in the large folio. This subject was also issued in the small folio, 8" by 12", by Nathaniel Currier.

A group of reproductions has recently come into the market and they are listed below. Measurements are listed to differentiate between the original and the reproduction.

Clipper Ship "Dreadnaught" off Tuskar Light. 8" by 10". Original was issued in the large folio only.

Winter in the Country."Getting Ice." 8" by 10". Original was issued in large folio only.

"A Home on the Mississippi." 9" by 12". This was issued by Currier & Ives in the small folio. The original is about 3/4" larger each way.

A Home in the Country. "Summer Scene." 9" by 12". The original was issued in a medium folio, 13" by 17½".

"The Roadside Mill." 9" by 12". Original was issued by Currier & Ives, 7-3/4" by 8-3/4".

"Hunting, Fishing and Forest Scene." 9" by 12". Original was issued in a large folio, 16¼" by 24¼".

"Winter Morning." (Winter Country Scene). 9" by 12". Original was issued in a medium folio, 11½" by 15½".

"A Race for Blood." (Horse Racing Scene). 11" by 14". Original was issued in a large folio, 18¼" by 28-5/8".

"Geo. M. Patchen, Brown Dick and Miller's Damsel." 11" by 14". Original was issued in a large folio, about 17-3/4" by 27-3/4".

"The Cattskill Mountains." 11" by 14". The original was issued in a large folio, 14¼" by 20".

"American Railroad Scene." 11" by 14". The original was issued in a large folio.

"The Old Homestead." 11" by 14". The original was issued in a large folio.

"The Old Farm Gate." 11" by 14". The original was issued in a large folio.

Reproduction prints have no value as collectors' items. Most of them sold originally for 10¢ to $1.00 each and this is their present value, whether they are one or forty years of age.

Within the past twenty years, china plates have been manufactured with Currier & Ives scenes. These plates have no value to collectors of authentic antiques.

The writer has compiled these lists for the convenience of collectors and dealers. He regrets that he cannot correspond with the readers regarding the differences between the originals and the reproductions. Due to the pressure of business and the considerable amount of travel that it entails, the writer feels that he cannot devote the time required to adequately answer inquiries on the subject.

As was previously stated, if the folio size of a print differs from the size given in the check-list, it is an indication that it is a reproduction. If there is doubt as to the authenticity of a print it is advisable to contact a reputable print dealer in one of the larger cities.

RECENT REPRODUCTIONS OF CURRIER & IVES PRINTS

During the latter part of 1968, a book entitled "The World of Currier & Ives" by Roy King and Burt Davis was published. This book contains more than fifty prints which are considered by experts to be the finest of the Currier & Ives group. The prints from the large folios have been reproduced to sizes of 10¼-11" by 15½". The reproductions from the small folio are actual size.

Fortunately, the beginning collector as well as the advanced collector, can readily determine that the prints are new because of the printing which appears on the back of each page. These pages are buff-colored and each one bears a description of the print along with a historical background of the print appearing on the following page.

Below is a listing of the prints which have been reproduced in this collection. The frontis page is "Skating in Central Park" and it has no margin.

THE PORT OF NEW YORK--The Waterfront That Built the City

STATEN ISLAND AND THE NARROWS--Guardians of New York

NEW YORK CRYSTAL PALACE--Our First World's Fair

CENTRAL-PARK, WINTER -- When The Park Was
Young

THE HUDSON RIVER STEAMBOAT "ST. JOHN" --
Queen of the Night Boats

THE CATTSKILL MOUNTAINS--Washington Irving
Country

THE GREAT RACE ON THE MISSISSIPPI--The Mil-
lion-Dollar Race

"ROUNDING A BEND" ON THE MISSISSIPPI--Pure-
ly American Design

"WOODING UP" ON THE MISSISSIPPI--Not A Moment To Spare

A COTTON PLANTATION ON THE MISSISSIPPI--Ro-
mance Of The Delta

THE LEVEE--NEW ORLEANS -- Heart Of A River
Empire

GREAT FIVE MILE ROWING MATCH FOR $4000 &
THE CHAMPIONSHIP OF AMERICA--The Little Gi-
ants of Rowing

THE AMERICAN NATIONAL GAME OF BASE BALL--
America Finds Its Game

THE HOME OF THE DEER--An Indispensable Animal

THE CARES OF A FAMILY -- The All- American
Bird

A RISING FAMILY--A Glow Of Woodland Light

CLIPPER SHIP "FLYING CLOUD" --The Fastest Thing That Sailed

CLIPPER SHIP "RED JACKET" -- A Gold Ship Rounds The Horn

AN AMERICAN RAILWAY SCENE, AT HORNELLS- VILLE, ERIE, RAILWAY -- The Heyday Of The Hard Sell

THE "LIGHTNING EXPRESS" TRAINS--Heroic Po- etry Of The Rails

THE ROUTE TO CALIFORNIA -- Conquest Of The Sierras

AMERICAN RAILROAD SCENE -- Man Of Legend In The Snow

ACROSS THE CONTINENT--A Prophetic Panorama

THE ROCKY MOUNTAINS -- Wagons West--In The Shadows Of The Alps

GOLD MINING IN CALIFORNIA--Yellow Riches Of Eldorado

HON. ABRAHAM LINCOLN / "TAKING THE STUMP" OR STEPHEN IN SEARCH OF HIS MOTHER-- Mr. Lincoln As He Was

BOMBARDMENT AND CAPTURE OF ISLAND "NUMBER TEN"--Conquest Of The Mississippi

THE FALL OF RICHMOND, VA. ON THE NIGHT OF
APRIL 2ND, 1865--Funeral Pyre of Rebellion

PEYTONA AND FASHION--The Race Of A Century

THE CELEBRATED HORSE LEXINGTON -- A Great
Grandsire Of American Racing

"TROTTING CRACKS" AT HOME -- When The Horse
Was King

BENJAMIN FRANKLIN: THE ART OF MAKING MONEY
PLENTY / THE STATESMAN AND PHILOSOPHER--
Poor Richard And The American Character

SHAKERS NEAR LEBANON -- The Fervent Shaker
Quadrille

THE PROGRESS OF INTEMPERANCE / WOMANS HOLY
WAR / THE FRUITS OF TEMPERANCE--When Temperance Was in Flower

LIFE ON THE PRAIRIE (THE BUFFALO HUNT)--The
Slaughter Of A Species

LIFE ON THE PRAIRIE (THE TRAPPERS DEFENCE
"FIRE FIGHT FIRE")--A Matter Of Life And
Death

A PARLEY--A Tense Moment In Enemy Country.

THE LAST WAR-WHOOP -- Defiant To The Last

CAMPING IN THE WOODS--The Good Life In The
Wilderness

AMERICAN HUNTING SCENES--Sportsmen In Paradise

TROLLING FOR BLUE FISH -- The Blues Of Long Ago

BROOK TROUT FISHING--The Sport Of Gentlemen

ARGUING THE POINT--The Latest News

"HUSKING" -- The Peculiarly American Grain

AMERICAN FOREST SCENE -- The Sweet Season

AUTUMN IN NEW ENGLAND--The Universal Beverage

PREPARING FOR MARKET -- A Simple, Cash-Free Economy

AMERICAN COUNTRY LIFE -- The New Leisure Class At Home

WINTER IN THE COUNTRY--(The Old Grist Mill) Rural Industrialist

WINTER IN THE COUNTRY (A COLD MORNING) A Traveler's Haven

THE ROAD -- WINTER -- The Eternal Christmas Card

THE LIFE OF A FIREMAN (THE NEW ERA. STEAM AND MUSCLE)--Volunteers At Bay

THE LIFE OF A FIREMAN (THE METROPOLITAN SYSTEM)--A New Day In Fire-Fighting

THE "HEATHEN CHINEE" -- Humorists And The Yellow Peril

THE WHALE FISHERY "LAYING ON"--The World Of Moby Dick

BUTTERICK & CO.'S SEMI-ANNUAL REPORT OF NEW YORK FASHIONS--High Style For The Housewife

SECTION II

Kellogg Prints, Sarony & Major, Haskell & Allen, Duval, Prang, Miscellaneous Engravings and Prints.

INDEX

KELLOGG PRINTS

To many collectors, Kellogg Prints are confusing because of the various combinations of initials appearing before the Kellogg surname and the other names incorporated with it. Kellogg prints, as we refer to them today, are the combined efforts of four brothers and their various partners and selling agents.

The Kellogg brothers were all born in Hartford, Connecticut, in the first decade of 1800. The eldest, J. G., studied engraving in Boston and practiced the art there. A second brother, D. W., joined J. G. in his business and learned the trade.

While in Boston, D. W. appears to have also learned the lithographic trade, for in 1833 he commenced a lithographic business in Hartford, Connecticut, under the name of D. W. Kellogg & Co. In this enterprise he was assisted by his younger brother, E. C. Kellogg. In 1836, D. W. decided to move to Wisconsin. He turned the business over to his brother E. C., or Elijah, as he was known to his family and friends, who operated the business under the name of E. C. Kellogg until 1843.

In 1843, Edmund B. (E. B.) Kellogg, the youngest of the brothers joined with E. C. to form the partnership of E. B. & E. C. Kellogg. This business arrangement continued until 1865, when Charles E., a son of E. B., became a partner. In 1869, the senior partners sold their interest to Eliphelet Bulkley and his son, William

H. Bulkley. The new firm, Kellogg & Bulkley, followed the same policy of issuing prints until about 1875. At that time the partners realized that prints were becoming passé and went into commercial lithography. It is reported that the firm is still in business.

It appears that for a short time J. G. Kellogg, the engraver, became associated with Samuel Hanmer, Jr. in a lithographic business in Hartford, Connecticut. The duration of their association was a little more than a year, 1844-45. The partners used the name of Kellogg & Hanmer.

The Kelloggs had sales agencies in New York and Horace Thayer was their agent from 1844 to 1848. Prints sold through the agency were inscribed Kellogg & Thayer. From 1849 to 1852, J. G. Comstock acted as sales representative with the prints being imprinted Kellogg & Comstock. After 1852 the firm established their own sales agency which continued for approximately ten years.

It has been stated that less than 1000 different subjects were issued as a result of the combined efforts of the Kelloggs and their partners. The prints were issued in smaller quantities and are scarcer than those of N. Currier and Currier & Ives. Although the list which follows is short, it is probably the most complete catalogue of current prices available on these prints.

KELLOGG PRINTS

Abigail, Girl at Spinet, E. E. & E. C. Kellogg ....Small .$ 20.00
Ann; Kellogg .... Small.. 20.00
Battle of Malvern Hills, Va., July 1, 1862 .... Small.. 35.00
Birthplace of Henry Clay, Hanover County, Va. .... Small.. 30.00
Bloomer Costume, The; E. C. Kellogg .... Small.. 36.00
Brave at Home; (Genl. McClellan, his wife and children). Small.. 22.50
Brother and Sister; Kellogg ....Small.. 30.00
Caldwell, Lake George; Kellogg ....Small.. 40.00
Canary Bird, The; Kellogg ....Small.. 25.00
Caroline; Kellogg & Thayer .... Small.. 20.00
Children in the Wood; Kellogg & Comstock .... Small.. 20.00
Death of John Quincy Adams; Kellogg ....Small.. 25.00
Death of Major Ringgold, The; Kellogg & Thayer ....Small.. 20.00
Embracing an Opportunity; Kellogg ....Small.. 25.00
Emeline, (¾ length portrait); Kellogg ....Small.. 20.00
Emma, E. B. & E. C. Kellogg ....Small.. 20.00
Farmers' Pets, The; Kellogg & Comstock ....Small.. 35.00
Flower Girl, The; Kellogg & Comstock .... Small.. 30.00
Fruit Girl, The; E. B. & E. C. Kellogg .... Small.. 30.00
General Andrew Jackson (On horse); Kellogg ....Small.. 27.50
General Andrew Jackson, Hero of New Orleans (On rearing
    white horse); Kellogg ....Small.. 35.00
George M. Dallas, Vice President of the U. S.; 10 x 14'' ·
    Kellogg & Thayer 30.00
Happy Mother, The; Kellogg ....Small.. 35.00
Holy Family, The; 12 x 16''; Kellogg & Comstock 15.00
Home and Friends; Kellogg & Comstock ....Small.. 32.00
James K. Polk, (On horseback); Kellogg ....Small.. 35.00
James K. Polk, The People's Choice; Kellogg & Thayer..Small.. 35.00
Jenny Lind; (¾ length portrait); E, C. Kellogg ....Small.. 30.00
Lady Washington; Kellogg ....Medium 40.00
Last Supper, The; Kellogg ....Small.. 12.50
Lincoln at Home; Family group; E. B. & E. C. Kellogg...Small.. 35.00
Little Brothers, The ....Small.. 30.00
Little Charlie; Kellogg ....Small.. 25.00
Love among the Roses; Kellogg .... Small.. 35.00
Lovely Breeze, The; 12¼ x 16''; Kellogg 20.00
Lovers' Reconciliation, The, (Two ¾ length figures);
    Kellogg & Comstock ....Small.. 20.00
Major Genl. George B. McClellan on his Favorite Horse
    "Daniel Webster"; Kellogg ....Small.. 32.50
Major Genl. Winfield Scott, U. S. Army; E. B. & E. C. Kel-
    logg ....Small.. 32.50
Major Genl. Zachary Taylor — "The Hero of Buena Vista"·
    Kellogg ....Small.. 35.00
Married; (James Baillie, artist); Kellogg & Thayer ....Small.. 30.00
Prodigal Son Receiving His Patrimony; Kellogg ....Small.. 22.00
Prodigal Son Returned to His father; Kellogg ....Small.. 22.00
Queen of Angels, (Full length in oval) .... Small.. 12.50
Queen of May; Kellogg & Comstock .... Small.. 22.50
Queen Victoria; Kellogg & Comstock ....Small.. 25.00
Rivals, The, (Two young women); Kellogg.................. Small.. 22.50
Roses, Hare Bell & Sweet Pea; Kellogg ....Small.. 30.00
Sailor's Adieu, The; Kellogg & Comstock...................Small.. 25.00
Silhouettes by E. B. & E. C. Kellogg, 1844; John Quincy
    Adams .... Small.. 30.00

```
John Quincy Adams ........................................... Small ...$   30.00
Henry Clay .................................................... Small ...   30.00
Thomas Cooper ............................................... Small ...   32.50
John Forsyth ................................................. Small ...   32.50
Felix Grundy ................................................. Small ...   32.50
William Henry Harrison ..................................... Small ...   30.00
Andrew Jackson .............................................. Small ...   35.00
Richard Mentor Johnson ..................................... Small ...   30.00
Dixon Hall Lewis ........................................... Small ...   30.00
Alexander Macomb ........................................... Small ...   30.00
John Marshall ............................................... Small ...   35.00
Richard Channing Moor e .................................... Small ...   30.00
Joel Roberts Poinsett ....................................... Small ...   30.00
Samuel Lewis Southard ...................................... Small ...   30.00
Nathaniel P. Talmadge ...................................... Small ...   30.00
John Tyler ................................................... Small ...   35.00
William White ............................................... Small ...   30.00
Henry Alexander Wise......................................... Small ...   30.00
Levi Woodbury .............................................. Small ...   30.00
Silas Wright ................................................. Small ...   30.00
Single, (James Baillie, artist); Kellogg & Thayer .......Small ...   30.00
Sisters, The, (Primitive type); Kellogg .....................Small ...   22.50
Soldier's Adieu, The, 12 x 16; Kellogg ...................Small ...   25.00
Spirit of '76, The; (Family arming for war) ................Small ...   48.50
Summer Scene in the Country; Kellogg ....................Large...  125.00
Vase of Flowers, Kellogg ...................................Small ...   40.00
Washington, (Full length); Kellogg ........................Small ...   35.00
Washington at Prayer; Kellogg & Thayer ................Small ...   30.00
Washington at Prayer; (Kneeling on one knee); Kellogg &
     Comstock ................................................ Small ...   30.00
Washington's Reception by the Ladies at Trenton, N. J.,
     April, 1789, (Washington on a white horse); Kellogg. Small ...   35.00
Which Will You Marry? (Two girls, two verses)........... Small ...   20.00
```

SARONY & MAJOR

The firm of Sarony & Major made its entry into the lithographic field in 1846, in New York City. The partners, Napoleon Sarony and Henry B. Major worked for Nathaniel Currier for several years prior to commencing their own business.

Napoleon Sarony was born in Quebec, Canada. In 1836, he came to New York City to study art under Archibald Robertson who was the foremost painter in New York at that time. Sarony was later engaged by Nathaniel Currier as an artist.

The first address of the firm was #99 Nassau Street during the years of 1846-47. From 1847 to 1857 the address was #117 Fulton St. In 1855, Henry B. Major died and was succeeded by his son, Richard Major. No change was made in the name of the company. However, Sarony apparently established a separate business at the smae address from 1853 to 1857, known as Sarony & Co., while still maintaining his interest in Sarony & Major. In 1857, Joseph H. Knapp became a partner and the firm was then designated Sarony, Major & Knapp.

In 1868, Sarony retired from the company and opened one of the first Photographic studios in New York City. It was known as Sarony & Co., Photographers and is reported to still be in business. The lithographic firm was afterwards known as Major & Knapp until 1871, when Richard Major withdrew and Joseph F. Knapp operated under the name of Knapp Litho Co., as a commercial house until about the turn of the century.

The prints of Sarony and his partners and successors are rather scarce for they were, generally speaking, not issued in vast quantities as were the prints of Currier & Ives.

SARONY & CO.

SARONY & MAJOR

SARONY, MAJOR & KNAPP

Battle of Cerro Gordo, Fought April 17th., 1847
    Sarony & Major ....Small.... $ 40.00
Bivouac, January 28; Sarony, Major & Knapp .... Small....   35.00
Canadian River near Camp 38; Sarony, Major & Knapp... Small....   45.00
COO-CHE-TO-PA Pass; View looking up Salwatch Creek
    (Western scenery); Sarony, Major & Knapp ....Small....   40.00
Comanche Camp on Shady Creek; (Indian Camp); Sarony,
    Major & Knapp ....Small....   40.00
Death of Warren at the Battle of Bunker Hill, 1775; Sarony
    & Major ....Small....   40.00
Fort Smith, Arkansas; (Boat on River with town in the
    background); Sarony, Major & Knapp ....Small.... 100.00
Head of the First Canon of Grand River; (Western scene)
    Sarony, Major & Knapp ....Small....   50.00
Lucy; Sarony & Major ....Small....   30.00
Marriage, The; Sarony & Major ....Small....   20.00
New York and Environs from Williamsburgh, 1848; Sarony
    & Major..Small.... 100.00
Peaks of the Sierra Blanca, from near Ft. Massachusetts,
    Sarony & Co. ....Small....   40.00
Perry's Victory on Lake; Sarony & Major, 1846 ....Small....   45.00
Pride of the West, The; Sarony & Major....................Small....   32.50
Rio Colorado near the Mojave Villages. View #1; Sarony,
    Major & Knapp ....Small....   45.00
Rio Colorado near the Mojave Villages. View #2; Sarony,
    Major & Knapp ....Small....   45.00
Rio Colorado near the Mojave Villages. View #3; Sarony,
    Major & Knapp ....Small....   45.00
Salisbury, North Carolina, Sarony, Major & Knapp ......Small....   65.00
San Francisco Mountain, from Leroux's River; Sarony,
    Major & Knapp ....Small....   50.00
Valley of Bill Williams Fork. (Western View); Sarony & Co.
                                        Small....   40.00
View of Ordinary Lateral Ravines on Grand River; Sarony,
    Major & Knapp ....Small....   35.00
View of the Black Forest, Mount Hope and Sierra Prieta;
    (Western scenery); Sarony, Major & Knapp ....Small....   40.00
Washington, The Patriot, the Statesman, and the Warrior;
    Sarony & Major ....Small....   35.00
Which Will He Marry? Sarony & Major ....Small....   20.00
Z. Taylor, Rough and Ready; Sarony & Major ....Small....   35.00
Zuni Sacred Spring, (Indian Spring); Sarony & Co. ....Small....   37.50

HASKELL & ALLEN

The firm of Haskell & Allen operated in Boston, Mass., from about 1867 to 1875. Little information is available concerning the men who operated the business.

The concern closely followed the lead of their contemporary, Currier & Ives, in producing Hunting, Horse, Western and other scenes. After 1870, the ordinary lithograph was on its way out, having been replaced by the chromo-lithograph. The partners were apparently unable to produce the new type of print and terminated their business.

HASKELL & ALLEN

Almont, The Great Sire of Trotters	Large	$200.00
American Girl and Lady Thorn	Large	250.00
American Trappers; 10 x 14"		125.00
Autumn on Lake George,	Small	65.00
Boston Common	Small	80.00
Breezy Day Outside, A	Small	50.00
Brush for the Lead, A.	Large	450.00
Colisseum	Small	35.00
Coming from the Trot	Large	250.00
End of the Brush, The	Large	425.00
Ethan Allen (Horse)	Large	275.00
Flushing a Woodcock	Small	85.00
Frontier Lake, The	Small	60.00
Going to the Trot	Large	250.00
Goldsmith Maid (Horse)	Large	275.00
Harry Bassett (Horse)	Large	285.00
Home in the Country, A	Small	30.00
Home in the Country, Summer	Large	75.00
Leaving Brighton Hotel	Small	60.00
Little Blossom	Small	25.00
Little Charles	Small	24.50
Little Sarah	Small	20.00
Mattie; 10 x 14"		20.00
Midnight Race on the Mississippi	Small	100.00
Old Grist Mill, The	Small	55.00
Old, Old Story, The (Comic)	Small	25.00
Sleigh Ride	Small	275.00
Summer (Trotters)	Small	65.00
Summer Scene in the Country	Large	100.00
Trading on the Plains	Large	2,400.00
Trip down the Harbor, A	Small	60.00
Winter (Trotters)	Small	75.00

DUVAL PRINTS

Peter C. Duval, a French artist and lithographer, was brought to this country in 1830, by C. G. Childs of Philadelphia, who had gone to Europe to study lithography. Duval worked for Childs and his partners, Henry Inman and George Lehman. Childs' first partner was Inman and they operated as Childs & Inman. He also worked simultaneously with his other partner under the firm name of Childs & Lehman.

Childs retired in 1836. The business continued as Lehman & Duval until 1838, when Lehman retired. For a period of less than one year, 1838-39, the firm was known as Dow & Duval. From the latter part of 1839, Duval continued the firm as P. C. Duval until 1857, when his son entered the business. It was then known as Duval & Son.

Duval made a number of portraits, historical views of cities, sporting and other prints. Today, examples of his works are scarce and often difficult to locate for they were issued in small quantities.

PRANG PRINTS

Louis Prang, the son of a Prussian textile manufacturer was born in 1824. In 1848, he was forced to flee his country because of having been on the losing side of a political revolt. He married a Swiss girl and they emigrated to New York in the Spring of 1850.

Prang formed an immediate dislike for New York and moved to Boston, where he became a free-lance wood engraver and finally was Chief of the Art Department at Gleason's Pictorial. He later became chief artist for Duval.

He formed a partnership in 1856 with Julius Mayer, a lithographic printer. Their first color job was a "Bouquet of Roses" which appeared in "The Ladies Companion" for 1857. A number of views of towns and other subjects were issued until the beginning of the Civil War. During the war period, the firm prospered and in 1864 Prang went to Europe.

In England, he met William Harring, an artist and lithographer. They produced their first "Chromos" or oil lithographs together in 1865. The finished product had a glossy surface similar to a varnished painting.

Christmas cards were practically unknown before 1874. Prang issued the first cards in America and the public demand became so great that the company prospered beyond the dreams of the owners.

MISCELLANEOUS LITHOGRAPHERS

The brief histories heretofore presented are of the leading print-makers in America. Other lithographers such as A. E. Bellows; Joseph Hoover, of Philadelphia; Knapp Lithograph Co., successors to Sarony & Major, New York; Ehrgott, Forbridger & Company; Middleton, Strobridge & Co., of Cincinnati; Otto Krehs of Pittsburgh; William M. Donaldson, of Cincinnati; Otto Krehs of Pittsburgh; William M. Donaldson, of Cincinnati; Shober & Carqueville and Kurtz & Allison, of Chicago; Milwaukee Lithograph Co., Milwaukee and Britton, Rey & Co., of San Francisco were all important producers of prints and chromo-lithographs after the Civil War Period. It is possible that at some future date collectors will recognize the works of some of these lesser known lithographers and begin the serious quest of gathering their works.

MISCELLANEOUS PRINTS and ENGRAVINGS

"Where There is Smoke There is Fire"; Prang .... Small...$25.00
Cavalry Off; Remington ....Small... 35.00
Arizona Cowboy; Remington.....................................Small... 35.00
Fortress Monroe, Old Point Comfort and Hygeia Hotel, Va.;
    Lithographed by E. Sachse & Co., 1861, 18 x 28 .... 48.50
View of Washington, D. C. (With key); E. Sachse & Co., 9 x 16.... 65.00
Bird's Eye View of the City of Annapolis, Md., Charles
    Magnus; 1863; 11 x 17 .... 75.00
Harper's Ferry, Va., E. Sachse & Co., 9 x 15 .... 50.00
Running the Blockade; (View of Wilmington, N. C.); Lithographed
    by Charles Magnus; 18 x 21 .... 30.00
Telegraph Chart of America and Europe; "Celebration all over the
    United States in honor of ocean telegraphing Sept., 1858."
    Gives also the Queen's message to Buchanan and the Presi-
    dent's message to the Queen. Lithographed by Charles Magnus,
    1858. Very Rare; 18 x 23 .... 95.00
Atlantic Telegraph Game; Charles Magnus; 21 x 24½ 100.00
Battles of the Rebellion; Charles Magnus; 1863; 20½ x 23 .... 40.00
Abraham Lincoln, "Sixteenth President of the United States,"
    Lithographed by F. Fuchs, 13½ x 16½ 35.00
Washington's Farewell Address; Engraved by J. C. Butre; 11½ x 17
    25.00
The Lincoln Family in 1861; Engraved by J. C. Butre, 1873; 18 x
    24 .... 40.00
The Dawn of Liberty; Lithographed in colors by Rosenthal; 16 x
    22 .... 35.00
Richmond, Va., Lithographed by Charles Magnus, 1865, 15 x 18 .. 40.00
Bird's Eye View of the City of New York; Charles Magnus, 6 x 9. 35.00
View of San Francisco; Steel engraving by Charles Magnus, 1858,
    4½ x 7 .... 20.00
View of Cincinnati, Ohio; Steel engraving by Charles Magnus,
    1858; 4½ x 7 .... 20.00
Maj. General Peck's Headquarters at Suffolk, Va., Lithographed in
    colors by E. Sachse & Co., 1863; 9 x 16 .... 40.00
Camp Hamilton, Fortress Monroe and Rip Raps, Va., Lithographed
    in colors by E. Sachse & Co., 9 x 16 ....48.00

Encampment of the U. S. Troops at Newport News, Va., Lithographed
in colors by E. Sachse & Co.; 9 x 15 ....40.00
Soldier's Home, Washington, D. C., Black and white Lithograph by
Charles Magnus, 1863; 9 x 17 ....30.00
Bird's Eye View of Texas and Part of Mexico; Lithographed by
John Bachman; 1861; 18 x 28 ....35.00
Bird's Eye View of Virginia, Maryland and Deleware; John Backman;
18½ x 28 .... 35.00
Bird's Eye View of Kentucky and Tennesee; John Backman; 18½ x
28 .... 35.00
Panarama of the Mississippi Valley and its Fortifications; Litho-
graphed in colors by Charles Magnus; 23 x 25 .... 30.00
Map of Virginia with border of Generals; Octagon shaped map of
Virginia lithographed in colors by Charles Magnus; 18 x 18 .. 21.50
Map of the State of New York with view of Niagara Falls; Printed
in colors by Charles Magnus; 1854; 19 x 24 .... 24.00
New York City and County Map, with vicinity of entire Brooklyn,
Williamsburg, Jersey City, etc., printed by Charles Magnus;
20 x 33 .... 27.50
Lincoln and Davis; A curious lithograph in colors showing Lincoln
and Davis on white horses. The Northern and Southern fanatics
"imprisoned for life" and the dove of peace with "Union hence-
forth, Now and Forever." Extremely rare Lincoln item. Charles
Magnus; 13 x 16 ....125.00
Father of Our Republic; Lithograph of George Washington in
colors by A. Muller & Co., 1879; 22 x 31............................ 35.00
General U. S. Grant; Engraving by W. E. Marshall; 1868; 16 x 21.. 35.00
Abraham Lincoln; Engraving by W. E. Marshall; 16 x 21 .... 45.00
Andrew Johnson; Lithographed by Kramer; 13 x 17.................... 20.00
Winfield Scott, Lieut. General Com., U. S. Army; Lithographed by
Conrad Huber; 1858; 13 x 15 .... 27.50
The Charge of the First Maryland Regiment; Rare lithograph by A.
Hoen; 18 x 25½ 45.00
President Lincoln and his Son, Tad; Engraved by A. B. Walters;
Published by Bradley & Co., 9 x 10½ 30.00
Second Battle of Bull Run, Va., August 30, 1862; Charles Magnus;
1863; 12½ x 16½ 35.00
Battle of Gettysburg, Pa., July 3rd; 1863; Charles Magnus;12 x 19
40.00
Battle of Gettysburg, Pa., (4 scenes); Lithographed in colors by
Charles Magnus; Each scene 4½ x 7½ 30.00
Sixteen Military Camps, lithographed in color in 1862 by L. N.
Rosenthal:
   a. Camp Chase, 15th Reg. Conn. Volunteers; 6 x 10½ 25.00
   b. Camp Chase, 11th Reg. N. H. Volunteers; 6 x 10½ 25.00
   c. Camp Worcester, 34th Mass. Volunteers; 6 x 10½ 25.00
   d. Camp Vermont, Va., 4th Del. Infantry; 6 x 10½ 25.00
   e. Camp 19 Regiment Conn. Volunteers; 6 x 10½ 25.00
   f. Camp Brightwood; 6 x 10½ 25.00
   g. Camp Hathaway, 141st Regt., N.Y.S.V.; 6 x 10½ 25.00
   h. Camp Chase, 147th Regt., N.Y.S.V.; 6 x 10½ 25.00
   i. Camp Seward, 170th; N.Y.S.V. 2nd Regiment Corcorans Le-
      gion; 6 x 10½ 25.00
   j. Camp Tom Casey, 26th Maine Regiment; 6 x 10½ 25.00
   k. Camp Hicks, near Frederick, Maryland; 6 x 10½ 25.00
   l. Camp of Webster Regiment, 1st Brigade, Banks Division; 6
      x 10½ 25.00
   m. Camp Pomeroy, 111th Regiment, New York; 6 x 10½ 25.00

n. Camp Brightwood, Winter quarters, 7th Mass. Volunteers;
 6 x 10½ .... $ 25.00
o. Camp of Second Massachusetts Regiment; 6 x 10½ 25.00
p. Fort Ethan Allen; Garrisoned by the 4th New York Heavy
 Artillery; 6 x 10½ 25.00
Mt. Pleasant Hospital, Washington, D. C.; Charles Magnus; 1864;
 11 x 17 .... 42.50
Bird's Eye View of Camp Convalescent, (Near Alexandria, Va.);
 Charles Magnus, 1864; 11 x 17 .... 42.50
Douglas and Stanton Hospital, Washington, D.C.; Charles Magnus;
 1864; 11 x 17 .... 42.50
Lincoln Hospital, Washington, D. C.; Charles Magnus, 1864; 11
 x 17 .... 42.50
Cliffbourne Hospital, Washington, D. C.; Charles Magnus; 1862;
 9 x 16½ 40.00
Campbell U. S. General Hospital, Washington, D. C.; Charles
 Magnus; 1864; 11 x 17 .... 40.00
Harewood Hospital, Washington, D. C.; Charles Magnus; 1864;
 11 x 16½ 40.00
Carver Barracks, Washington, D. C.; Charles Magnus; 1864; 11
 x 17 .... 40.00
Camp Fry, Washington, D. C., 9th and 10th Regiment's Veterans
 Reserve Corps; Colored lithographed by Charles Magnus;
 1864; 11 x 17 .... 45.00
Soldier's Rest, Alexandria, Va.; Lithographed by Charles Magnus;
 1864; 11 x 17 .... 45.00
Soldier's Rest, Washington, D. C. (Troop train in foreground and
 Capitol in vista; Charles Magnus; 1864; 11 x 17 .... 42.50
Finley U. S. General Hospital, (Capitol in distance); Charles
 Magnus; 1864; 11 x 17 .... 40.00
Satterlee U. S. A. General Hospital, West Philadelphia; Pub-
 lished by Jas. D. Gay; 1864; 11 x 17 .... 32.50

Lithographed and Engraved Portraits of Famous Americans

AUDUBON, J. J., Lithographed by D'Avignon; 1850 ...9½ x 11..$ 35.00
BAINBRIDGE, WM., Engraving by Edwin; Circa 1815...3½ x 4 ...25.00
BIDDLE, NICHOLAS, Engraving by Sartain .... 7½ x 9½.. 25.00
BOONE, D; Engraving;1896 ....6 x 8 .. 25.00
CARROLL, CHARLES, OF CARROLLTON; Engraving.8 x 10 .. 35.00
CLAY, HENRY; Lithograph by D'Avignon; 1850 .... 9½ x 11 .. 32.50
CLINTON, DEWITT; Engraving by Ames; Circa 1830...7½ x 8½.. 25.00
DECATUR, STEPHEN; Engraving by Meyer; Circa 1815
 6½ x 8 .. 60.00
ELLSWORTH, OLIVER; Engraving by Maverick .... 3 x 4 .. 25.00
FULTON, ROBERT; Engraving by Leney; 1815 .... 4 x 5 .. 20.00
JACKSON, STONEWALL; Engraving; Circa 1860 ...... 9½ x 11 .. 25.00
JONES, JOHN PAUL; Engraving by Chapman; 1796 ... 4 x 5 .. 25.00
LEE, CHARLES; Engraving by Hart; Circa 1870 ...... 6 x 8 .. 35.00
MacDONOUGH, COMR. THOMAS; Engraving by Gimbrede
 8½ x 10 .. 40.00
MONROE, JAMES; Engraving by Gimbrede, 1817 .... 7½ x 9½.. 70.00
MORRIS, GOUVERNEUR; Engraving; 1783 .... 4 x 4½.. 22.50
PENN, WILLIAM; Engraving by Lawson, 1797........... 4½ x 7½.. 22.50
PERRY, COMR. OLIVER H.; Engraving by Meyer; Cir-
 ca 1815 .... 7 x 8   70.00
PUTNAM, ISRAEL; Engraving by Shepherd, 1775 .... 9½ x 12½. 45.00

RITTENHOUSE, DAVID; Engraving by Gobrecht; Circa
    1785 .... 4 x 5 ...$ 25.00
WEBSTER, DANIEL; Engraving by Ritchie, 1863 .... 7½ x 8 ... 25.00
WEST, BENJAMIN; Engraving by Spilsbury; Circa 1780. 5 x 6 ... 25.00
WOLCOTT, OLIVER; Engraving by Durand; Circa 1825.' 7 x 8 ... 27.50

Hand-colored Lithographs of the Viviparous Quadrupeds of North
America, by J. J. Audubon, 1845. Approx. 20'' x 27''

Armadillo .... $	35.00	Mink	$50.00
American Badger	28.50	Ocelot	30.00
American Black Bear	50.00	Virginian Opposum	37.50
American Elk	50.00	Canada Otter	30.00
Cinnamon Bear	45.00	Common Skunk	50.00
Grizzly Bear	40.00	Wolverine	30.00
Polar Bear	60.00	Raccoon	50.00
Cougar and Young	30.00	Prong Horned Antelope	45.00
American Red Fox...........	45.00	Buffalo	50.00
Silver Fox	50.00	Common Deer	55.00
Jaguar	30.00	Rocky Mountain Goat	45.00
Canada Lynx	25.00	Moose	25.00
Texan Lynx	20.00	American Beaver	40.00
Black Tailed Hare...........	20.00		